THE STORY OF POETRY

The Story of Poetry

DAVID HOPKINS

and

TOM MASON

with wood engravings by

Hilary Paynter

BROADSIDE BOOKS

First published by Broadside Books,
4 Cotham Vale,
Bristol BS6 6HR.
(an imprint of Broadcast Books)

ISBN 1874092 04 4

Page design by Jessica Caws
Cover design by John Meek

Printed by The Bath Press, Bath, Avon

Acknowledgements

The authors owe a considerable debt both to those many who assisted directly in the composition and to all those who have read or heard parts of this book over the years (including several generations of undergraduates at Bristol University), and whose advice, smiles, frowns and yawns have helped to shape successive drafts. Sandra Hopkins cleared the final draft by exercising 'the last greatest art: the art to blot'. The greatest debt, however (and far larger than is customary), is owed to Geoffrey Chaucer, Edmund Spenser, Philip Sidney, William Shakespeare, Benjamin Jonson, Andrew Marvell, Abraham Cowley, John Milton, John Wilmot, John Dryden, Joseph Addison, Alexander Pope, Thomas Gray, Samuel Johnson, William Blake, William Wordsworth, Samuel Coleridge, Percy Shelley, John Keats, Alfred Tennyson, Robert Browning, Matthew Arnold and Rudyard Kipling, without whose help (and words) this book could not have been written, and who may be held responsible for nearly all its peculiarities and oddities.

Table of Contents

Book One: The Progress of Poetry

Book Two: The Arts of Poetry

Book Three: The Arts of Listening

Book One

The Progress of Poetry

Part One:
The Story of Art

1. Our Hero

The Story of POETRY is part of the Story of ART which is part of the Story of HUMANITY which is part of the Story of MANKIND which is part of the Story of the WORLD.

It is not an easy story to tell. It is one of those stories that cannot be told without a string of wild generalizations, dubious analogies, weak jokes, dangerous guesses, lumbering allegories, over-long similes, over-extended metaphors, enormous borrowings, wholesale purloinings, systematic thefts, and a few downright lies.

There is one lie which (in this case) is so like a truth that it will serve almost as well as if it were true indeed. It is a lie told by a Greek called Pythagoras. Pythagoras lived one life some two thousand years ago, and another life (so he *said*) five hundred years before, when he had fought in the Trojan War. He even recognised his old shield when, one day, he saw it hanging on a temple wall.

Every good story needs a hero. The Story of POETRY covers a million years and contains a thousand characters. But if it might be imagined that Pythagoras was right — that one soul might animate various bodies at different times and in miscellaneous places — then this story will need only one protagonist.

His (or her) spirit is very special, but it is special only in degree. His personality (as such) is not remarkable: he is as other men and women are — only more so.

He is endowed with more lively and quicker sympathies than the rest of his species. He has more enthusiasm and tenderness, a greater knowledge of human nature and a more comprehensive soul than are supposed to be common among mankind. He is affected more than other men by absent things almost as if they were present, and he rejoices more in the spirit of life that is in him.

He has all the natural human capacities and potentialities in super-abundance and in such fine and perfect equipoise, one with another, that his character combines elements not often co-existing in humanity — a searching intelligence and a delicate fancy; agility and weight; strength and sweetness of soul.

The fundamental principle of his mind is GOOD SENSE. He has a prompt and intuitive perception of what goes with what and what belongs where; what is likely to be the case and what is not. He sees quickly which of his own ideas to keep and which to throw away. He knows what to copy and what to shun in the notions of others.

He has JUDGEMENT to separate the essence of a thing from what goes with it and to select from human life or from nature exactly what is needed for his present purpose.

His UNDERSTANDING is uncluttered; his ideas clean and distinct. He can find his own halting way through the labyrinth of thought.

His SENSATIONS are powerful but precise. His sight is clear, his hearing acute, his touch discriminating. The various shapes and sounds of nature, the incidents of life and the energies of human passion are impressed upon and exist within his IMAGINATION with such vividness and quiddity that his INVENTION easily forms new trains of thought and new combinations of images.

To assist these powers, he has great strength and exactness of MEMORY. What he hears or sees or feels is not easily lost. He has before him at all times not only what his own meditation suggests or his own experience supplies, but what he has found useful or engaging in the minds of others.

These benefits of nature he improves by incessant and unwearied DILIGENCE. His mind is prompt, watchful and eager. His CURIOSITY knows no limits. He lets pass no opportunity to be informed. His powers of ATTENTION are great but not absolute. His mind, whether he wills or no, is perpetually selecting notions and collecting impressions, continually combining and re-combining feeling and sensation, constantly giving new life and movement to images and ideas.

His mind is active, ambitious, and adventurous, always investigating, always aspiring; in its widest searches still longing to go forward, in its highest flights still wishing to be higher; always imagining something greater than it knows, always endeavouring more than it can do.

He is irresistibly drawn to whatever is just beyond the reach of thought and feels himself to be born for whatever is arduous.

To this end he has two capacities which are the result neither of art nor of study but which are purely the gifts of Heaven.

His first gift is an AMPLITUDE AND ELEVATION OF SOUL. Where other men and women take the easier path, he has a natural antipathy to what is low or mean. He is impatient of all prevarication, every evasion, any mendacity. He rejoices in the presence of truth and never ceases to wonder at the world.

His desire is to know and then to tell (or to know *by* telling) the truth or truths about the sum of human life – in general and in particular.

His second gift is a SOVEREIGN ELOQUENCE. Like other men and women, he has the colours and forms and sounds of human expression before him. He can shape his thought with delicacy, variety, weight or elegance. But he has, more than other men and women, an ability (by nature, by instinct, or by inspiration) to pour forth the richest treasures of his mind in answering splendour. He possesses a vivacity, a vitality, an energy of expression which gives *his* forms grace, abundance, and beauty. He has a force and a fire of soul which gives body to thought, which gives life to dead matter and which calls new powers into being.

The mind of Our Hero is the image of all other minds. Nothing human is alien to his soul. He is capable of thinking whatever a human being may think and of feeling whatever a human being may feel. He can put himself in the place of another and of many others. The pains and pleasures of his species are his own. He can draw the bounds and sound the depths of human nature. His mind is as a mirror upon which all things are reflected and in which they compose one image, one form.

This great soul (according to the fancy employed in this book) is fated, or doomed, or damned to re-appear on earth sometimes in one place and sometimes in another; incarnated sometimes as a man, sometimes as a woman; sometimes as a pauper and sometimes as a king.

Sometimes he is born to fail and sometimes to triumph: sometimes to be revered and sometimes reviled.

Sometimes he comes to the world with more force, sometimes with less.

Very occasionally Our Hero returns to the world to wield the strength and force and fire of thirty living souls.

And that is when life becomes intensely interesting – to him, and to us all.

2. The World Before Art

Our Hero (we may suppose) would have been there even in the earliest morning of human time, trailing along after a small pack of man-creatures, sneaking and slouching, creeping and stumbling along the edge of the jungle, between the dark trees and the grassy plain. Like the rest of the pack, he would have been permanently confused and absolutely terrified. He would have been living what little life he had in a state of perpetual horror.

He would have been confused and horrified because he was at the same time an animal and something much more than an animal.

His body, like the body of every other living thing, would be continuously sending him messages that he could not hope to understand – impulses of fear, of sudden elation and just as sudden torpor, of lust and of hunger, of sickness and of pain – messages that had to be obeyed instantly and without question but by which he was almost always deceived or betrayed.

At some moments his body would do things Our Hero would very much rather not have done. When he thought he was standing bravely in the path of the charging bison, he would discover that his legs were carrying him away. When he thought that he was letting his enemy go, he found himself crushing brains and tearing flesh.

At other moments, his body absolutely refused to do what he wanted to do. Sometimes when he wanted to run, his legs didn't work. He wanted to shout, but his mouth was too dry. He wanted to work something out, but his head hurt. Often he would have liked to fly like a bird, but he could never get more than a few inches from the ground.

His body, it was clear, lived by the iron laws that govern all matter. But what laws did *he* live by?

He began to notice that his brain did not work properly. Whenever something seemed to half-happen in his mind, everything went blank. He forgot his half-thoughts even as he half-had them. It was like chasing a snake in pitch darkness. Or a nest of snakes – for his mind would never settle on any one thing at a time.

He would stare at his feet or his navel, but his head would fill with images of the stars. He would try to concentrate his whole being on hitting a rabbit with a stone, but as he concentrated and stared, the rabbit turned into a tuft of brown grass.

Nothing could be trusted, not his body, not his mind, certainly not the world around him.

Our Hero could be sure of only two things – that nothing was sure and that he was the most wretched of creatures.

The difference between the way an animal fears and the way our man-creature feared, was that he knew (or half-knew, or half-thought he half-knew) that he was afraid. He had noticed or half-noticed that even the strongest, the quickest and most careful of his (or any) kind could not long preserve that quickness and that strength. He had one enemy from whom there was nowhere to hide. And he was afraid.

Worse, the outside world and his body (he couldn't always distinguish between them) seemed to be full of fearful, nameless powers.

They came when he was hungry. They came in the dark. They came when his mind went blank. They came in his sleep. They wore the face of the moon, or of a snake, or of a sabre-tooth tiger. The most terrible came when he was losing all sense of what was real and what was not – of who or what or if he was. These wore no face at all. And he was afraid.

Conscious or semi-conscious fear transformed itself into something else. It turned into misery.

Our Hero tried to make the best of it.

He found a companion – who was eaten by a leopard.

He found another – who stole his hand-axe.

He ran away from the pack of man-creatures with a young female – who died of starvation.

And so Our Hero, broken, dwelt with his fellows in toil and in misery, sneaking and slouching and stumbling along the edge of the jungle, between the dark trees and the grassy plain.

He could not hope to be the leader of the pack. The leader of the pack was a great power who had the leanest meat, the most juicy berries and all the females. Whenever the pack-leader glared, Our Hero's legs and brain and bowels turned instantly to water. Our Hero could not come within ten feet of him without covering his own face with mud, bowing and scraping, crawling in the dust and making a long whimpering howl of elaborate submission.

Without a pack-leader, Our Hero half-knew, there would be no pack, and without a pack he could not exist. But living with the pack he had always to lick the feet of those stronger than himself. He was growled at constantly by those at whom it was impossible to growl back. The best pieces of meat never seemed to come his way. The female he wanted so much was always the pack-leader's favourite. His sleeping place was always the rockiest and most draughty. Whenever he stepped out of line, he was beaten or bitten into submission and encouraged to recall (or half-recall) that he was only a frail man-creature, obeying the inexorable law of his kind.

Yet, despite his misery, Our Hero had the shadow of an inkling, somewhere among the dance of impulses inside him, that he was different from all the other creatures on the earth – different, too, from the rocks and the stones and the trees.

He also had the glimmering shadow of a suspicion that, where everything else was doomed to repeat the same round of actions over and over again for all eternity, he might one day, some day, possess an instant or find a place that was all his own – an instant or a place in which he could know and be himself.

He would have liked to have shared these half-guesses and suspicions with the rest of the pack. He would have liked some help. He longed to know if he was as other man-creatures were and if other man-creatures were as he.

But, clearly, it was impossible.

Clearly, he was born to suffer and suffer – to suffer and say nothing.

For the only sounds he could utter were a few snarls, hunting-cries and whimpering howls of elaborate submission.

3. The First Moment

Nothing changed for millennia. Nothing could change – without a miracle.

The Story of ART began (or so it might be imagined) when that miracle occurred – when Our Hero, in one of his stronger incarnations, had his first really good day.

The time was not propitious. It was mid-winter in an Ice-Age. All the children had just died of influenza. The pack-leader had been mauled by a bear. The fire had gone out. It had been snowing and sleeting and hailing for months. No-one had fed for a week. The night seemed to have no end. There was serious doubt whether the sun would ever rise again.

There was much howling and wailing and moaning and groaning from the pack – from Our Hero especially. He had discovered or developed a particular aptitude for wailing and howling and moaning. Wailings and howlings and moanings enraptured, entranced and enthralled him. Now he stood up and howled very loudly and very piercingly.

He was trembling with terror. He was, at the same time, dreaming about being wrapped up under a warm bear-skin with a young female, and of suckling next to the heart of his dam. There was a pounding in his head as if he had been running down a gazelle, or axing a snake, or standing on the edge of a waterfall.

Strongest of all his impulses was a passionate wish to stay alive – a longing not to be taken by the unknown powers or swallowed by the dark.

He stared into the blackness where the mouth of the cave should have been, and longed for the sun.

And he moaned and he howled and he wailed. And as he moaned, he began to sway. His sway was the sway of misery, but also half-reminded him, in some half-understood way, of the swaying of trees and the flowing of rivers.

And so he moaned to his swaying and swayed to his howling. It was as if he had been able to bring his body and his mind together in one great sway and wail.

Suddenly, mysteriously, all the impulses which had been fighting within him, driving him relentlessly and confusedly hither and thither, sinking him in chaos and in terror, seemed for a moment to be tamed, controlled, harmonised.

The other members of the pack heard his moan and felt the pattern of his swaying in their minds and their bodies.

The pack began to chant and sway along with him.

The cave was filled with the great swell of the moan.

From deep in their bellies the pack wailed the great HOWL.

Suddenly, mysteriously, Our Hero, and then the whole pack, began to chant a man-creature's sound. It was the howl they used when cringing in submission before the pack-leader. Though no-one had ever used it before in circumstances like these, this sound, clearly, wonderfully, was the RIGHT SOUND.

Our Hero hurled this sound into the dark, desperately, defiantly, imploringly.

AND THE SUN CAME UP.

And as the sun flickered from a suspicion to a glimmer, Our Hero felt such a joy as he had never felt before. The joy came so fast that it had no time to replace the misery. It simply included it.

The joy seemed to come, simultaneously, from inside himself, and from the others in the cave, and from the outside world – from the sun.

The tears that were running down his cheeks turned (without altering) from tears of misery to tears of exultation.

The howl which included and excluded everything – which seemed to make the whole world irrelevant by embracing that world within itself – became a shout of triumph which was also a plea and a lament.

Again and again Our Hero howled his howl, shouted his shout, swayed his sway, while the pack laughed and cried and the sun rose high in the heavens.

THIS WAS THE FIRST WORD.

It contained within itself the seed of the first song, the pattern of the first dance, the germ of the first prayer, the promise of the first science, the root of the first myth, and the embryo of the first poem.

Our Hero was the first story-teller (even though his story was only one sung-gesture long).

The members of his pack were the first human beings.

It was a great discovery – greater than flint, greater than fire. The word-story brought all the joys and terrors, the pleasures and pains of life together, and made them dance a human dance.

By using the howl of submission for the sun, Our Hero had shocked and delighted the members of the pack into knowledge of themselves. Now they *knew* that the sun belonged to their world, and they to the sun's.

No-one, not in ten thousand generations, had dreamed that a sound used in the pack could be applied to the universe beyond the pack.

The pack-members stood around Our Hero wondering delightedly, incredulously, and then fell on their faces in worship of the celestial sound. They *knew* with every fibre of their bodies that no mere creature could have spoken so sweetly and so well – no mere creature could have invented such a WORD. The first speaker had obviously been visited by great and good powers, powers who swayed and howled through him.

Only the spirits could have joined heaven and earth with a single sound.

For what had happened?

The whole universe had been made, for one infinitely precious (but repeatable) instant, to exist within the mind of a man-creature.

And for one infinitely precious (but repeatable) instant, the mind of a man-creature had extended to the whole world.

IN THIS MOMENT WAS CREATED THE FIRST ELEMENT IN THE INTELLECTUAL UNIVERSE OF HUMAN THOUGHT.

4. How Stories Grew

And then (or so our story goes) *everything* began to change. After the miraculous moment which had given birth to the first WORD, the pack-members began to see every morsel of their lives anew and afresh – as a man who has been blind and is given sight looks round in astonishment, and, with slowly dawning recognition, sees for the first time his familiar well-handled tools. Once they had heard a howl of animal submission applied to the sun, the pack could never again look on the world around them as something *entirely* alien to their own minds. They were accordingly delighted every time Our Hero (or in some incarnations, Our Heroine) invented or discovered or was taught a new WORD (which happened every thousand years or so – with luck).

Whenever he was incarnated in more propitious circumstances and managed to live more or less to maturity, Our Hero tried to apply pack-sounds and pack-gestures to various parts of the world, or to things in the world (or to things out of the world). Increasingly he began to connect the sounds and the gestures one with another to form a STORY that was also a LANGUAGE – as he or she (and the guiding spirits) began the slow, painful, sudden, joyful, process by which man-creatures made sense of themselves and their circumambient universe.

It was not planned. It happened. Often it went wrong. For, however hard he tried, Our Hero could never know how his stories would turn out before he began them.

Every word, every story, every sentence, every dance seemed to contain within itself the seeds of other unknown and mysterious tales of new and far-off lands – if only he could find them. One dance led to another – if the spirits were willing.

Each new story, every new word, was like a new journey into a strange territory. He could never be sure if the spirits were accompanying him, whither he would be led, or what he might be prompted to do and say. Sometimes Our Hero was simply appalled by what came out of his mouth. If the territory into which he ventured was too strange and arbitrary, the pack could not connect the imagined terrain with that which they knew. They became angry or bored, and the WORD died. But if the new territory was *not* strange or extraordinary, the pack were left with all their old doubts and terrors, howling in a land that was all-too-familiar, and again the WORD died.

Clearly, it was the most difficult business of life, this finding or making words and this finding or making the connections between them.

But one fine day, in one fine incarnation, the spirits came rushing at Our Hero and invaded him all at once with such fury that he was not able to resist – giving him for some moments double strength. On recovering from his fit, he found himself leading a whirling dance where one member of the pack danced as the sun and made courting groans to another pack-member, who was dancing and moaning – it became suddenly and wonderfully apparent – as the moon.

The new dance, the new WORD, was a success: the moon shone every night and the river flooded in Spring.

Some centuries later he suddenly felt the need (or was suddenly inspired) to elaborate the dance so that a Sky-figure murmured soft grooming noises to an Earth-dancer twisting in ecstasy.

This was the third WORD, and that year there were nuts in abundance.

As the centuries passed, Our Hero began to associate the nameless and confused feelings of terror and joy to which he, like the other pack members, was continuously subject, with his dancers, with the dance, or with the sounds made by the dancers in dancing.

In one incarnation, watching his tiger-dancer, Our Hero suddenly realised that this figure concentrated everything he had ever felt about real tigers in the jungle, about the jungle itself, about the great father of all tigers, and also seemed to express everything that had half-happened in his mind in those moments when he had gone beyond himself with a rage like the tiger's. And then he saw his moon-dancer reflecting all the pale silvery stillness of the moon on a clear night, and also everything that was female and therefore mysterious and powerful in himself and in the world.

In another incarnation (in another land, another tongue, and incarnated as a woman) Our Heroine began to imagine that, if the earth was the mate of the sky, then the fishes and the trees MUST be the children of this union, begotten by cosmic copulation. As she watched the dance, pondering, delighted, she began to see that, since the pack-howls could be used for Nature and the Heavens, then the various forms and processes of Nature and the Heavens MUST be related one to another just as the members of the pack were related. It seemed clear, for example, that the bravest and most powerful pack-leaders were mighty lions, great begetters and, simultaneously, bright suns in the sky.

The possibilities were, suddenly, endless, inexhaustible. Not only could pack-gestures be applied to things in a way that seemed magically right, they could also be applied in a way that seemed magically *wrong*.

So one day when the pack-idiot crawled out of the corner (where he usually crouched burbling happily at spiders) and tried to join the dance, Our Heroine found herself calling him with and by the first danced WORD (which by now was associated with the pack-leader, with the lion, with the sun and with a rage like the lion's or the sun's).

It was a dangerous moment. For a while it looked as if the pack might tear Out Heroine (and the idiot) to pieces.

The pack-leader, in particular, was not amused. But then they smiled, they laughed, they wept, and embraced one another, gleefully.

THAT STORY WAS THE FIRST JOKE.

When the members of the pack were in the presence of Our Hero's (or Our Heroine's) new stories, moving in song and dance, they felt that the world they lived in was, after all, comprehensible and therefore bearable. In such precious moments they found their lives easier to endure and easier to enjoy. They began to revere the world because of the stories and the stories because of the world.

The stories were kept alive in the memories, on the lips and in the dances of other members of the tribe, even at times when there was no living reincarnation of Our Hero. And even when (as generally happened) one tribe was overrun and enslaved by another more powerful, the conquerors learnt their slaves' and concubines' stories and chanted and whirled them in their own way.

It was *surprising* how quickly the stories spread and grew and mingled with other stories.

It was *astonishing* how long they lasted.

It was a MIRACLE that they pleased tribes in distant lands with quite different preoccupations, predilections and principles.

It seemed that the stories were powerful because the great spirits had forced the composer to dream, think, feel or know, not as one man dreams, thinks, feels or knows, but as *all* men and women – in the very depths of their souls – might dream, think, feel, know.

THE BEST STORIES, IT SEEMED CLEAR, WERE NOT OF A SINGLE MOMENT OR A SINGLE TRIBE, BUT FOR ALL THE TRIBES THAT HAD BEEN, ALL THE TRIBES THAT WERE, ALL THE TRIBES THAT MIGHT BE.

5. A Golden Time

And so (or so it may be *supposed*) everything went on changing. Our Hero found himself in some extraordinarily interesting and rewarding incarnations.

By now he knew three thousand wise words and a thousand and five sung dances. They told of the trees, from the great cedar tree that grows in Lebanon down to the hyssop that springs from the wall. They spoke also of beasts and of fowl and of creeping things and of fishes, of crocodiles and of frogs. They told how the world was made, and how the stars and the sky. They told how the great spirits made man-creatures (and how sometimes they wished they hadn't). They told how the great spirits were not very different from pack-leaders and did what they did because they hated or loved or were jealous or wanted more power or honour or more possessions.

And so these stories served a double purpose. They explained why things are as they are – why lightning strikes here and not there; why that mountain is covered in clouds; why the good do not prosper – at the same time as showing how man-creatures behave, and how they might conduct themselves in a world made for human beings.

Our Hero's stories now seemed to have given a shape to the whole of life and his tribe began to live, or tried to begin to live, in, or by, his precepts.

And so Our Hero came to be looked upon as the pack's most precious possession. The wisdom of a tribe that included an incarnation of Our Hero among its members excelled the combined wisdom of all the peoples who had no stories. It seemed that the powers which spoke through him were indeed the greatest spirits of the universe.

A mouthpiece for the gods must be heard; his judgements must be respected and feared. Knowing stories and possessing surpassing wisdom were, it was clear, one and the same thing. The gods had given Our Hero wisdom and understanding and largeness of heart as abundantly as the sand that covers the shore of the sea. And since the gods had granted Our Hero such wisdom and knowledge, it seemed only proper and provident that he should also be given riches and wealth and honour such as no king had ever had before.

All the people and their leaders came to hear the stories, to watch the dances and to admire the wisdom of Our Hero. He was asked to organise ceremonies, to adjudicate disputes and to preserve customs. He became, at one and the same time, the tribe's High Priest, its Composer, its Choreographer, its Historian, its Law-Giver and its Prophet.

He was given one tenth of all their possessions – thirty measures of fine flour and three score measures of meat, twenty fat oxen out of the pastures and a hundred sheep, hart and roebuck and fallow deer and fatted fowl. And he was given forty thousand stalls of horses for his chariots, twelve thousand horsemen, and seven hundred wives (all princesses) and three hundred concubines.

Our Hero was now a person of great power and influence, but his duties were arduous indeed. He had to foretell the future.

In the first place he had to predict his *own* future. If, for example, he were choosing a new princess, he would have to invent a story about how she might look if she were old, how she might comfort him if he were sick or troubled, how she might conduct herself towards emissaries from other tribes and how he (and she) might feel about it.

He had also to predict the future of his tribe; the future for his charioteers for example. If they were storming this or that citadel he would have to invent a story about their glorious victory or their noble fortitude in defeat. His most difficult and most important task (by far) was to predict the future of the gods. He had to invent stories about where they might like to spend their mornings and their afternoons. He had to compute how many smoked entrails of how many sheep would be necessary to placate them.

All these things had to be in his stories, and all these things had to be right.

But with resources like those at his present disposal, his sung and danced stories could perform wonders.

On one great day, and by means of a great ceremony, he had a temple built which would be a home for the great gods and for the lesser spirits of the kingdom; a temple that was also a castle and a theatre and a city – and itself one of his best and most convincing stories.

"Send me," he said, "men cunning to work in gold and in silver and in brass and in iron and in purple and in crimson and in blue. Send me also fir trees and cedar trees out of Lebanon. For the house which I am to build shall be wonderful and great."

The builders, dancing and singing and chanting, adorned the temple with gold, with carvings of crocodiles and with precious stones. They made a golden throne from which Our Hero might issue his judgements and conduct his ceremonies. They built and decorated chambers and chapels for his assistants: a chapel of Wisdom, a chapel of Power, a chapel of Truth, a chapel of Law, a chamber of Dance, one of Colour and Form, and one of Chanting and Sound.

When the Temple was built Our Hero burnt sweet incense before the gods, morning and evening.

"The gods told me," he said, "that they wish to dwell in thick darkness and I have surely built them a house for them to abide in forever."

And he offered a sacrifice to the gods – the smoked entrails of two and twenty thousand oxen and the blood of an hundred and twenty thousand sheep – and he chanted and swayed and whirled continuously for three days and three nights.

And all the people said, "May the Great Spirits save our Wise and Wonderful King, All-Powerful, All-Knowing, Teller of Stories, Dancer of Dances, Singer of Songs, Builder of Buildings, Inventor of Pictures, Interpreter of Gods, and Giver of Laws."

They chanted and swayed and whirled and rejoiced with great joy, so that the earth seemed to be rent with the sound.

FOR THE GREAT GLORY OF THE GODS, THE GREAT GLORY OF THE WORLD, THE GREAT GLORY OF MANKIND, THE GREAT GLORY OF HUMANITY, THE GREAT GLORY OF THE TRIBE, THE GREAT GLORY OF ART, HAD FILLED THEIR NEW TEMPLE, AS IT HAD FILLED THEIR HEARTS, EVEN TO BURSTING.

6. The Players Perform

But mortal happiness does not last. Fortune, turning her bright face away from Our Hero, danced in the wind, shook her wings and would not stay. Things began to go wrong.

As the centuries passed, each time Our Hero was reincarnated, he found he had more work to do.

As well as all the new stories which the spirits inspired him to tell and the new temples which the gods instructed him to build, there were all his old stories to re-learn and re-tell. The demands on his time and energies were now so many, and so dauntingly various, that instead of performing his sung stories himself, he was forced more and more to delegate. He still composed the words and music and laid down the dance movements which should accompany his sung stories, but increasingly left the detailed working-out of the performance to his disciples.

Unfortunately not all these disciples were friends of the spirits who inspired Our Hero with nightly visitations. At times they seemed, indeed, to be inspired by demons of their own.

It was therefore inevitable that one day a disaster would occur.

Our Hero had composed a ceremony to celebrate the new year and to praise the great spirit of the sun. It told the story of the creation of the crocodile and of the river snake and of the frog.

The dancer who represented the sun-spirit would arise majestically from among one hundred and fifty dancing girls whose undulating steps and chaste demeanour would represent the sacred waters of life. The sun-dancer would have union with his clenched fist, and join himself with the embrace of his shadow, casting his seed back into the waters. He would then chant a discourse of some fifty thousand words on the glory of the created world, on his own wisdom, power and might,

and on the wonder of crocodiles. This would be interspersed with beautiful digressions on the problems of determinism, the duties of citizens to the state, the humorous antics of wood-demons, a complete family tree of the gods, together with awful warnings to those who were slow in getting their tithes to the temple.

Our Hero described and recited his composition to his assistants and gave them detailed and scrupulous instructions on how it should be performed.

He was nowadays so busy that he could not always attend rehearsals of his works, but on this occasion he was able to be present.

What he saw and heard horrified him.

His assistants had cut his oration and replaced it with a catchy chant of some four or five words, endlessly repeated, on the sexual habits of frogs, accompanied by lascivious gyrations from a group of naked slave girls. The whole performance was now to culminate in a spectacular display of gymnastics, fire-eating and juggling from the chief dancer.

Outraged and appalled, Our Hero went to his chief assistant and demanded an explanation.

To his surprise, the player was unrepentant, even defiant.

"O Wise and Wonderful, All-Powerful, Teller of Stories, Singer of Songs, Builder of Buildings, Inventor of Pictures, Knower of Gods and Giver of Laws, just indeed are thy ways and justifiable, but your composition (tremblingly I say it) was hardly suitable for the modern temple.

We players have been troubled for some time. You seem to have lost interest in keeping the audience happy and entertained. There are only a few fanatics who are prepared to bear with your tedious (if I may use such a term) *prolixity* and (dare I say it) *didacticism*.

If we had performed this new work of yours according to your directions, the listeners would have been yawning and shuffling in their seats within minutes.

Any oration which sends the listener to sleep is good in vain. You make more demands on every one of your audience than flesh and blood can bear. A master-performer keeps his audience in pleasing captivity: his departure from the stage should be seen with an eye of sorrow such as a traveller casts upon departing day.

The modern temple-goer does not want to be *told* things. He wants to see for himself – and judge for himself. He wants something to happen, here and now before his eyes. He wants to be taken out of himself – to have the miseries of life instantly lifted and lightened. He wants to sit back in the expectation of immediate pleasure. He wants to feel that he is part of the performance – part of a shared *experience*. He wants variety. He admires skill. The last thing he needs is to feel that he is back at school.

Resign the stage to a fresh-comer with some new ideas (and fewer words)."

Our Hero, at this moment, found himself indeed speechless.

"Would you not," continued the Player, "even you, rather see my girls than listen to a tedious oration about crocodiles and the creator of the world?"

Our Hero refused either to confirm or to deny this suggestion but tried to gesture wisely with his hands. The Chief Player was undaunted.

"My charming assistants and I have something to show you. Look at the faces of the audience during our performance. You will see how happy we keep them."

The player and his girls began to dance a wheeling, serpentine dance. Despite himself Our Hero was enthralled. He saw the temple fill with frogs and crocodiles and all the beauty of reptiles – every kind and type of reptile expertly impersonated. He willingly believed that the world was overflowing with frog-spawn. He saw a great god emerge from the frog-spawn like the spirit of life itself.

The scene changed. Now he saw a great and wise man behaving like an ass.

He laughed till the tears ran down his face.

He could not stop laughing even when it dawned upon him that the great ass was himself.

Our Hero saw that he had been shown a story without a teller, a story which spoke to his heart without words.

And then he wept.

7. The Lovers of Colour and Form Astonish

Deep and dark was the gloom into which Our Hero was thrust. He began to wonder whether his talents were, after all, of surpassing use and interest to his fellow human beings. With anxious care he planned a new Grand Ceremony to make use of another group of his servants – those who built the temples, provided the costumes, the body-paints, the wall-paintings and the masks for his performances.

"Lovers of Colour and Form," he began, "a terrible thing has happened. The players tell me they no longer need my words or my stories. They *maintain* that·they can give and take delight without me. But you, surely, will continue to need me. Your golden temples, your colourful wall-paintings, your bright masks, your awesome costumes, would make no sense without the connecting threads of my narrative and the shaping power of my great thought. Every picture tells one of my stories. Here is a new story about the universal ingratitude of men and women (and the crass insensibility of players and dancers in particular)."

And he explained his latest plan. The temple would be plunged in darkness. He himself would walk slowly into the central area wearing the mask of Absolute Agony, baring a flaming torch towards a brightly painted sculpted form which he would invoke as the God of Retribution.

He would then orate for some three or four hours upon the beginning of the world, the creation of crocodiles and the stupidity of performers. At various points in the narrative, sculpted female forms (representing some of the more voluptuous dancing girls) would be wheeled into the playing area. These, he would explain, were Folly, Greed and Self-Love. The prevailing colours should be brown and blue.

The Lovers of Colour and Form listened politely, coughed, shuffled their feet, and stared, fixedly, at the ground. At last, the chief painter (idly describing

a perfect circle in the dust with his left foot) began:

"O Wise and Wonderful, All Powerful, Teller of Stories, Singer of Songs, Knower of Gods and Giver of Laws, just indeed are thy ways and justifiable, but your instructions (tremblingly I say it) are at once too general and too precise. You say, for example, that you want brown and blue. Perhaps you could tell us *which* brown and *which* blue – precisely."

(A junior servant at this point came forward with a slab of slate on which were painted a hundred thousand hues.)

"These three thousand might be described as blues, and these five thousand as browns. Pray choose."

(Our Hero could not. Words failed his eyes.)

"And when you speak of sculpted forms of the more voluptuous dancing girls – which ones did you have in mind – precisely?"

(Our Hero was presented with a slate on which were depicted the right ankle of two thousand maidens, each distinguished from each, all voluptuous.)

"Pray choose."

(But again he could not. He had, he found, too many in view and none in mind.)

"And again, when it comes to the mask of Absolute Agony, there is more than one possibility."

(Our Hero was led into the Chamber of Masks – a glorious addition to the temple of which he had been unaware – and then into the Sub-Chamber of Masks-of-Agony).

"Pray choose," said the Chief Painter.

(No, it was impossible. Our Hero saw agonies beyond name.)

"And the little matter of the God of Retribution. As it happens, we have something to show you."

The Lovers of Colour and Form pulled back a curtain to reveal ... Our Hero knew not what but flung himself prostrate on the ground, grovelling.

"Great god," he moaned, "have mercy upon me and upon my presumptions".

It was some hours before he noticed that the painters were not, like him, prone on the cold ground, but that those who had not drifted away were smiling and laughing softly amongst themselves with an air of surprising satisfaction.

"We are glad you like our sculpture, and that you recognise that it is more than an illustration of one of your stories. We had been suspecting for some time that you are, to all intents and purposes, blind. Because we have taught ourselves to see, we include and illuminate in our work infinitely more of the visual world – the world of colours and shapes and volumes and forms – than you can dream of. Now with our new God (of Retribution or what-you-will), we can give in an instant what it would take you three hours to describe – even if you had seen it in the first place."

(Our Hero was quick to concede that he had not).

It was at this point that he noticed that the sculptors' new god was only six inches tall.

But it seemed to exist in the inner space of the temple with an overwhelming presence – more than he had himself.

Each of its buttocks seemed to weigh as much as an elephant. Every fear and every hope which he had ever had seemed to be summed up in the power of its frown, the thickness of its neck, the cold enamel of its eyes.

Our Hero, feeling the power of the eye's mind, realised, sadly, that the skills of his former assistants were great and mysterious indeed.

With the utmost regret, the Lovers of Colour and Form told him that they feared they too no longer needed him or his stories, but would henceforth practice their Art without his (and here they paused) *interference*.

Our Hero hardly heard them. He could not remove his eyes from the tiny figure of the great god.

8. The Lovers of Sound Triumph

Our Hero was plunged from deep into deepest gloom. He began to wonder whether his talents were, as he had confidently assumed, an asset to mankind. He looked for consolation. There was one group of his assistants of whom he had become moderately fond. He quite respected (and even, occasionally, mildly admired) the delicate power and strong sensitivity of their voices, which seemed to adorn the beauty and deepen the wisdom of his great chants and stories. To these favourites Our Hero now turned for sympathy and support.

"My friends, we have fallen upon evil days and evil tongues. The players and the dancers and the Lovers of Colour and Form tell me they no longer need my words or my stories. But you will, certainly, continue to need me. Sound alone makes no sense. There can be no song without words. I have here composed a little something on the creation of crocodiles and of ants and of grasshoppers. My composition teaches the superiority of mind over body (with particular reference to the superiority of wisdom, prudence and the inner life over dancing, profligacy and the visible world). Please perform it for me. We shall need some sweet-voiced eunuchs to compensate for the absence of dancing girls and costumes, but the central figure should be a man of great authority, grandeur and dignity of voice. If you begin at daybreak the performance should be completed before night falls."

But Our Hero found that even his favoured assistants were not much interested in his problems. He had only just begun to recite the end of the preamble to the foreword to the introduction to the preface of his new composition when the Master Chanter interrupted him.

"O Wise and Wonderful, All-Powerful, Teller of Stories, Knower of Gods and Giver of Laws, just indeed are thy ways and justifiable, but your composition (tremblingly I say it) has too many (far, far too many) *words*. My assistants and I have something to show you. We have discovered that it is possible to make pleasing sounds without any need for stories. Indeed (and I say this with the deepest regret) so magically do these sounds work, that words seem (how shall I put it?) to get in the way, to be (if I dare be so bold) an ugly and tedious *irrelevance*. If we do use words nowadays we find that we have to subordinate them completely to the demands of the new sounds which we make with our natural voices and with instruments which we have fashioned for ourselves from wood and reeds and bronze and cat-gut."

Our Hero was more than a little sceptical about these claims, and was not impressed when showed the new inventions (which seemed capable of a huff or a plunk at best). So the Lovers of Sound invited him to a Grand Ceremony of their own.

Aloft in regal state Our Hero sat on his priestly and imperial throne. The loveliest of his concubines reclined beside him like a blooming eastern bride in the first flower of her youth and beauty.

The Master Chanter placed himself and his tuneful choir in a high gallery unseen. He stroked his lyre delicately. Trembling notes curled round the pillars, climbed the walls, and ascended to the very roof of the temple.

Our Hero was not conscious of hearing anything. But he began to feel much better. All his old confidence came back. He felt content. He felt happy. He felt joyful. He felt the power of his own unconquerable soul. He felt god-like. He *was* a god. He glared imperiously at those who sat around him, defied heaven and earth and seemed (to himself) to be shaking the stars.

The Master, like a nightingale who sings to cheer its own dark solitude, now played a sad soft tune.

Our Hero was entranced by the melancholy of the unseen musician, feeling that he was being moved and softened, yet knowing not whence nor why. His mind filled with the troubles of the world and his own present discontent — a great sea of sorrows. With downcast looks our joyless Hero sat, revolving in his mind the various turns of chance on earth. Now and then he sighed, and tears began to flow.

The mighty Master, up in the gallery, smiled secretly to himself. In gentle tones he soothed Our Hero's soul, inspiring pleasure and soft desire.

Our Hero, unable to conceal his feelings, gazed on his fair concubine and sighed and looked and sighed and looked again. At last, oppressed with love and happiness, our vanquished Hero sunk upon her breast.

The Master struck the golden lyre with a louder and yet a louder strain. The trumpets and drums sounded, breaking the bands of sleep. Our Hero roused himself and started up as if he had heard a rattling peal of thunder or the sudden clash of arms.

And then he realised that he was hearing something more sublime and more serene than any sound he had ever heard or ever imagined. It was a miracle. Either the Lovers of Sound had raised a mere mortal to the sky or they had drawn a spirit down from the very heavens.

For it seemed to Our Hero that every pain and every pleasure — every possible human feeling — could be first prompted and then ruled by tunes and harmonies. And yet the emotions which this music produced were infinitely more beautiful and therefore infinitely more pleasurable than anything he had experienced in ordinary life. They seemed to give his soul complete tranquillity and fulfilment, perfect peace. And yet, again, when listening to the Lovers of Sound, he seemed to feel more truly and more fully alive than he had ever felt before.

Now the Master was singing again, softly in the silent temple.

Our Hero listened, enthralled, enraptured, entranced. It seemed that the heavy and weary weight of the unintelligible world was lightened and lifted. His breath and even the motion of his blood seemed almost suspended. He felt himself to have been laid asleep in body and to have become a living soul, while with an eye made quiet by the power of harmony and a mind stilled by the deep power of joy, he saw (or seemed to see) into the heart of things.

It was long, long before he realised the song was sung in a language to him unknown.

And then he wept.

29

9. The Men of Power Take Control

Mortified, abashed, humiliated, humbled, and once again broken, Our Hero decided from now on to make his stories in words alone. Some of the people, perhaps, would still be prepared to come to the Temple, some of the time, to listen to him. For although he had now parted company with the players and dancers, the Lovers of Colour and Form, and the Lovers of Sound, he still retained his influential positions as Law-giver and Priest and source of all Wisdom. Where but in his stories could laws be found? How else could the gods be known?

But then one day a group of his disciples who had assisted him in the interpretation and administration of the laws and the running and ordering of the Temple and the State came to him suddenly and denounced him saying:

"Wise and Wonderful, Teller of Stories, Knower of Gods, you of all men are least fit to be our Law-Giver and to wield power in our State.

Firstly, you dream endlessly in your stories of how men might be, but your dreams are always contradictory. You say little or nothing of how men and women might best manage the practicalities of life as it must be lived from day to day.

Secondly, you offer us heroines and heroes whose conduct is monstrous and who do nothing but weep and whine and moan and howl. Indeed you seem to approve of weeping, wailing, whining and howling.

Thirdly, you stir up the passions when you should be inculcating the virtues of obedience, self-control, duty, loyalty and a proper respect for the State.

Fourthly, your imaginings are irresponsible and opportunist. You do not seem to be able to resist making subversive suggestions – which are all the more wicked because they make us laugh.

Fifthly, your stories are full of giants and dragons, monsters and self-aggrandising super-men. The State needs men (like us) who deal in reality, who will suppress personal feeling and fight and die manfully for what is right.

You are escapist, unmanly, and a danger to us all. If we keep listening to you the fabric of society will dissolve. Civilisation will crumble.

The only use of your orations is to aid the memory and persuade the people. You have three choices: drink this cup of hemlock, accept perpetual banishment or confine your activities to the recitation of these our LAWS."

With that the chief Man of Power began to describe his edicts.

Our Hero listened grudgingly but was forced to see that here was a system of laws which protected the weak and controlled the strong; which ministered to the needs of the poor while punishing the idle; where justice was tempered by mercy, and where mercy acknowledged the demands of justice. Here was a system where the rights of the one were balanced against the needs of the multitude and those of the multitude against those of the one, so that the punishment meted out to each offender was proportioned to his crime and those were rewarded who served their country well. It was a system by which the the bad might be distinguished from the good; which combined morality with pragmatism.

It was a system which also, Our Hero noticed, contained (in a codicil) the most terrible penalties – incarceration, suffocation, bifurcation, precipitation – for tellers of stories which did not inculcate a proper respect and observance of LAW.

Our Hero struggled manfully with himself for a while beneath the glowering frowns of the Men of Power. But then he broke down and wailed like a beaten child.

From that moment onwards Our Hero was excluded from any position of real influence in the Temples or Palaces of the Law-givers – where his former disciples now held absolute sway.

10. The Priests Protest

Faced with the new Men of Power who believed that the only good stories were those which celebrated their rule, Our Hero (defeated, routed, and once again humiliated) retired to an inner Temple where there were still a few devout men and women willing to hear his stories of gods and men and crocodiles.

But all was not well for long. A substantial and influential group among his audience began to to hold secret meetings in a side-chapel – for they, too, had become seriously dissatisfied.

"Have you noticed," asked one, "that the story the Teller told about the gods this week entirely contradicted those he told last week (which entirely contradicted those he told the week before)?"

"Indeed," said another, "and have you noticed that he sometimes tells the same story in a different way which gives it an entirely different significance?"

"But worst of all," said a third, "he plays fast and loose with the stories he has brought with him from his previous incarnations. He expands and he abridges, he varies and he combines just as the spirits take him. This cannot be right."

"Perhaps," whispered a fourth, "the spirits which inspire him are not true gods at all?"

"Is it not our clear duty," said a fifth, trembling, "to distinguish those stories about the gods which *are* true from those which are damnable lies?"

"I feel," said a sixth rising to his feet, "I feel a spirit within me crying that WE are the true priests, and that the Teller of Stories is a false prophet who must be exposed before he does more harm."

So they came to Our Hero and denounced him saying:

"Wise and Wonderful, Teller of Stories, for your own good, and that of your immortal soul, we must tell you that all your works are dangerous blasphemies. You invent new gods, and new actions for the old. You seem to think that the gods have their birth in your own fanciful mind. We must tell you that there are a fixed number of gods, and that they live, not in your mind, but in their holy places. Not only do you ignore what has been revealed with certainty about the gods, but you describe, at great length and with loving care, that which cannot possibly be known. You describe heaven and hell with as much certainty as you would describe a nearby village. You forget that these are places whose mysteries cannot be known this side of the grave. And you forget that you yourself are destined to reside in one or other of these places after death. If hell is to be your home (as we think likely) you will suffer torments which are beyond human imagining.

When you tell your stories, you forget, and you encourage your audience to forget, that the gods are real, that they observe all things, and that they are WRATHFUL. You and your audience have the wrong attitude, the wrong expressions on your faces. Even when you are describing angry gods, you are relaxed, smiling and at ease. You should be prostrate and trembling.

The presence of a true god is felt in the terror which turns the mind and heart – and the bowels – to water. The gods do not want stories made by men. The gods do not need your tricks to decorate their power and their glory. The gods require obedience, supplication, repentance, sacrifice, burnt offerings, blood. If you were really possessed by a god, as you sometimes claim, you would not have *time* for your ornaments, for all those honeyed words, those pretty metaphors, elegant comparisons and paltry fictions. You would be on your knees, begging for forgiveness, in fear and in trembling.

And your stories are doubly dangerous because you let anyone tell them. You have taught them to foreigners, and you have let the musicians make songs of them. But only the initiated can praise the gods properly, and interpret their Will. Holy stories can only be told under the direction of a true priest: in other mouths the true gods become gods of lies.

The purpose of religion is to pay those honours to the gods which they demand and to ensure that men behave as the gods desire. Your compositions may make men happier; they do not make them

better. But all is not lost. Your soul may yet be saved. We will help you to repent."

And they displayed their whips, their sacrificial knives and their everlasting bonfires.

Our Hero instantly submitted to the will of heaven and retracted all his stories, whimpering.

11. The Lovers of Wisdom Mystify

Rejected by his former associates – the players, the musicians and the Lovers of Colour and Form – expelled from the seats of power, banned from officiating in the temples of the gods, Our Hero was forced to live in retirement and seclusion (in a hut in the garden of the Temple) as a Wise Man.

All went well until a group of his fellow Wise Men began to conduct tests; tests on matter; tests in their minds; tests on numbers and on forms. They began to suspect that there was only one kind of wisdom, and that it was entirely different from the kind which Our Hero claimed to possess.

The Chief Lover of Wisdom and Truth came to Our Hero and said:

"Teller of Stories, I must tell you that five or six friends have been meeting at my chamber and discussing some of your stories and have found themselves utterly confounded by the difficulties and problems they found. Your compositions seemed to be riddled with what appeared to be *logical contradictions*. You seemed to make no distinction between observable reality and the fanciful notions of our ancient ancestors. Indeed (and I speak with trepidation) we have come to suspect that your stories might be FICTIONS.

This is how it happened. For a while we were puzzled by your stories. Then it came into my thoughts that we were taking a wrong course, and that before we set ourselves upon inquiries of this nature, it was necessary to examine your abilities, and see what objects your understanding was or was not fitted to deal with.

For the purposes of ordinary life, it is sometimes necessary to adopt opinions which are demonstrably uncertain, but we wished to give our attention solely to the search after TRUTH, so we thought that an exactly opposite procedure was called for: we ought to reject as

absolutely false all your opinions in regard to which we could suppose the LEAST GROUND for doubt.

At the end of this experiment in thought, nothing of your stories remained. We found ourselves unable to understand your methods – if methods there were – or follow the process of your thought – if thought there was. The most heterogeneous notions – if notions there were – seemed to be yoked together by sheer violence of imagination. You did not appear to be capable of maintaining the separation of your IDEAS – if distinct IDEAS were there at all. In your compositions, the minds of men turn into their bodies, and their bodies into the bodies of animals, and the bodies of animals into the stars."

"But what is truth, and where may it be found?" asked Our Hero flippantly.

"Certainly not in your compositions", was the stern reply.

"We have discovered that you are (at least) as open to error as anyone else. Our conclusion is that we must reject as *almost certainly false* all the stories that we had previously taken as demonstrations of absolute truth.

Solid TRUTH, it has dawned upon us, can only be found by ignoring the senses and the emotions and living by the light of REASON alone.

REASON is the hand-maid of TRUTH. It proceeds by a series of ordered steps, constantly scrutinising its own premises. It concerns itself with questions which can be disproved. It is a discipline of the mind, purely.

It has become apparent to us that when you are composing your poems you cannot separate what you are thinking from the way you are feeling, and the way you are feeling from the moon and the rain. In your orations, the grounds where truth might grow are constantly shifting and sliding. You present human opinion as infinitely various, but real TRUTH, to be known and loved, must be single, constant and uniform. In your stories what is thought is always muddied with distracting emotion and sensation, confusing images and useless analogies.

Above all, it has become plain to us that you use entirely the *wrong words*. The pursuit of TRUTH would certainly have been very much more advanced in the world if the endeavours of ingenious and industrious men (such as ourselves) had not been encumbered by your vague, affected, and ultimately unintelligible terms. Your un-meaning forms of speech have too long passed for the mysteries of knowledge. Hard or misapplied words have for too long been mistaken for deep learning and for the height of all possible speculation.

Your stories and your words, we have concluded, are the covers of ignorance and a hindrance to true knowledge. We will try to clear the ground a little, and remove some of the rubbish that lies in the way. To break in upon your sanctuary of vanity and ignorance will be, I suppose, no small service to human understanding.

You must no longer consider yourself a Wise Man: your truths are lies and your knowledge is as nothing. You are ignorant of your own ignorance and are therefore as ignorant as dirt."

To demonstrate the veracity of his last proposition,

the chief Lover-of-Wisdom then asked Our Hero a few short sharp questions:

What is mind and what is matter?

Where does the body meet the soul – at the base of the spine or the nape of the neck?

Is the will free? Or are all things predestined?

What kind of fish is the crocodile?

Are the gods happy?

And what is happiness?

Why are bees generated from the stomachs of dead goats?

Is there one way of living that is noble and another that is base?

Or are all ways of living equally futile, equally vain?

Why do ships not fall off the edge of the earth?

What is the good? Must the good be eternal?

How large is the sun? How deep the sea?

Is there such a thing as true wisdom?

Our Hero's answers to these questions (or failures to answer these questions – except, perhaps, the one about the crocodile) were ample demonstration that he (if, that was, he might be spoken of as having a separate individual existence) did indeed know nothing, or did not know anything about anything, or did not know what it might be to know anything (or nothing), or if there was any thing to know, or anything to knowing.

12. The Last Straw

Our Hero, once so revered and so privileged, now lost all his power and his pre-eminence, and found his lustre sadly tarnished. He was still sometimes permitted to act as an assistant to those who had formerly served him. He was from time to time instructed to compose hymns to the gods. The painters occasionally asked him for a few phrases to grace their latest monument. The musicians now and again needed some words for a song. The Lovers of Wisdom once in a long while invited him to praise the purity of Truth. The Men of Power twice or thrice ordered him to celebrate this great victory, or that great tyrant.

But whenever he was given an important job, he botched it. When asked for a song, he produced a sermon. When he was ordered to describe the king or the gods as noble and glorious beings, they always emerged as somehow slightly stupid. Whenever he was compelled to celebrate a great and famous victory, his work seemed more like a condemnation of war. When told to praise the virtues of wisdom and peace, he couldn't help hinting at the pleasures of folly and the wild excitements of complete destruction.

His reputation withered as a flower in a cold wind. He was, once again, a person of small importance and no repute, stumbling along behind the crowd of men. He rediscovered his old interest in moaning and wailing, and set off heart-broken for his secret place, to howl.

On the way he met a merchant going to market with his wife and child. Falling in together, they turned aside for a few minutes at a wayside inn. The merchant was surprised to find Our Hero in such a condition. Some signs of former grandeur could be discerned amongst his rags. Our Hero, glad of a sympathetic ear, spoke of his misfortunes and how he had been rejected and spurned by all his disciples.

"But perhaps you and your good lady might enjoy the occasional recitation? Perhaps something about how the crocodile became? – quite wrong of course, horribly inaccurate, but possibly entertaining? Something to while away the long evenings? I know I am old-fashioned, but gentlefolk of your obvious discernment might be prepared to overlook some deficiencies here and there? My voice is nothing to crow about, I must admit, and I can only shuffle."

"Teller of Stories," said the merchant, "I used to go to the Temple in my younger days of course – had some good times there too – the Song of the Frogs' Spawn – excellent piece – was that one of yours? – and that God of Retribution – did you make that? – I could sell any number of those – but since I became a man I put aside childish things – And besides I have no time – wife and children to support – nose to the grindstone. But my wife, now she is fond of a good story."

"Well I used to be," replied the merchant's wife, smiling at the child in her arms. "But now I haven't the time – you know how it is."

"That is very sad," said Our Hero.

"What you need is a new trade," said the merchant. "There are so many opportunities nowadays for someone with a bit of go in him. I am sure I could find you something. You had – I remember – some sort of gift with words, didn't you? Perhaps we could make a salesman of you yet. You'd have to clean yourself up a bit of course and get rid of that high-falutin manner. What do you say?"

"I'm not sure I am fitted for such an occupation," said Our Hero.

"If you don't mind me saying so, that is the trouble with people of your generation – all that stuff about crocodiles and who made the world – no sense of utility! Now priests, priests we do need – for without religion there can be no ethics – and without at least *some* morality, commerce – I can tell you – is difficult. And laws, obviously we must have laws – and lawyers too (though it goes against the grain to have to say it). And Lovers of Wisdom – funny lot – but there's money to be made from their discoveries –

they know a thing or two, believe me. But stories? – Where's the utility? We've got to have men of power too – Can't have brigandage, instability and disorder – bad for business, very bad. Not too keen on wars myself, but the Barbarians must be kept down, and you never know where the odd penny can be picked up – Prepared to pay for it too – Taxation no tyranny – if you get my drift – if it's not too steep. And Players? Why it's good to go to a tavern of an evening to watch a juggler or two – join in the odd chorus of the old Frog Song – and (while my wife isn't listening, just between you and me) to see the dancing girls – helps a man relax after a hard day's work. But stories – long stories in fancy dress? – What's the point of that? – Now me, I help to keep the whole system going – five slaves and a freedman I feed and clothe. Where do you think your robes came from? – (that's real gold braid isn't it?). That doesn't grow on trees, you know. Without me and my kind we'd all be living in caves. But stories – what's the use? – where's the profit?"

"I fear they may have little utility. Clearly there is no profit."

"In that case I don't think we can do business. There doesn't seem to be much call for stories nowadays. I've forgotten those I used to know. Still – sorry to hear things are bad and that you've been hoist by your own petard, to coin a phrase. Neither a borrower nor a lender – that's my motto – cash on the nail. It's a hard, hard world out there – nature red in tooth and claw, I say. Still kind hearts are better than coronets, and hard cash better than either. Put money in your purse I always say. Go back to your former associates – I mean to err is human, to forgive is divine. There's method in their madness. Fools rush in, don't you know – and get yourself a good wife. Ever had a wife? – A few, a few? – Yes better to have loved and lost than never to have loved at all, I always say – don't I love? – None but the brave deserve the pretty little things.

Still, must be off. Sorry I can't help."

Our Hero began to cry. The Merchant's wife kissed him.

"Don't mind my husband – he's not a very sensitive man. I did like your ceremonies sometimes (especially the ones about the loves of the gods) but they went on too long and I fell asleep. There were too many hard words, and long ones. I would rather be outside in the sun. But you are old and love old things – old stories and old gods – but there is a life to be lived here and now, or," (and she glanced, blushing, at her stomach) "three lives now. I love life you see. I love it at first hand. I love my husband, fool though he sometimes is, and my pretty prattler and my flowers and this sunny evening with the shadows now and my young friends and (in your ear and between ourselves) a young man of our town. I can see you are a kind and gentle man. Would you mind blessing the baby – just for safety's sake and for old times? Here is some money."

Our Hero took the Merchant's coin. There was nothing else to do.

"Thank you – and for the drink."

13. A Complaint

Heart-broken Our Hero went to his secret place to moan.

His secret place was a garden which contained a solemn grove. This grove was the dwelling place of his great secrets – or so our Hero had always believed.

His great secrets were his personal spirits or demons.

They did not always come when he called.

It was sometimes hard to tell if they were speaking. Or was it the wind in the trees? Or the ripples of the fountain? Or his own disordered mind?

The Spirits had never revealed themselves. (When he was in their presence Our Hero considered it decorous to keep his eyes firmly on the ground.) But he knew (from some sneaked glimpses) that they were beautiful beyond dreams, powerful beyond terror, and wise beyond imagination.

He was, always had been, always would be, their slave.

Our melancholy Hero lay down where the yew's unlucky green mixed with the mourning willow's care-full grey; he lay down and wept.

He spoke from the sickness of his heart. He spoke to the hills and the trees, and to the world. Most sonorously of all, he spoke to the Spirits themselves. His complaint, even as he uttered it, contained, he felt sure, some masterly strokes:

"O woods and fountains, hills and dales and bowers, I taught your woods to ring with other tones than these of woe. How is my greatness fallen, fallen! For I, so lately the glory of the world, a wise and wonderful King, a teller of stories, a dancer of dances, a singer of songs, a builder of buildings, a knower of gods and a giver of laws, am now accursed, abused, despised, rejected, grieved. Hide me from the face of gods and men, ye shades. From earth I was made and to earth I shall return.

Did I request you, O Spirits (Demons rather), to mould me a man of unusually delicate sensibilities, to make me an inveterate dreamer of dreams, and a compulsive teller of stories? Did I ask you to promote me from quiet obscurity, and place me in the forefront of men? I thought once that you loved me, cherished me, honoured me, nourished me, but now I know you could not bear more hatred to any mortal than you have shown to your most devoted slave – than you have shown, cruel Spirits, to me.

You betrayed my early, tender, simple youth. When I lay in the cradle, innocently, helplessly, you wicked Spirits stole my will away and carried my soul into new-found worlds – I know not where – where you forced me to dream the dreams of the tribe. You winged my thoughtless youth with vain desires of greatness. You misled my manhood with wandering fires. I followed your false lights; and when their glimpse was gone, my pride struck new sparkles of her own. O fleeting joys of pride, dear bought with lasting woe!

And then you planted me in a world – a cruel, false world – where only the basest fools flourish; where the only arts are the arts of envy; where pride and ignorance are the only result of learning.

This was my error, O my Spirits, this my gross mistake – to do your bidding in a world that has no regard for you, or yours. I have been climbing on rotten boughs. I have been casting pearls before swine. I have been wasting my great talents and your fine powers on creatures who have no taste; offering bread to those whose appetites are dead. No one takes me seriously, no one regards me. I am thought a trifler or worse – a corrupter and trivializer of all things serious and weighty. My occupation has gone. I am maimed and unuseful to the government and the state. The world has no need of me.

So farewell! False world, farewell! My part is ended on your stage. I see now that all your forms and customs are studied deceits, and what are called your gifts are traps and snares. This whole wide world is a shop of toys and trifles where every good is up for sale.

Now you have deserted me, O Spirits, left me without hope and without capacities. On all matters there are men and women who know (or profess to know) more than I know – who claim to excel me as the sun outshines the stars. The exercise of power is beyond me. The only laws I know are your laws – and those I do not understand. I have clay feet and cannot dance. I have cloth ears and cannot sing. I am a liar who cannot think, a dauber who cannot see, and a devil-worshipper who cannot pray. I am less than

nothing. I would gladly lay me down to death as in my mother's lap. I will embrace oblivion as a bride and hug it in my arms. Into what an abyss of fears and sorrows have you driven me – out of which I find no way, from deep to deeper plunged."

On the ground outstretched Our Hero lay, on the cold ground, and cursed his creation, lamenting loud through the still night.

His wails and moans and howls echoed impressively through the silent garden.

Part Two:
A History of Poets

14. A Heavenly Spirit Replies

When, Lo! a heavenly spirit appeared before Our Hero's wearied eyes, a spirit seen in and by a blinding light. She stepped – or seemed to step – from the pool or from the fountain. She bore – or seemed to bear – a golden lyre with silver strings in her lovely hands. She wore – or seemed to wear – a wondrous hieroglyphic robe, rippling in the air with loose pride, a robe which was adorned with all the colours and all the shapes that nature or fancy can create.

She touched Our Hero gently on the arm and raised him from the ground. The shaken strings of the lyre resounded melodiously.

"Renegade! Ingrate! Have you returned at last to your forsaken secret place? Have you returned at long long last to me? You Prodigal who wasted the good estate of all your youthful years, have you returned here, fearing too soon and repenting too late, to gather up some dry husks of learning – now that the rich harvest time of life is past and winter marches quickly on?"

"Husks of learning? O Spirit, I do not understand."

"I meant to adopt you as my chosen son. I assigned to you as learned a portion as ever any of my eight sisters gave their dearest children. I resolved to exalt your name among the Spiritual Lords of Peaceful Fame."

"The Lords of what?"

"But, Changeling! you were bewitched with noise and show, and forsook me for the courts and cities of men. You longed to see the world and to have a share in all the follies and the tumults there. You wanted to be *something* in a State and to make business for yourself – business, the thing which I hate above all things, business, the contradiction of your Fate!"

"For a while things were well."

"But what have you now?"

"Nothing, is what I have now – no honour, no wealth, no power, no influence, no wives, no concubines, no ... "

"That is entirely as it should be."

"It is?"

"A Poet can serve only one mistress. A Poet must leave father, mother, and cleave to his Muse alone. He must have the constancy of a martyr to suffer for her sake."

"A what?

"A POET."

"... and his what?"

"His MUSE. I am your Muse – the Muse of Poetry."

"You are? But I thought there were many of you."

"There was your mistake. One is enough for any genius – so vast is art, so narrow human wit."

"But, Celestial Being, I have been denounced by many, rejected by all. Will one art, however vast, make me rich and powerful in the world?"

"In the *world*? Certainly not! Come, forget the loathsome world. Have not proud and impudent fools usurped your sacred seat in the Temple?"

"They have, they have."

"Let their empty minds and vapid mouths run on and rage and rave; they were not made for you, still less you for them."

"They weren't? I wasn't?"

"Strike a disdainful strain, so that these fools will envy your song, and see that there is no weakness in *your* brain, no palsy in *your* soul. Leave things so prostitute and take up my lyre."

"Your lyre? And will that make me rich and powerful again?"

"My child, you have not understood. The Lyre is a symbol."

"A symbol?"

"You, my Chosen One, are a POET – a maker. POETRY is what you will make. I am your MUSE, your inspiration, your guide – the source and end and test of your Art."

"And what, O Heavenly Spirit, is poetry?"

"Poetry is the image of Man and Nature."

"I see," said Our Hero (seeing nothing at all).

"Poetry is the record of the best and happiest moments of the happiest and best minds."

"I see," said Our Hero (blankly).

"Poetry turns to shape the creations of the Imagination and the Invention; giving a local habitation and a name to airy nothings. It animates matter, embodies sentiment and calls new powers into being. Poetry is a comprehension and expanse of thought which fills the whole mind with rational astonishment and ravishing transports of delight, and fills the hidden recesses of the heart with sudden sweetness."

"I see," said Our Hero (in total confusion).

"Poetry makes immortal all that is best and most beautiful in the world; it arrests the vanishing apparitions which haunt the interlunations of life and veiling them in language, sends them forth among mankind bearing sweet news of kindred joy."

"I see," said Our Hero (with mounting desperation).

"Poetry, like the unchanging sun, clears and improves whatever it shines upon; it turns all things to loveliness; it exalts the beauty of that which is most beautiful, and it adds beauty to that which is most deformed; it marries exultation and horror, grief and pleasure, eternity and change."

"I see," said Our Hero (floundering wildly, helplessly, hopelessly in the dark).

15. The Poet's Fame

Our Hero, though raised from the cold ground, was kept on his knees by a mixture of awe and simple astonishment. Eventually his lovely Muse sat down beside him in the long dewy grass and embraced his shoulders lightly with her slender arms.

Though bemused, he was much comforted by the heavenly apparition. He looked around his secret place contentedly. It was a garden so lovely that it appeared to have been created by Nature herself. Here it was perpetual spring and eternal autumn: the boughs of the trees were covered with laughing blossoms and tender buds, and at the same time laboured under a weight of ripening fruit. A dimpling fountain supplied many a stream which meandered through the matted grass, watering flowers of every hue, and gathering again in a pool as calm and smooth as a mirror of crystal.

By day the garden was quiet and wholesome. On one side, there were shady grottoes and caves of cool recess over which the mantling vine displayed her purple grapes. On another side there was a pleasant arbour – formed, it seemed, by the trees' own inclinations, by the trees themselves knitting their branches part to part and enticing the wanton Ivy and the Eglantine to climb amongst them. The joyous birds sung like a choir and the leaves trembled in harmony. The rich trees wept odorous gums and sweetest balm.

"I cannot promise you riches, nor concubines as a matter of course, but LOVE, My Poet, enduring LOVE, and lasting FAME, will be yours in abundance – eternal, universal FAME."

"But I have fallen upon evil days and evil tongues. No one loves me. No one remembers me. I have no fame at all. I am, O Heavenly Spirit, generally despised."

"There is a world of difference between LOVE and popularity, between eternal FAME and temporary renown. I challenge Time to declare whether the FAME and GLORY of any of your former disciples will compare with that of my Greater Poets."

"How can this be? The players and the dancers, and the painters and the sculptors, and the singers and the musicians, have each and all excelled me at what I once thought was my very own game."

"I am more powerful than my sister-Muses."

"You are?

"Ours is an exceptional medium."

"What is our medium?"

"Why words, my Poet, words, words, words. Language is produced by the human Imagination and has relation to thoughts alone. Language may be expressed in gestures, or embodied in sounds, or denoted in written signs. It is a purely human invention; its laws are purely human laws. But all other materials, instruments and conditions of art have relations among each other, which limit and interpose between conception and expression. My sisters, unlike myself, must obey the secondary laws of matter."

"Alas, alas, Heavenly Spirit, I do not understand a single word you speak."

"Language is as a mirror which reflects: sound and colour and wood and stone are like a cloud which enfeebles the *force* of human thought and feeling," said the Muse, trying hard to accommodate herself to her pupil.

"(You wouldn't say that if you had seen the little god of Retribution, or had heard the Master Chanter's song to my enchanted soul.)"

"Hence the FAME of sculptors, painters and musicians will never equal that of my POETS – my POETS, who will use the wonders of language as the means of colouring, translating, picturing, presenting, embodying, expounding, expressing, arranging, aggrandising, communicating, trapping, stilling, moving or creating their thoughts. The renown of my POETS will extend ..."

"But the Priests, the Men of Power and the Lovers of Wisdom and Truth – their fame already extends to the furthest boundaries of the world."

"There is a difference between renown which extends across one age and eternal FAME. The FAME of founders of religions and the FAME of inventors of systems of government alone will exceed that of my POETS. But their FAME is dependent upon the course of the world and is affected by chance events: yours is carried alive into the heart by passion and by love. It will be co-extensive with the spirit of humanity."

"Co-extensive with the spirit of what? How can this be?"

"The original inspiration of the founders of religion and the inventors of laws (often, I must admit, provided by myself) will be diluted and modified by Time and changes of custom. No civilisation, no arrangement of political, economic and legal bonds between beings wanting or forced to live with one another will ever come near to embodying the full range of potentialities, or to acknowledging the full power of the limitations which you mortals find within yourselves (when you think deeply). The history of civilisations will be a cyclical history. Something will be gained by each but something will also be lost. Political systems, economic organisations, social arrangements of all kinds,

laws, even systems of thought and religions will survive the civilisations that produce them only in tenuous and modified forms. One Lover of Wisdom and Truth will replace another. Laws will be silently repealed in letter and in spirit. Ancient gods will die. But your work, My POET, your spirit, your flame, will live again and again in every age with all the fire and force (and sometimes more) of its first inception."

"O Heavenly Spirit, my fire (if I had one) is quite extinguished. I have no force at all."

"On the contrary," said the Muse, raising herself to her full height and almost chanting, "you are a great begetter. You, Soul of all Future Poets, are the rock of defence for human nature: an upholder and preserver. In spite of difference of soil and climate, of language and manners, of laws and customs; in spite of things gone silently out of mind and things violently destroyed you will bind together, by passion and knowledge and by the power of Love, the vast Empire of Human Society as it is spread over the whole earth and over all time."

"But I cannot sell my stories; no, not for the price of a drink."

"In your future incarnations (or some of them), when your great soul inhabits human form, you will find that Poetry will be considered as the highest learning and will be regarded with a veneration approaching that which men pay to the gods."

"The highest learning, you say, but alas, I know nothing. It has been conclusively demonstrated that I am as ignorant as dirt."

16. The Poet's Task

Our Hero's confusion increased with every word that fell from the lips of his Muse. He was more convinced than ever that his ignorance was boundless and unyielding. He began to feel hungry, and glanced at some overhanging grapes with longing eyes – while feeling that it would be somehow not quite proper to interrupt his fair Instructress (who seemed to be warming to her subject).

"Now you are a Poet, you must see everything with a new purpose. Your sphere of attention must be magnified."

"With which subject shall I begin?"

"No kind of knowledge is to be overlooked."

"I must know *everything*?"

"You must range mountains and deserts for images and resemblances, and picture to your mind every tree of the forest and every flower of the valley. You must observe with equal care the crags of the rock and the pinnacle of the palace. You must wander the mazes of the rivulet and watch the changes of the summer clouds."

"Of what use to a poet is a knowledge of the weather?"

"To a Poet nothing can be useless."

"Nothing?"

"Whatever is beautiful and whatever is awe-inspiring must be familiar to your Imagination – must exist in your mind with all the quiddity it has in the world. The plants of the garden, the animals of the wood, the minerals of the earth, the meteors of the sky, must all come together to store your mind with inexhaustible variety; for every image is useful for the decoration or expression or embodiment of truth; and he who knows most will have most power of diversifying his scenes and of gratifying his audience with remote allusions and unexpected instruction."

"My allusions have often been remote but, alas, seldom gratifying. My audiences do not seem to have shared my great fondness for cedars and crocodiles ... and (now I think of it) grapes."

"Knowledge of nature is only half the task of a Poet. You must be acquainted likewise with all the modes of life."

"All? Did you say *all*?"

"You must estimate the happiness and misery of every condition, observe the power of all the passions in all their combinations, and trace the changes of the human mind, as they are modified by various institutions and accidental influences of climate and custom, from the sprightliness of infancy to the despondency of decrepitude."

"*All* the passions? *Every* condition? It is not possible."

"It is essential. For you must divest yourself of the prejudices of your age and country."

"But my age and my country make me what I am."

"You must consider right and wrong in their abstract and unvarying state."

"How can I do that? I am what I am. I know what I know."

"You must disregard *present* laws and opinions, and rise to general and transcendental truths which will always be the same."

"Always the same? In a world of perpetual change?"

"In the eyes of poets and of gods, always the same."

"And then, Heavenly One, I will be rich and famous?"

"You must therefore condemn the applause of your own time, and commit your claims to the justice of posterity – to the warm Love of *future* generations."

"I was afraid of that," said Our Hero, sadly, to himself.

"You must write as the Interpreter of Nature and the Legislator of Mankind."

"I will be the law-giver to the world?"

"Yes, but unacknowledged – the unacknowledged legislator of mankind."

"(Just as I feared – another catch.)"

"You must consider yourself as presiding over the thoughts and manners of future generations as a being superior to time and place."

"I see," said Our Hero, who, since he had met his Muse, had in fact seen nothing but her glowing form. "When shall I begin?"

"Begin! When you have learned all these things you will still be only on the foot-hills of knowledge. You must know many languages and you must, by incessant practice, familiarise yourself with every delicacy of speech and grace of harmony. Then your words may be worthy of your thoughts, and your thoughts worthy of your words. You must learn the DANCE OF WORDS, THE SONGS OF THOUGHT, THE IMAGES OF WISDOM – for by these means you may peer deep into the abyss of the Human Soul."

"The abyss of the human soul? Enough, Bright Goddess, you have convinced me that no human being can ever be a Poet!"

"It is quite true that no individual, no single mortal, could be a Poet. Behind every Poet a thousand, thousand other Poets will sing – your sons, your future selves. You must not expect to be a Poet in your first incarnation, nor in your five-hundredth, but a Poet, I swear, you will be. You will bless savage nations with the soft arts of peace, and fill the world with Love."

"I do not doubt your veracity but wonder how this can be. Do words have such power?" asked Our Hero – for whom words seemed to have no power at all.

"Long is the road, and life, alas, allows but one ill winter's day to each incarnation. But triumph you will, and over every difficulty, even those which might lead a weaker spirit to despair. You, my Chosen Soul, shall triumph even where most of my sisters' progeny fail. You will root, blossom and flower where they find a barren and rocky soil. To comfort and inspire you I will tell the story of one of your future triumphs – an astonishing and famous victory – over the most intractable obstacles ever to be faced by a Poetic Soul."

17. The Muse's Greatest Conquest

"Far, far from here, far from the Garden of the Muses, there is a damp, dour little island pounded by a cold northern sea. There will be few places in the whole wide world less hospitable to those of our delicate, sensitive and profound disposition. It will be a fen of stagnant waters where mud flows from a muddy spring. Long, long after many other parts of the the world have welcomed my sisters and myself with open and with longing arms, this island will be peopled by a grumbling, headstrong, moody, murmuring race of brutish, slow-witted savages – haters of thought, haters of Art.

Although, at last, they will make a few impressive buildings, and although an occasional Lover of Wisdom and Truth will argue a strong case, the inhabitants of this island will have precious little painting, or music, or sculpture of which they might be proud or from which they might take sustenance.

And yet, enclouded in insensibility, cloth-eared, dull-eyed, they will hardly notice this loss, this impoverishment, this spiritual disability. They will be unashamed, indeed proud, of their crass and eternal mediocrity. Instead, they will rejoice in their prowess as Men of Power – as traders, pirates, inventors, exploiters, administrators, prevaricators, soldiers, thieves. It will not matter to them that the civil peoples of the world will regard them as a nation of cold hypocrites, dull philistines and perfidious shop-keepers. They will laugh when their own sharpest minds call them the most miserable race of vermin to crawl on the face of the earth.

Their language will be capable of infinite distinctions and therefore of infinite evasions. There will always be *something* that they will prefer to naked truth. They will have no language of love or tenderness and will seem to their neighbours to be incapable of true belief or real passion. Even their religion will be godless, a compromise, an evasion. Their temples (fine buildings some of them) will be places where dilettante, delicate-handed priests intone the platitudes of complacency and self-congratulation.

Their national characteristic will be a combination of meekness (or false modesty) and arrogance – the masks of dullness, fear and pride. They will be content to dwell in decencies for ever: in decency without generosity. They will grumble perpetually at their lot, at the same time having an absolute conviction that nothing is managed better elsewhere; that what they do not know is not worth knowing; that what they cannot do is not worth doing.

They will act always with an eye to the main chance. The principle of Self of which money is the visible incarnation will be the true god of their world. They will believe that they live by bread alone. Friendship, brotherhood, fatherhood, love, will freeze in the icy waters of cold-blooded calculation. The poor will believe there is no sin but to be rich, and the rich that there is no vice but beggary.

The inhabitants of this Isle will enlarge the limits of empire over the external world while becoming circumscribed in the internal world. The more they seem to know and rule the outer world, the less the inner world will be open to them. Having enslaved the elements, they will remain slaves to their own unknowingness of themselves.

And yet, (if you learn your lessons well) your descendants will succeed in harmonising this slippery language and mollifying the harsh souls of this tribe of brutes. I myself will forsake the pleasant groves of this garden for those wet dales and, for years on end, will adopt that dour island for my chosen dwelling. Together, my Poet, we will fill this northern land with gentle murmurs, sweet complaining, and sighs that warm the embers of desire. By virtue of our works (and our works alone, *alone*! I say) this Northern Clime will become a green and pleasant land, an isle excelling all others, a seat of pleasure, of Poetry, and, My Chosen Soul, of Love.

18. The Temple of Poets

"Such a conquest," said Our Hero, "is surely beyond me. All that I have had to endure in previous incarnations is nothing to this horror – to the sterility of this grim land."

"I will show you your sons," replied the Muse complacently, "sons who will throw off the encumbrances and circumscriptions of that Northern Isle like dewdrops from a lion's mane."

As the Muse spoke, Our Hero felt the ground billowing gently beneath his feet. "O ye gods who live in perfect bliss," he cried, "save and preserve me from witchcraft and demons, from fantasy and illusion!" He had a distinct sensation of rising. Where there had been green hills there were now rosy clouds. The Garden of the Muses was floating softly upwards. But the birds still sang and the fountain still played.

"O gods that created all things," said Our Hero, "is there no other way for me to die?"

The floating garden tilted slightly, flinging Our Hero, tottering, to the flowery bank which now formed the margin of his world. Below him he saw now fields and plains, now hills, valleys, forests and rivers, now cities and tiny ships sailing on a golden sea. He clung desperately to a rose tree which, luckily, was without thorn.

"Do not fear," said the Muse, settling beside him, and cooling his fevered brow with her silken hand, "we are entering an over-extended, over-elaborated *fancy*."

"I see," said Our Hero. "When will it end?"

Slightly below him and to one side, a large building hove into view constructed entirely out of the finest adamant. If all the men and all the women who have ever lived were to pool their wisdom and their eloquence, thought Our Hero, they could never describe the beauty of this building as it catches the rays of the morning sun in the clear blue sky.

"This," said the Muse, "is the Temple of Poetry, and the home of some of the Future Lords of Peaceful Fame."

"I see," said Our Hero (bedazzled).

The Temple of Poetry floated on a cloud, as now did the Garden of the Muses. The two clouds drifted slowly together but there was a noticeable gap of pure but wispy cloud betwixt and between.

"Let us enter," said the Muse.

"Not today," said Our Hero.

"Have faith," said the Muse. "You shall tread like an airy spirit."

"Am I here in spirit or in body?"

"Body and soul," said the Muse, embracing her pupil with a firm arm.

The Temple of Poetry, which had filled Our Hero's view, even when he had seen it from a distance, now seemed as large as a mountain. It was constructed, it appeared of massy towering pillars forming ever lessening squares, receding towards a centre which was hidden from his view but from which shone a peculiarly clear, bright, unchanging light.

"Here dwell," said the Muse, "the shades of your future selves – or possible future selves. They are owed a body by Fate but their existence depends on you – depends upon the purity of your attention to my words and on your more-than-human courage, faith, fortitude and endurance. (Their position in the Temple, however, depends in part on the love and praise of future men and women.) They are the images of lives and minds and bodies which are destined for you, my Chosen One, for you. In this place they await their time in the world, and to this place they will return when all their work is done. Long, long has my soul desired this time and this place, to set before your sight your glorious race, so that presaging joy may fire your mind to undergo the incarnations designed by Destiny! Let us survey this airy throng of your most honoured progeny."

The Muse and her Poet stepped lightly from their cloud and walked or drifted or floated or flew towards the gleaming pillars of the Temple of Poetry.

19. Failed, Forgotten and Lesser Poets

A vast swarm of shades reclined on the cloud around the Temple of Poetry or sat on the lower steps leading to the first set of pillars. Some cast longing eyes towards the inner regions but made no attempt to ascend the stairs. Our Hero noticed that the feet of many were pointing in the wrong direction.

"These," said the Muse (who, now as almost always, had divined Our Hero's thought), "are shades of the Failed Poets – those who will write verse instead of Poetry (and nothing is more ridiculous than a would-be Poet). Here also are the shades of those who will *want* to be Poets, but lacking the courage, will compose nothing at all or (what is the same to me) choose mere prose. They are our friends, however. They will provide us with useful plots and telling phrases from time to time. We shall smile upon them as we pass (but condescendingly)."

The Muse was lightly ascending the first step of the Temple of Poetry when Our Hero was distracted by jeering, snarling, jarring, sneering sounds which issued from small barred windows let into some of the lower steps – a cacophony which seemed to be incited anew by the sight of our Hero and his Muse.

"Those," said the Muse frowning, "are not our friends – they are the critics – lice in the locks of literature. But do not mind them: they make good subjects for satire." Our Hero peered into the subterranean gloom and saw innumerable figures preening each other and themselves, each with a mirror in his hand.

"Their mirrors, which they take to be Mirrors of Art, are in fact only the mirrors of Self. You need have no pity for these. Such as they are, they are content to be. They are the waste disposal system of the Temple of Poetry. If any unwanted morsel floats down they tear it into shreds and

devour it – converting it into their own dull matter where it becomes quite harmless."

Our Hero and his Muse passed through the first set of towering pillars. Before them a multitude of shades with steady, silent, unwavering footsteps trod and trod again an endless circle round the Temple of Poetry.

"Behold your sons and daughters," said the Muse. "This is the region of the Undeservedly Unfamous, the Forgotten Poets. They are, as I see you are thinking, almost without number. But though of some the names, and of others the works will be lost to Fame, they will be important to you in your successful incarnations and essential to the continuing life of our Art."

"But no one will speak their name?" said Our Hero, pained.

"Not for generations. But they live in constant hope. It may always happen that a Forgotten Poet will be rediscovered and pass, yea, even into the inner regions of the Temple."

"How can it be that so many of my sons and daughters will be so forgotten? Are they true poets? Can you not save them?"

"Some I will visit only very occasionally: their True Poetry will be lost among a pile of trash. Others, though genuine incarnations of your spirit and fully loved by me, will have the misfortune to compose in a language that dies beyond recovery. Many will never tell another living soul of what they have made. Some will belong to tribes that are obliterated. Many will suffer from the accidents to which all mortal things are subject. Most will compose before there is a means by which their makings may be easily given to the world."

"Alas! Let us leave the region of the Undeservedly Unfamous," said Our Hero, not much elated by the prospect before him.

The Muse led her poet on past a second set of columns into a chamber filled to bursting with the shades of men and women, talking and reciting at the tops of their voices and with an energy and vehemence which took Our Hero somewhat aback.

"A Forgotten Poet, I might add, may quite easily become a Lesser Poet – whose noble region we are now entering," said the Muse, smiling. "You have no need to be dejected for these your children. The term 'lesser' is entirely relative. Here, at the outer edge, are sons who will manage only a little, but that little will be sufficient to ensure an everlasting Fame. Some will earn an eternal place even for a single poem; many for a select handful. Those towards the centre of this region will be widely loved and much esteemed. In many ways, they will be loved more than the Greater Poets whose shades reside in the innermost region."

"Why should this be?"

"The ways of mortals are strange. The innermost circle of the Temple is for those most warmly loved and revered by other Poets, by me and by the gods. Their names will be sacred. But some mortals will seem to find the Lesser Poets easier to know and therefore to love. For mortal beings, there seems to be something daunting, almost repulsive, in the *sublimity* of great achievement. The compositions of Lesser Poets will sometimes have a very human incompleteness and a very human limitation of mind. But do not be downcast. These too live in hope, and those Lesser Poets near the centre can easily pass their waiting years in sweet discourse with the sacred shades in the innermost region."

"Celestial Goddess, may I make an observation? The nearer we come to the centre, the fewer *female* shades there seem to be. Why should this be? I seem dimly to recall inhabiting the bodies of priestesses and queens in past incarnations (when I enjoyed life eight times more than I do now). Will I cease to be reincarnated in female form?"

"This matter is a mystery – a mystery even to me, and possibly to the gods themselves. If you should visit the Temples of my sister Muses you would see the same pattern repeated. It is a mystery because Poetry and the other Arts will not, like war, be taken as the peculiar province of males. Despite all male contempt, despite the obligations of maternity, despite the malignancy of patriarchies, you *will* compose Poetry in your female incarnations. And even while inhabiting a male body, women will be the subject of your compositions and women will be (at least) half your audience. A Poet endeavouring to speak for all mankind must inhabit (in reality or in imagination) the souls of both men and women. And yet the fact remains. Few female shades wait near the centre. I should warn you that though many aspiring Poets will be called, few will be chosen. Legion are those who will think of being Poets, and multitudes are those who will fail to be Poets. Small is the number of those who will earn the glorious name even of Lesser Poet, and there are few, few indeed of either sex, who will inhabit the innermost region of the Temple of Poetry."

20. A Banquet of Greater Poets

The innermost region of the Temple of Poetry is illuminated by a shaft of ethereal light from above. All is peace save for the soft music of delicate laughter. At the centre stands a golden table at which the shades of future Poets sit, or recline on couches, their brows crowned with roses, with myrtle and with laurel. The banquet is not large; the chamber, though not overflowing, is full.

"We are now," said the Muse, "in the hallowed place where the shades of the Greater Poets reside in perfect bliss. These are the Future Lords of Highest Song placed here by peaceful Fame and right Rumour. Behold the legislators of Mankind – your sons!"

Our Hero was not impressed. He thought he had seen fairer forms than any he saw before him now. The Muse, however, seemed rapt with joy.

"Forever green with bays each Greater Poet sits, far above the reach of sacrilegious hands, secure from flames, from envy's fiercer sting, destructive war, and all-involving age. From each region of the earth the learned will bring their incense. In all tongues consenting paeans of just praise will ring. The general chorus of mankind will resound their Fame even to the four corners of the World!"

"You say my sons are apportioned their places according to the dictates of Fame and Rumour," said Our Hero (who had taken a dislike to the hierarchy of the Temple of Poetry). "What is the distinction between these goddesses?"

"The distinction is not clear."

"Not even to you?"

"Particularly not to me."

"Does that mean that these banqueters are here on false pretences? Or that they can be suddenly ejected and sent to live in the outer regions?"

"No, their place is assured. Their work (as I promised) will be co-extensive with humanity."

"How can this be? If Fame is no more than the servant or executor of Rumour, how can the Greater Poets preserve this security? And how may they be distinguished from the Lesser?"

"The chambers of the Temple of Poetry (as you have seen) are not sharply distinguished one from another but allow considerable free passage to and fro. However, most of your descendants (those you have already seen) will master only a few of my Arts, and only fragments of their work will last for ever."

"Does life allow *more* than this?"

"Yes, indeed. The Poets at the centre of this inner chamber will compose at least one great work or a large body of interrelated shorter Poems by which the whole of mortal life will seem to be illuminated and in which all humanity will seem to be included, encapsulated."

"How can this be?"

"In these incarnations, you will rise above all others as the eagle soars above the wren or as the cypress towers over the waving field. The Lords of Highest Song will be revered for having advanced the claims of mankind to be a sentient species."

"All you are saying is that they are here because of a concurrence of favourable rumour?"

"Because many generations and many nations will concur in the same decision, and, most of all, because they themselves will agree with the choice."

"I do not understand."

"These Lords of Highest Song (your sons) will place their predecessors in this hallowed chamber and justify their veneration by the power of emulation."

"Emulation?"

"*More* than emulation. These banqueters are placed here by true lineage and descent. Each will derive his supremacy from a predecessor, and by acknowledging his debt he will ensure that predecessor's longevity of Fame. The Lesser

Poets will (by and large) also agree as to who should inhabit the inner regions of the Temple. They will admire superior sense and doubt their own."

"What are the conditions by which one can become a Greater Poet?"

"It is not easy to say. Madness is an obstacle to greatness, of course, but so are laziness, dishonesty and lack of nerve. Great Poets will have greater powers (for I will give them such) – particularly of Imagination and Invention."

"To what end?"

"In the first place, they will imagine that greater things can be *done* with Poetry, and they will then do those things with larger and more active Imaginations. Their minds are larger; their souls more comprehensive: their skill infinitely greater. They are *driven* to compose Poetry, and they are driven by me personally and not by a sacred hunger for Fame. I will love them, and they me. Most will die in my service."

"So they are Greater Poets only because they will compose more."

"Yes and no. Some of the shades of the most prolific composers of future verses are confined to the outermost regions of the temple: their great works will serve only to send mankind to sleep."

"All that labour to so little end!"

"The distinction of greatness is not conferred by simple diligence and tenacity – though every Greater Poet will have these qualities in abundance. But they will certainly perform more than Lesser Poets. Little poems can only do little things, however lovely. To ordinary mortals the minds of the Greater Poets will appear to know no bounds. These Greater Poets will also be able to sustain their exceptional skill through large tracts of thought and passages of narrative. As they will fly higher, so they will continue longer on the wing. Let us approach!"

The Muse and her Poet walked hand in hand towards the table where the Greater Poets hold their everlasting banquet. Our Hero saw a table set with all that might delight the human appetite, or that of gods. The genial bowl went round and laughing nectar overlooked the lid, but none of the shades appeared in the slightest intoxicated. Their aspects were serene – distorted neither by joy nor sorrow. Their conversation was forceful but discreet. Most (but not all) bowed their heads in deep reverence as the Muse approached, and while she spoke – or (as our Hero heard it) chanted.

"Hail Bards triumphant, Lords of Highest Song to be born in future time, immortal heirs of universal praise, whose honours will grow with the passage of ages, as streams roll down enlarging as they flow! Nations unborn shall sound your mighty names, and undiscovered worlds applaud your mighty makings!"

The Muse, having returned the bows of her assembled Greater Poets, turned aside to introduce the slight form of Our Hero (who found himself shaking with apprehension).

"Behold! Behold your ancestor, your Great Original, who as yet on weak wings and from a far plain imitates your future flights, glows while he listens but trembles as he contemplates his future labours! Inspire his mind with courage. Your existence on the earth depends upon *him*!"

The shades of Greater Poets, the Lords of Highest Song, looked at the Muse and her pupil with varying expressions (all of which Our Hero found most confusing). Were they smiling, perhaps? And were their smiles expressions of beneficence? Or derision? Or were they laughing? With happiness? Or with contempt?

"O Goddess excellently bright," he said at last, "I am in perplexity. I couldn't help noticing that all the Lords of Highest Song were not equally respectful to me or to you. Some turned pale at your approach: some even averted their eyes from yours. I do not understand. Will you not care for me in all my incarnations?"

"My Poet, though you are as dear to me as my own skin, I must warn you that our relations will not always be easy. What I will want will, alas, not always be what will seem best to you."

"That (though with deep respect I say it) I can well believe. But what is that great shimmering disk which stands before them and to which the Lords of Highest Song direct their gaze?"

"Before them stands the Mirror of Life – for the end of Poetry is, has been, and will always be, to hold the mirror up to nature: to show virtue her own feature, vice her own image, and display the essential imprint of every age and time. Here the shades watch the passage of the generations, waiting their turn. Here you may learn the progress of your Fate – or Fates. You see the shades of your future sons without knowing the nature of their triumphs. The time has now come for you to know some few of them – fathers and families – and hear of their great works, so that you may believe that you will succeed and triumph – yes, even in that wretched isle pounded by a bitter northern sea."

21. The First of Poets and of Cities

Our Hero looked in vain for cold Northern Isles in the Mirror of Art. Instead he received an indistinct impression of thirsty, sun-baked lands, gleaming, sun-bleached rocks, and glittering, sun-drenched seas.

"You will have progeny in almost every land on the face of the earth," began the Muse, softly, soberly, as one setting out on a long journey. "Your future ancestors, your future sons in that wretched Northern Isle (as well as half the world) will think with eternal veneration of Asia Minor as the place where their particular Poetic family began – as their father's home."

"Asia Minor? I do not understand."

"For it will be there, or thereabouts, one fortunate day (soon may it come!), that you will be reincarnated with ten times your normal powers."

"Ten times? I do not understand" said Our Hero, staring vacantly into the face of his Muse.

"Well perhaps a hundred times your *present* powers – or a thousand. In this incarnation your gigantic soul, uniting all mortal and all Nature's strength, will rise above the mass of mankind. Let us venerate the Father of Poetry!"

The Muse directed her pupil's attention to a figure at the very centre of the banqueting table. The ethereal light from above shone so brightly upon this form that Our Hero was unable to discern any features, to be certain of the sex, or even if he or she were one shade or several. And yet Our Hero felt a degree of veneration unknown before, and was relieved when the Muse made no attempt to call this ancient figure from his honoured seat.

"Behold the First of Poets, Prince of Men! In this great incarnation you will collect the stories and words of hosts of your predecessors. You will mould and arrange, abstract and combine, amplify and distil these stories (the work of

Forgotten Poets) to make a great sung story which will last to the end of human time."

"What kind of story can I make out of so many stories?"

"Your story will tell of the insatiable wrath of one man and of bloody battles around the walls of the distant city of Troy."

"Not crocodiles? Will I be trying to please the Men of Power?"

"No, for although this story will be filled with killing and with the deaths of heroes, it will be loved by men of peace as much as by warriors."

"How can this be? Of what interest are battles to a contemplative soul?"

"Because it will be far more than a story of war. It will tell of gods and men and women and the nature of things. It will concern the whole of life, its joy and its suffering."

"How will this Poet – how will I with my mortal limitations – be able to tell of the *whole* of life?"

"Because in this incarnation you will tell old stories as if you had invented them for yourself. It will be agreed by all future Poets that in this incarnation you will have the greatest Invention of any Poet whatever. Fire and Rapture will be so forcible in your compositions that no man of a true Poetical Spirit will be master of himself while he listens."

"Why will they not be masters of themselves?"

"Because everything in this Poet's work will be of the most animated nature imaginable; everything will move, everything will live and will be put in action."

"Everything will live – in a mere *story*?"

"If in the story a council is called or a battle fought, your audience will not be coldly informed of what is said or done as if by a third person; the listener will be hurried out of himself by the force of your Imagination, and will think that he hears not your words but the words of your heroes. He will believe that he *witnesses* their great deeds."

"How will I manage that?" asked our hero, whose incredulity was now at breaking point.

"These are mysterious Arts which you have yet to learn. In this incarnation you will be said to be the Poet who found the 'living words'; there will be more daring figures of speech and metaphors in this work than in those of any other author."

"Living words?"

"Your arrows will be 'impatient' to be on the wing, your weapons will 'thirst' to drink the blood of an enemy, your ...."

"Isn't that an absurdly exaggerated way of speaking? asked Our Hero, interrupting his impassioned Muse."

"No. This Poet's expressions will never be too big for his sense. It is the depth and strength of his thought that will swell and fill out his language."

"Is such mastery possible for a mortal?"

"More than this – for in the same incarnation you will also sing a story about a man who saw and knew the cities of a world of nations, with all their manners, minds and customs; a story about the life and mind of men and gods, a story of realms of gold, of goodly islands and kingdoms, of enchantresses, one-eyed giants, and fearsome monsters – a wide expanse of pure serene thought couched in bright and bold language."

"Will not such a stupendous double triumph put an end to the need for further Poems?"

"It is true that it will sometimes seem to following generations that these Poems are so crammed with the essence of human life that henceforth Poets will be able to do little more than repeat and develop their incidents, their truths and their beauties."

"Alas for my selves, my sons – redundant before incarnation!"

"But what is daunting to a true Poetic Soul is also *inspiring*. Look in the Mirror."

Our Hero was dazzled by a nobly-built and sun-lit city beside a shining sea.

"Behold the Aegean shore! The air is pure and the soil light. This is Athens; the eye of Greece, the seat of intelligence and light, the mother of arts and eloquence, the native home of my best progeny and those of all my sisters. Incarnated here, you, like all the other little boys, will learn the Great Poem of Troy by heart. So you will learn the secret power of harmony and various-measured verse. So will the Father of Poetry beget a long line of wonder-working sons – souls who will see life steadily and see it whole, the mellow glory of their age, great teachers who will treat of fate and chance, and change in human life, high actions and high passions."

"How will I do all this?"

"You will rediscover the arts of joining plays and Poetry. The tragedies of the Athenian Poets (tales of incest, murder, rape) will be thought to be as mirrors in which the spectator beholds himself stripped of all but his essence. Audiences in later ages will feel that their imaginations are enlarged by a sympathy with the mighty pains and passions of the words which these great tragic Poets, AESCHYLUS, SOPHOCLES, and EURIPIDES, gave the players. Mortals, hearing these plays, will believe that their good affections are strengthened by pity, indignation, terror and sorrow."

"And all this will be owing to the Father of Poetry?"

"All this and more. The tribe of this first great incarnation, this Poet-with the-strength-of-ten-Poets, this HOMER, will claim to have based their whole civilization on his Poems."

The Muse bowed low to the venerable shade, almost invisible in brightest light. The lips of the soul of the future First of Poets moved, or seemed to move. Our Hero heard, or thought he heard, the words: "Fate gives the wound and Man is born to bear" (but what they meant, and whether or not they were meant for him, he knew not).

22. Romans

In the mirror Our Hero saw (or thought he saw) dark clouds, battles, heaps of dead, aqueducts, elephants, triremes, riots, temples, villas, a great city and a greater empire.

"Many years after the composition of the great Poem about Troy," said the Muse in explanation, "the first Greater Poet's tribe will be crushed and ruled by barbarians – by a more powerful nation, a brutal warrior people springing from a town in Italy."

"Alas, alas!"

"But even then the great Poem will not die. The cold conquerors will learn the language of the Poet-with-the-strength-of-ten-Poets just to be able to enjoy his Poem."

"That is some comfort."

"And they will do more. They will make new Poems of their own in close imitation. It will be through these imitations (rather than the originals) that the spirit of Poetry will survive many a dark age. Behold the true fathers of the Poetic family of the dour Northern Isle!"

Our Hero looked and saw five or six shades reclining at ease at tables heaped to profuseness. But among them he saw one man sipping clear spring water from his glass as if it were the most luscious wine, and eating green salad as if it were the richest venison.

"That man," said the Muse pointing and smiling, "that man will long wish to be a Lover-of-Wisdom-and-Truth."

"But he will be prevented?" asked Our Hero (fearing the worst).

"He will have the good fortune to fall in love with the great Poem about Troy and the even greater fortune of being seduced by me."

"O happy (and unhappy) man!"

"Even when possessed by me, this man will have a calm and lofty scorn of everything mean and low. He will sing, and sing with a voice of vigorous and imperious command,

about the nature of things – how everything comes in and out of being by a wonderful process of pure chance, how death is the end of all, and why, therefore, men should be happy, and enjoy their lives to the full in ecstatic peace, like the indifferent gods, neither joying nor grieving at things beyond their control. This great Poet, this LUCRETIUS, will sing a truth that stops the rolling torture-wheels and numbs the snakes of human fear, a truth which plucks the mortal soul from immortal hell."

"Who, Celestial Patroness, is that shade reclining beside him, and gazing upon him and upon the Father of Poetry with wonder and with love?"

"Beside him sits his greatest admirer – though a greater than he. This wonderful man will give the world its most haunting and mellifluous verse. He will wield the stateliest and most melancholy measure ever moulded by the lips of man."

"Of what will he sing?"

"First he will sing of the joys of country life and of all the wondrous processes of nature."

"First? Will that not suffice?"

"No, no, I will not let him rest there. This Great Poet, this mighty VIRGIL, will die in my service. He will die in the attempt to continue the great stories of Troy, singing of arms and a man, of the glory of Empire (and his Emperor) and of its cost, of love and death and the pain of human life. He will send his hero, Aeneas, on many journeys – even to learn the secrets of Fate in the underworld. He will try to include every beauty, every delicacy, every thought of all your previous incarnations. He will never be satisfied – I will never be satisfied."

"You, Celestial One? I notice he eyes you askance."

"I will torment his nights with wild inspiration," said the Muse laughing. "He will wake at dawn and spend his days attempting to order and correct. Our battles will not end."

"Will this Poet then be different from his predecessors?"

"Where HOMER will hurry and transport his listeners with a commanding impetuosity, the second Poet of Troy will lead his audience with attractive majesty. HOMER like the Nile will pour out his riches with a sudden overflow; great VIRGIL, with a gentle and constant stream, like a river within steep banks."

Our Hero glanced from one table to the other, studying the faces of both Greater Poets. He saw (or fancied he saw) the older Poet boundless and irresistible in his conversation; the younger Roman Poet calmly daring, undisturbed in the midst of action, disposing all about him and conquering with tranquillity – but all with a strange and all-pervading melancholy.

"His does not sound like an easy life, nor does he seem light of soul."

"Do not grieve for yourself, for your son. No Poem will be more constantly admired or more frequently emulated down the ages than his great work."

"Is this, then, to be my greatest incarnation?"

"Your most influential, certainly. Knowledge of HOMER's language will be scarce in many a dark age. But love of VIRGIL will endure through every vicissitude. His works will be a fixed star in the Poetical firmament. So deeply will his Poem be revered that many will attribute magic power to its author and will think that his work foretells the entire future of mankind."

"He seems well-attended with companions," said Our Hero, cheering up.

"Yes, he will live at one of those wonderful periods in history when your spirit will take more than one body in the same place and at the same time."

"Who is his friend whose features seem to combine good humour with wisdom?"

"This Poet will be an exquisite and a mighty artist. His verse will seem to crown distress with garlands, and to charm the human soul into a happiness like that this Poet will enjoy (or dream of enjoying) on the Sabine farm he will love so well. His shorter Poems will dance with briskness, delicacy, jollity and good-humour, while he advises his audience to shun the deeps and rocks of life. With light but earnest voice he will eulogise peace, leisure, freedom, moderated desires, and a joyful inner content. Even when rebuking the vices of men, this Poet will speak with the voice of the most genial of drinking companions and he will seem to be looking on all that err with silent pity. He will appear to talk his audience into sense with graceful negligence. In this incarnation, loved as a life-long familiar friend, known as HORACE, you will also be a great and clear-voiced teacher of future Poets."

"A clear-voiced teacher *and* a Poet!" exclaimed Our Hero, whose experience of conversing with the Muse had not suggested that the two roles were easily compatible.

"You will judge with coolness though you will sing with fire. You will prune the superfluous branches of wit, giving new and useful rules. You will direct your sons how to moderate the force of my inspiration (often, I must admit, a necessary lesson)."

"That rather portly shade with the enigmatic expression, who is he?"

"The Roman Poets you have so far seen will be loved almost as gods might be loved. This man will charm listeners in childhood, entertain their middle years, and haunt their imaginations in old age."

"How will he do this? He looks half-drunk to me."

"He will sing the oldest and most brutal stories about men and gods in the newest, wittiest and most subtly sophisticated way. This OVID will combine pathos and comedy as never before or since. He will sing of the metamorphoses and flux to which all people and things are subject, transforming in his verse the ordinary feelings of men and women – sorrow, anger, horror, love – into a calm delight, felt as a delicate twinkle in his eye. However barren, rude or mean his subject, the play of his restless imagination will seem to gild the scene with fire."

"And the fifth figure with the wild and rolling eyes, who is he?"

"He will live a century later than the other three. In this incarnation, too, you will rebuke the vices of men but more in the manner of a jester, revelling in contemptuous hyperbole and in the power of your own scurrilous imagination. You will, however, be remembered best as an earnest moral prophet, scorning the world and scourging mankind in righteous indignation," said the Muse to Our Hero's complete confusion. "Known as JUVENAL, you will give your future Poetic admirers as much pleasure as they can bear. Your vexations (or assumed vexations) will directly arouse theirs. You will drive your audience along with you. The fertility of your satiric imagination will be such that when you abandon a topic it will be assumed that the subject is exhausted, and that the wit of man can carry it no further."

Our Hero exchanged a few words with each of the Roman Poets in turn, but, although the conversation was warm and often witty, he came away with an overpowering sense that human life, even (or particularly) at the centre of a great empire, was a condition in which there was little to be enjoyed and much to be endured.

23. A Table of Italian Poets

The mirror grew dark and misty. Our Hero was able to discern some shadowy shapes and figures, some terrible destructions, some burning cities perhaps, and a deal of butchery, but nothing was clear.

"The shadows in the mirror," said the Muse, "are the men and women of the years which men will call the Dark Ages. Some of these we met in the outer regions of the Temple – true poets of power and distinction; but various mischances will cause their work to be lost or obscured and so it will not enter the minds and hearts of later poets, your sons."

"Alas! Alas, to be incarnated in vain!"

"The mists are now clearing. The mirror has carried us forward many centuries. We are still in the land of the Romans, but their empire has now crumbled. In its place are many small princedoms and cities governed by powerful priests and tyrants. In these cities I and all my Sisters will find fruitful soil indeed. Behold the Italian Poets!"

Our Hero's attention was directed towards a group of shades eating furiously and talking with a mixture of vehemence and mellifluousness which he found surprising. He was unable to tell if they were carousing or boasting or quarrelling – or even guess at the subject of their concern. But, clearly, their conversation was intense, extreme.

"The first of the Greater Poets to write in Italian (the language of the new lands) will be the greatest of all. He will sing a story of his own journey down to Hell (guided by the shade of the Greatest Roman Poet) and then up to Heaven. He will describe with greater clarity than anyone else all the human passions."

"ALL the human passions again!"

"He will examine them one by one and enter into each of them so completely that his verse will have an authority that no other poet will ever achieve. The sheer power of his Imagination and Invention will never be

equalled. He will plumb depths and scale heights few others will ever dare, and will find a voice for joy, grief, rage, despair, hope, pride and love which will direct men's understanding of these feelings forever and forever."

"O Celestial Being, I notice that when this shade looks at you he does so with the air of a man whose soul is devoted (if I dare say it) to higher things."

"It is true," said the Muse with a secret and (to Our Hero) terrifying smile, "that the intellectual framework of his poem will be a set of beliefs called Christianity. Nevertheless it is *me* that this Poet, this DANTE, will serve – and serve well. Despite all his best intentions, his true religion will be that of my Poets."

"The religion of your Poets? What is that?"

"My Poets must combine an intense involvement in the affairs of the world with the detachment of a Greek god. This Poet, obeying me despite himself, will therefore be loved equally by those of his religion and by those to whom his religion is anathema."

"He will be loved? He looks daunting to me."

"He will be loved both in his native land from the first, and in the wider world to the last (though even his warmest admirers will not be able to say quite *why*). You will see that the Greater Italian Poets have invited two friends from other regions of the Temple. They are men of great and  rich learning. One, PETRARCH, will fill the world (yes, even that cold Northern Isle) with the name of Laura his love, and will be crowned Poet Laureate in Rome. The other, BOCCACCIO, a great collector and famous teller of tales both in prose and in verse, will be the first to tell the world of DANTE. See with what admiring eyes they gaze upon the face of this Great Italian Poet of Heaven and Hell!"

"They admire him because he will be the perfect poet?"

THE STORY OF ART: A TABLE OF ITALIAN POETS

"Not quite perfect. He will have one terrible fault; though he will make grim jokes, he will never smile."

"Alas!"

"Do not lament. There to the right of the table is ARIOSTO, your next Italian incarnation, in which you will, by way of compensation, never stop smiling (in your works, that is. I say nothing of your life.) In a great romantic epic full of knights and enchanters, you will smile at all the things at which men are usually incapable of smiling. You will delight in the madness of the world, the capriciousness of events and the vanity of human wishes. You will present the world as a thing founded on discord and confusion, but the smile in your voice as you utter this vision will sweetly and benignly knit all the world's disparate features together, and then unknit them all again."

"It sounds rather confusing."

"Your audience will see human life form and dissolve and transform itself under their eyes, and will love your inability to catch it in your hand."

"That inability, Celestial One, I can well imagine."

"Shortly afterwards in another Italian incarnation, known as TASSO, you will write of the religious wars which will liberate Jerusalem from the Saracens and of the battle between good and evil. But though your mind will be fired by the glory of this vision, you will also be absorbed by the exquisite sweetness of earthly love. Your verse will be virile, arduous and impulsive, and at the same time, languorous, sighing, sensuous and poignant. It will impress mortals as being both thrillingly manly and softly feminine."

Our Hero tried to enter the conversation at the Table of Italian Poets – in vain. As far as he could gather, the talk was not about love, or war, or Poetry (the topics he had been expecting), but about the finer points of Roman inscriptions and (more passionately) of who was in and who was out of power, who up and who down – in particular princedoms, in particular cities, in particular squares, by particular gleaming, sun-lit towers.

24. The Father of Poetry in a Northern Isle

"Now," said the Muse, "we must pass at last to the family of Future Poets who are to be born in that unpropitious Northern Island."

Looking in the Mirror, Our Hero saw, as from a great height, a little spot of land embraced by a shining sea. He saw green dales, leafy woods, gentle slopes, monarch oaks, noble firs.

"This land is not as barren as you would have had me believe, Celestial One."

"I was speaking of the souls of the inhabitants and the coarseness of their tongues. All the sunny lands which you have so far seen will be civilised by warm-souled mortals with musical voices. But in this cold land, the language will be harsh, the people – the people as I have described."

"How can I hope to be a Poet in such a land?"

"Because, my Poet, you will be re-incarnated here so frequently; because the family of Poets will be so numerous in this isle, and because so many of them will seem to include the whole of life in their work, each new Poet will be able to re-discover arts which have not been long lost or quite forgotten."

"I cannot see how such a thing may be done."

"Much of the credit will be due to the first great member or *Father* of this poetic family. This noble Poet will be considered the first to have enriched the language of this dour land with his rhymes, the first to break into my rich treasures, the first to speak in weighty numbers, and the first to delve in the mine of ancient knowledge for intellectual gold – which he will refine and make current. As much as this harsh language can express to men, he will make it do and be and say, and by his wondrous skill he will spread a love of Poetry in a barren land. Behold! his noble shade!"

Our Hero looked round in vain. The Muse seemed to be gazing at a corner of the table of Greater Poets where a massy column cast a venerable (but impenetrable) shadow.

"How will he do these things?" he asked blankly. "What method will he use? What materials? Which tools?"

"He will appear to his successors in the Northern Isle to have re-invented poetry almost without native assistance. He will take what he can from France, but most from Italy, from the re-discoverers of Roman Poetry, and from Roman Poetry itself."

"What will his story be? Of what worlds will he speak?"

"He will compose a great story of the joys and sorrows, the worthiness and vanity of love, set in the same city of Troy which had been the scene of the first great Poem (a work he will dream about but will not know). There he will tell of lovers musing night and day, mourning all alone without comfort when their loves are gone. Never again will such loveliness of detached god-like wisdom be combined with such warmth of close human sympathy. This Poem will be my darling care."

"O happy man to have such a mighty triumph!"

"But his labours will not then be at an end. He will die in the attempt to embrace the whole of life by telling all the stories that ever were from every possible point of view and in every possible style."

"*EVERY? ALL?* He will die in the attempt!"

"I will teach him to describe, from the outside and inside simultaneously, the thoughts and emotions of every class of men and women, from millers and shipmen to knights and prioresses. He will be a man of a most wonderfully comprehensive nature and will take into the compass of his poems the various manners and characters which will compose all ages and nations. Each of his creations will be both an individual and a species"

"How can this be?"

"As one age falls, another rises, different to mortal sight, but to we immortals always the same. Of this man's characters, as described in his last work, some of the names or titles will be altered by time, but the characters themselves will for ever remain unaltered, displaying the lineaments of universal human life beyond which Nature never steps. Nor can a mortal child be born, who will not be one of this poet's creations."

"What will his matter be? his manner? and his language?"

"His matter will afford pleasure and consolation to all suffering mortals. His terms will not be dark or obscure, but pleasant, plain, easy, and always to the point. He will be a perpetual fountain of good sense. As he will know what to say, so he will know when to leave off. He will invent the word-pattern which most of his sons will follow. He will be the first English Poet whose works will be continuously remembered by his successors. As he will be the Father of this nation's Poetry he will be held in the same degree of veneration as the Grecians and the Romans will hold theirs. Let us honour him."

The Muse turned to the shadowy corner and bowed low. Our Hero bowed lower.

"O dear pupil and dearest master," declaimed the Muse, "GEOFFREY CHAUCER, honoured son and reverend father, flower of eloquence, piercer of the darkness, illuminator of this benighted isle, harmoniser of a harsh tongue, well-spring of undefiled language, enricher of all succeeding generations, most sacred happy soul, infuse your sweet spirit into my pupil (your begetter) who will follow the footing of your poetic feet in the hope of finding the fullness and weight of your great sense."

Our Hero was expecting an imposing forehead and perhaps a great beard. What he saw (as his eyes became accustomed to the shadow) was the shade of a small, round man sitting in a corner as quietly and as fixedly as any stone and staring at the ground as if he were looking for something he had lost.

He had an air of absolute abstraction, as if he were a visitor from another world.

"That thee is sent, receive in buxomness," said the shade of the Future Poet (to Our Hero's complete incomprehension) and no more.

"After such a Father, what sons? What will happen next?"

"The art of this Poet will leave his immediate successors with little to do but emulate. There will then follow a Dark Time in this northern Isle."

25. A Gentle Moralist

As far as Our Hero could tell from the Mirror, this Dark Time was not as dark as others he had seen. There was a some slaying, some storming of castles, here and there some villages burning, but nothing to depress his spirits overmuch. And soon the mists cleared.

"Behold your second greater English ancestor and incarnation," said the Muse. Though a man of natural chastity, a serene, pure and lovely soul, this Poet's relations with me will be surprisingly close. He will recognise that he has inherited the soul of his great predecessor, the Father of the Poetry of the dour Northern Isle!"

"Will his work, then, resemble that of his Father? Of what will he sing?"

"The two great Poets could hardly be more different. This man will sing of heroic knights and of fairy lands. He will compose the beginnings of a vast and spacious Poem about warriors and maidens, enchanters and dragons, which would have been (were he allowed to live his life to the end) one of the most sustained and most passionately serene and beautiful meditations on the beauty and ugliness of the human soul ever conceived."

"O happy Poet!"

"His story will, however, be one of the most slow-moving and least memorable ever composed under my direction."

"Alas! Why?"

"He will sing of a strange and magical land where nothing is quite as it seems; where everything is distinguished from (and yet shades into) everything else; where all is subject to constant flux, to Mutability."

"How will he express such a vision?"

"He will bring beauty from all your past incarnations - particularly your Italian incarnations - to glorify the truth he sees, and to expound its perpetual mystery. "

"Will he succeed in this mighty task?"

"Not entirely. He will never end his song."

"Another *unfinished* masterpiece! In what manner will he sing?"

"His spirit will be naturally attuned to words of sacred wisdom. He will sing so elegantly, so delicately, with such command, in such melodious song that mortals will fancy that the angels themselves would wish to make him one of their associates in heaven's fair choir. By my inspiration and his own free fancy he will teach distrust of specious miracles; that mortal man cannot live in bliss on earth. He will explain how closely good and evil, joy and sorrow are allied."

"Will there be no happiness in his work?"

"His gentle story will picture a fragile happiness. He will have mortals understand that in his invented land alone can the war-worn and the sea-worn man find dateless leisure and unrepining peace. Only in fairyland can the human heart be stilled."

"Will he sing of the passions?"

"He will, indeed, sing well of all the passions."

"ALL the passions? This is what you say about each and every one of the Greater Poets. How will this Poet be distinguished?"

"In this incarnation you will bring in view those shadowy beings, the passions of humanity, and with a bold hand remove each dark disguise in which love, hatred, scorn, or anger lie hidden. By you, good and evil and all the shades between will be marked as Virtue's foes and friends."

The Muse then turned to the shade of the Future Poet and, smiling, said;

"Gentle bard, sweet Poet, dearest SPENSER, moving through your clouded heaven with the moon's beauty, and the moon's soft pace, arise from the dust and sing of bloody Mars, of wars, of jousts and those who wield the awful crown of state. Or sing of love, of knights' and ladies' gentle deeds."

Our Hero was astonished when this shade of a Future Greater Poet (with greater presumption than any other shade) began to address the Muse directly. He spoke in a voice of great loveliness, and proud humility.

"Divinest, heaven-bred, happy Muse, infuse your sacred power into my brain. Lay forth the antique stories of fairy knights out of your everlasting store. Come to my aid, O Great Lady of this greatest isle ..."

"Greatest isle?" whispered Our Hero.

"This Poet will be most patriotic," answered his Muse.

" ... augment my style so that my wings may stretch from East to West, so that with fierce wars and faithful loves I may moralise my song."

"That," said the Muse, turning to Our Hero with a soft smile, "that is how to speak to me. That is how to address a true goddess. I will reward him. He will be a great begetter. He will be dearly loved by sweet-souled boys and girls, and a fixed star for all the pure spirits of Greater Poets in this Northern Isle."

26. A Comprehensive Soul

"I do not," said the Muse, with an unusual quaver in her voice, "I do not expect the same respect from that *fellow* over there."

"Why so? Is his not the shade of a Greater Poet?"

"O yes, he will be the Greatest of the Greater Poets," said the Muse (rapt – but not, it seemed, with joy). He will live at the same time as my Gentle Moralist, but his glory will be matched only by that of the Greek Father of Poetry himself. He will be the (unacknowledged) pride of his own, and the open wonder of every age and nation. He will be the man who of all Poets will have the largest and most comprehensive soul. All the images of Nature will be constantly and effortlessly present to him. When he describes any thing, you will more than see it, you will *feel* it too."

"Celestial One, why does this shade not look at you? Why do his eyes not meet yours – or yours his?"

"He will write for the *stage*! He will have terrible problems with his players. I will not approve of his motives for writing. For though his admirers will call him 'the divine, the soul of the age, the applause, delight, the wonder of the stage, the matchless, the multi-faceted, the what-you-will', it will be for for sordid gain and not for sacred Poetic glory, that he will wing his roving flight."

"He will grow immortal in his own despite?"

"He will grow immortal to his own complete indifference!"

"Is that why you will not love him?"

"Not love him! I will love the man! I will honour him to idolatry! I will love him as much as – no, more, much more than – any. Together we will flow with such facility that sometimes his mortal friends will feel it necessary that he should be stopped. I myself will be proud of him, and will joy to hear his lines. I will love him so that my earlier favourites will please no more, but lie deserted as if they were not my progeny. That's not it."

"Will he not learn your lessons well?"

"He will, it is true, not study as hard as the other Greater Poets you have met and, beside them, he will have small Latin and less Greek. But that's not it. I will love him so that he will hardly *need* to study. Those who will accuse him of a lack of learning will be giving him the greater commendation. He will be naturally learned. He will not need the spectacles of other's compositions to read Nature. He will look inwards and find me there. As if by intuition, he will understand all the human passions in all their combinations, and every shade of human character."

"(Just like every other Greater Poet.)"

"Every single character in his work will be as much an individual as those in life itself. It will be impossible to find any two alike. And yet none will be a mere invention, a mere freak of his brain. Nor will he only excel in depicting character and the passions. His coolness of reflection and reasoning will be equally admirable. By a talent very peculiar (something between penetration and luck), he will hit upon that particular point on which the bent of each argument turns, or the force of each motive hangs. He will seem to have looked through the depths of human nature with one glance."

"Will he be a Poet of Nature *alone*?"

"Such a thing is not possible. Poets are made as well as born. He will sweat at his Art, and turn and turn again on the anvil of his Muse. His compositions will be like swords of profound human knowledge brandished in the eyes of ignorance."

"But he will have some faults?

"I cannot say he will always be consistent. Were he so, I should do him injury to compare him with the gods. He will often write flatly, insipidly; his comic wit will often degenerate into word-games; his serious verse will often swell into bombast and empty noise. At one moment, eagle-winged, he will take flight heavenward: the big stage will thunder, and the listener's soul awake. At the next moment, low on earth, he will creep like a reptile; his heroes will make cheap jokes, his stories will rush to the easy expedient of a happy ending and his hearers will fall asleep."

"That is why you will not meet his eye?"

"No, that's not it. He will always write magnificently when some great occasion is presented to him. No man will be able to say that when this Poet had a fit subject for his mind, he did not raise himself as high above the rest of Poets as the towering cypress above the bending reeds.".

"Why is it that he who can fly so high will also fall so low?"

"He will sacrifice virtue to convenience, and be so much more careful to please an audience than to touch the soul that he will seem to compose without any moral purpose – or any purpose at all. His plots will be often so loosely formed that a moment's thought would improve them, and so carelessly worked out that he will seem sometimes not to have fully understood his own plan. And that is not the worst. He will no sooner begin to move his audience than he will counteract himself with sheer carelessness. Terror and pity as they are rising in the mind will be blasted by some sudden frigidity, verbal distraction, or foolish joke. (Jokes will always exercise some irresistible power over his mind.)"

"He will compose like this because you will not love him *kindly*?"

"Because I will love him *too much*! Sometimes I will possess him like lightening in the night, that burns where it strikes, or, like a rapacious beast, I will devour him with unrelenting force, in my full and natural nakedness. His knees will knock and his head will whirl. Then he will compose with cool fury and calm intensity."

"But at other times?" prompted Our Hero (fearing the worst).

"But at other times I will slip into the minds and hearts of all the characters he invents so completely, so utterly,

that they will act as if by their own terrifying volition – as if possessed by demons – so that his stories will never turn out as expected or desired. Then (particularly when matters are coming to a head, when his heroes should be facing up to things) I will suddenly leave him, and he will be forced to fall back on feeble wit, low buffoonery, mere pomp, and unconvincing contrivance."

"You will leave him?"

"Only for the odd moment – when I can bear the fire of his soul no longer. He will desert ME forever! He will give up – pretending exhaustion or disdain. Disdain of ME! He will take to business. Business, which I (of all things) hate! Business, the contradiction of his Fate!"

"How can this be?"

"I must bring myself to confess, O my Chosen Soul, that this great Poet will not think his works worthy of posterity. He will have no further plans for the children of his brain than present popularity and present profit. When his plays have been acted, his hopes and cares will be at an end. So careless will this Great Poet be of Future Fame that he will retire to ease and plenty when yet little declined into the vale of years – before he could be exhausted with fatigue or disabled by infirmity. He will make not the *slightest* effort to preserve his works for future Poets or to save them from the corruptions and distortions that they will suffer at the hands of the players and printers. I tell you he will scorn ME! My Greatest Poet, my Beloved SHAKESPEARE will look on Poetry as a thing of no consequence, a mere dream of a shadow, as insubstantial and as passing as lightning that strikes once, and then is swallowed forever in the dark night."

"That is why you will not look him in the eye, Lamp of Light?"

"That is why," said the Muse, sadly and (if Muses can weep) weeping.

27. A Bold and Noble Poet

It was some time before the Muse regained her composure. She seemed unable to withdraw her contemplation from the Greatest Poet (whose shade remained studiously indifferent). But at last the clouds cleared from her brow and her mind.

"I can (I hope) look for rather more respect from the next Poet to whom you will be introduced. He may appear to have a gloomy and severe countenance, but he will have a just, happy, and holy love – even adoration – of me, and of all my ways. Our love will, indeed, be mutual. To later Poets it will seem that never before had such *force* of mind been combined with such amplitude and dignity of Art as in this Greater Poet's greatest work. He will be granted (a gift seldom indulged to man) a God-like mind – a mind as unlimited and as various as his theme; astonishing as Chaos, fair as the bloom of blowing Eden, soft as the talk of true lovers, and as sublime as heaven. See! see! he upward springs and, towering high, spurns the dull province of mortality! See! he shakes heaven's eternal throne and sets the almighty Thunderer in arms!"

(Our Hero saw nothing of the kind and looked round the table in vain for a figure such as that the Muse described.)

At the Muses's call however, he came. He came from where he had been conversing earnestly with the Greek Father of Poetry. He came, walking with a haughty carriage and majestic footsteps. Though he bowed low, his conduct was not that of a mean suitor. He seemed to Our Hero to meet his Muse as an equal. A look of deepest respect having passed between them, the shade of the future Poet sat down, threw one leg negligently over the arm of his chair and smiled affably at Our Hero (who trembled as he gazed).

"Of what will this Greater Poet – of what will I sing in this incarnation, Celestial One?"

"No vulgar subject will engage your mind in this life, nor will earth's wide scene confine your hallowed passion. You will attempt a story of Man's first disobedience to God, and the fruit of a forbidden tree whose mortal taste brings death into the world and the loss of Paradise. You will sing of the great enemy of mankind, Satan, the first artificer of fraud. You will sing, too, of battles in heaven – of a starry field won from warring angels, and of God triumphant in his victor Son. You will sing also with great joy of God's abundant goodness to mankind, and of sweet delight and mildest passion. At your bidding, Eden's blooming grove will breathe the rich sweets of innocence and love. With purest joy, you will sing of sweet converse between the first man and and first woman, and of how they received an angelic guest within their blissful bower."

"How can I know such things?"

"Your inner eye will be opened to that sacred sight with which the gods compensate the blind."

"(The BLIND! Alas, not again!)"

"You will see earth in heaven, and heaven on earth … and hell. And incarnated as this Greater Poet, you will consider yours a story not less but more heroic than that told by the Greek Father of Poetry – the story of the wrath of stern Achilles."

"Why will I choose such a mighty subject in this re-incarnation?"

"This future son of yours will have a naturally bold mind. This Poet will delight to sport in the wide regions of possibility; reality will be a scene too narrow for his mind. He will send his faculties out upon discovery into worlds where only Imagination can travel, and he will delight to form new modes of existence, and to invent the thoughts, feelings and actions of superior beings – to trace the counsels of Hell, or accompany the choirs of Heaven.

The characteristic quality of his Poem will be sublimity. He will sometimes descend to the elegant; but his natural element will be the great. He will pass the flaming bounds of place and time; the living throne of Heaven, the sapphire-flame, where angels tremble while they gaze!"

"How will he sing of these mighty subjects?"

"With the greatest mastery and fire imaginable. Whatever he describes will be more than seen; it will be felt by the inner mind that waits behind the eye. Every verse, arrayed in majesty, bold and sublime, will draw the listener's whole attention, and seem above the laws of Art. He will sing with so much gravity and ease that delight and terror will fill his listener's hearts at the same moment. His majestic song will draw the devout, not deterring the profane (or not all of them). He will soar aloft above human flight on strong, soft wings."

"Where could he find words of such comprehensive power? What tongue, what words of rapture, will express a vision so profuse of pleasure?"

"He will study longer and harder than any. He will decide early to be a Poet. He will spend much time choosing his subject for heroic song and he will begin late.

He will command the accumulated Poetic treasure of two thousand years. He will make his native tongue include the accents and meanings of the dead languages of the ancients. Many languages and many literatures will be known to him. And then, I myself will make nightly visitations to his bedside, and dictate to him slumbering: I myself will inspire his verse."

The Muse turned to address the affable and angelic shade.

"Great soul of a Greater Poet, a dour Northern Isle has need of you, you whose voice will be like the sea, pure as the naked heavens, majestic, free!"

The Blessed Bard replied:

"Heavenly Muse, Celestial Patroness, I invoke your aid to my adventurous song, that intends to soar with no middle flight, while it pursues things unattempted yet in prose or rhyme. O Great Spirit, instruct me, support me, so that I may rise to the full height of this great story. Descend from heaven, O Muse; I will follow your divine voice, soaring, and make something that men will not willingly let die."

"Your prayers, O Noblest Poet, will be granted – in full. Yours, JOHN MILTON, will be the most powerful starry influence on the course of Poetry in your native land."

28. Energy Divine

"We are now," said the Muse with obvious and glowing pride, "in the midst of a glorious time for this Northern Isle – a time when your soul will take various forms simultaneously, and when your incarnations will overlap. The soul of the Greatest Poet (he who will not speak to me) will not have returned here to the Temple before the Noblest Poet begins his great studies; and while the Noblest Poet still walks the earth, your soul will inhabit a very different form. Behold this Poet's less presumptious chariot drawn by the long-resounding pace of etherial steeds!"

Our Hero saw only a short squat man in a long wig. The countenance of this shade combined the extremes of modesty and pride in a way and to a degree that Our Hero had not seen before. He seemed to be very much a man of the world but also a man of other worlds – ancient, modern and unknown.

"Where the Noblest poet was born for whatever is arduous, this Poet," said the Goddess, "will be content to drift along the stream of time – to make of the moment whatever the moment allows. Life, alas, will not permit him the calm of mind (or the money, or the time) which is necessary for mortals to bring a great work to fruition. He will try to do what it is fashionable to do; to say what it is fashionable to say. He will be prepared to bow to custom, to power, to influence, to the pressure of events. He will flatter, and rant, and pander, and change his opinions and beliefs, and then change them again."

"O Lamp of Light, do you not *despise* him?"

"Not at all. He will face many difficulties. He will find it difficult, for example, to decide whether he should be a rake, a popular playwright, a celebrator of public events, a political satirist, a literary critic or a religious controversialist."

"Why will he be so confused?"

"Partly because he will be able to do all these things with ease and distinction; partly because he will fall in love with the world. Look in the mirror. He will be brought up in a time when the Men of Power and the Priests together forge a harsh, intolerant, austere, world – a world which will seem to successors to be without smiles, sweetness, or grace. In these dark and sullen years there will be many who judge every effort of the Muse a crime. And when the tired nation breathes again after civil war, and the arts revive in softer times, the vaulted roofs of palaces and glittering theatres will ring with easy laughter. It will be, for this poet, a very merry, dancing, drinking, and unthinking time. The court (a dissolute school of wit and wantonness) will swarm with a mob of scribbling gentlemen, who write with ease and without responsibility. A Poet who wants to be heard will have to compete with such poetasters. And compete this Poet will. He will out-rant the most extravagant, and out-bawd the most lewd. I will wince to hear his rank obscenity. I will run mad to see his bedlam heroes roaring on the cracked stage, scarcely capable of speaking one reasonable word. And (do what I will) he will be enamoured of his follies. He will try hard to be a tearing blade and will love to frisk his frolic fancy."

"O gracious Muse," said Our Hero, suddenly inspired, "will I indeed profane your heavenly gift of poetry? Will I prostitute and profligate the Arts? Goddess, from whom all miracles spring, avert this destiny! Inspire my numbers with celestial heat and add the power of chaste nobility to my lines!"

The shade of the Future Poet, who had been listening to the Muse's words and those of her pupil with attention (and some agitation), now rose, and bowing as elegantly low as his portly form would allow, spoke to his Muse:

"Virgin-Daughter of the skies, cease your celestial words a little space. Hear then a mortal voice. As I am a Man, I must be changeable. I do not excuse the lewdness of my fellows or myself, but do not deprive me of my veneration of Venus. Fat as I am, unfit for ladies' love, her power inflames my soul, and inspires my wit. For all Nature is her gift; earth, air and sea; and all that lives, the various progeny, stung with delight is goaded on by her. Love first invented verse, and formed the rhyme, measured its movements, harmonised the jarring sounds. Love enlarges the narrow-souled, softens the fierce, and makes the coward ..."

"Do not fear, Shade of a Greater Poet," said the Muse interrupting hurridly. "Ever anxious to redress the abuses of my sacred charge, I will help you to become a true votary. It will be found that your excellencies always abound more than your faults."

"I do not understand," said Our Hero and the shade of the Future Poet simultaneously.

"I shall not reveal myself to you fully until you are fifty years old, when (your fury for the fashionable extinguished and spent) you will vie for fame with ancient Greece and Rome. Then you will learn to study the Noblest Poet, the Gentle Moralist, and all the Fathers of Poetry. Then the spirits of all your darling poets of the Past will suddenly join and speak delightedly out of your mouth. The rich fervour of your rising spirit will prevail over all the infirmities of age, and, unimpaired by injuries of time, you will enjoy the bloom of a perpetual summer. Your fire in your last days will not be less than it was in your freshest youth. "

The Shade of the Future Poet beamed contentedly. Our Hero, however, was bemused. "Lamp of Light, I still cannot see why you praise this pusillanimous time-server so?"

"Though tossed by every storm, this Greater Poet will struggle with, and conquer, Time. He will be, not one, but all Mankind's epitome. He will pour out a tide of song, a strong stream of sense. It will be said by his immediate poetic successors that from this Poet's work that they were taught to think naturally and express forcibly. He will show how the poetic past may be made to live in the present. He will find the Poetry of this Northern Isle crumbling brick, and leave it lasting marble."

Our Hero, always the doubter, was inclined to question the Muse further, but she seemed carried away on the wings of ecstasy.

"Hark, his hands explore the lyre! See bright-eyed Fancy hovering above, scattering thoughts that breathe and words that burn! Hear how this Poet's varied songs bid the passions rise and fall! Hear how his verse turns with the turns of Nature herself! Other poets may be smoother and more flowing, but this Poet will discover how to join the varying verse, the full resounding line, the long majestic march, and energy divine."

"Energy *divine*, Celestial Being?"

"These are mysteries of which we must speak further. In monumental, everlasting verse, this Poet, Glorious DRYDEN, will grasp the whole eternal world with divine energy. No power but his could so animate his language and make it so shining, so musical, so *strong*."

At these words, the squat shade of the Future Poet bowed and rose from the table of Poets of the Northern Isle. Picking up a chine of boiled bacon, he strolled over to the Table of Roman Poets where (to Our Hero's surprise) he was greeted with open arms, with fellowship, and with answering love.

29. *A Little Poet With a Magnanimous Soul*

The Muse followed the departing figure of the squat Poet of Energy Divine with eyes full of laughter and light.

"That man's warmest admirer (after myself) will be the next Greater Poet, a man who will ensure (or try to ensure) – by his own endeavours (and some cunning) – that his life is a complete contrast to that of his Great Predecessor. By an enormous effort of sheer *will*, this man will master his own destiny and his own Art. He will keep the Men of Power at a distance that is fit. He will be the first to insist on the proper dignity of the Poet. He will be truly Great (and conscious of it). Behold!"

Our Hero was not impressed. He saw a cripple, a chronic invalid, a fine face wracked with pain.

"Do not grieve for this Poet. Though more hated, vilified, and attacked than any of your other sons, he will wring respect even from the very teeth of men who know he holds them in contempt."

"Vilified, Alas! Attacked! Contempt! And respect only? Chief of Nine, is this a just reward?"

"This Poet will be admired more than loved by the generality of mankind. But neither time, distance, grief, nor age will diminish the veneration which his true Poetic admirers – your truest progeny – will feel for him. He will seem to his warmest admirers to have assembled all the moral wisdom that a good and great man can gather together, clothed in consummate beauty. It will seem to those who love him that his works are a complete literature in themselves."

"This little man will have extraordinary powers?"

"Those that live immediately after this man will feel that a thousand years must roll away before such another Poet could be hoped for in their land."

"What will this Poet do to earn such praise, to arouse such love?"

"Best of all, he will give his nation the great Poem of Troy in a form which can be taken to their hearts. They will see (or think they see) the soul of the god-like Greek breathe again in his frail form."

The Muse turned to the little shade and, smiling, said:

"To you, Mighty Poet, the hereditary poetic soul will descend – will descend and triumph. You will bring the voice of the Greatest Greek to the inhabitants of the northern Isle, you will set him free to live again! See, the Greek Father of Poetry himself honours his successor!"

"Great Lady," said Our Hero (seeing nothing of the kind), "something puzzles me. Why is the shade of this Greater Future Poet not more elated to hear of his – of your – of our – great success? Why does he seem so downcast by the contemplation of his time on the earth?"

The shade of the little Poet fixed Our Hero with his bright eyes, and spoke with clarity and quiet certainty, as one who has travelled far and suffered much:

"Soul of my soul and of all Future Poets, my Friend indeed, you must hear, and learn, and *know* that unhappy Poetry, like most human gifts, does not repay – does not repay *half* the envy which it brings. Envy pursues poetic merit as if it were its shadow. Those who cannot compose will scorn Poetry and envy those who have acquired its arts. Mortals are urged to base ends and use abject means when driven by the sacred lust of praise! The life of a Poet on earth is a perpetual warfare. Whatever you do, whatever you make, you are sure to vex some, and certain not to please all."

"Knowing this," said Our Hero (appalled to have his worst fears confirmed), "why will you aspire to follow our great Muse?"

"Why will I compose? What will lead me to this folly? While still a child and not yet a fool of Fame, I will lisp in verse – for verse will come unasked to my lips. The Celestial Muse will promise to help me through the long disease, my life, and teach me to bear my being. And I will meet with some success. My verse (at first) will be soft and innocuous. I will do always as the Muse requires. No one will work harder than I at the task. I will study by day and meditate by night. I will always admire superior sense and doubt my own: no one will pay more attention to advice than myself. Why, even the friends of the Great Poet of Energy Divine (from whom I will learn whatever I will know) will love and respect me. And yet, despite all my efforts, all my cares, Pride, Malice, Envy, Folly will rise against me as they will have risen against my Great Predecessor. I will be forced to sing another tune."

"Forced? What will force you?"

"You ask what provocation I will receive? – the strong antipathy of good to bad. When Truth or Virtue receives an affront, that affront is mine, my friend, and should be yours."

"Friend, are you not strangely proud?" asked Our Hero (amazed at his own temerity).

"Proud, yes, I am proud; I must be proud to find men who are not afraid of God, afraid of me. Unbowed, unbribed, no man's slave, I will brand the bold foreheads of shameless, guilty men; lay bare the mean heart that lurks beneath the purple gown. Yes, while I live on earth, no rich or noble rogue shall walk the world unquestioned to his grave."

Our Hero was terrified by this outburst, but the Muse seemed strangely placid.

"Hail, happy Poet, Great POPE," she began, "whose generous mind, will be at courts unseen, unknown. May the best companions (chiefs out of war, and statesmen out of place) grace your retreat with a feast of Reason and a flow of Soul. Let those who defame you (scribblers or peers) be alike one undistinguished, unregarded mob of fools. Leave such to those whom folly pleases and whose follies please. Above all flattery, all thirst of gain, and mortal only in pain and sickness, may you touch human verse with god-like grace and so give mortal thought new beauties not its own."

The little shade of the Greater Poet bowed to his Muse with politeness, but (or so Our Hero thought) without complete assent, and sat down to renew his meal of boiled lampreys.

"What effect," asked Our Hero, "will such a poet have on my sons and selves who follow?"

"His verse will seem to have an exact and perfect harmony, to be absolutely disciplined, complete, compact. But his musical finesse will be such, so fine his ear, so delicate his touch, and so varied and so extensive his subject matter, that he will seem to many to have made Poetry a merely mechanical art. Every would-be-poet will be able to string together his phrases and think he has the mighty tune by heart."

"What then?"

"There will then follow, if not a dark, at least a gloomy time."

"A gloomy time?"

" – a time when, in many of your incarnations, you will run stark mad."

"Alas!"

"But within sixty years there will begin what will seem to be a golden age for you, for me and for this blessed Northern Isle."

30. A Man Rejoicing in the Spirit of Life

"Behold! our next Greater Poet," said the Muse with mounting excitement, "he with the wrinkled forehead and humble-lidded eyes, he who stands as one half-bowed before the sovereign thought of his own great mind, made meek with proud inspiration. He is a man of free and noble vision. He will sing a song of high and passionate thoughts, chanted to their own music. He will sing of the great spirit whose dwelling is the light of setting suns, and which rolls through mountains and lakes and through the mind of man. His joy in the spirit of life will be as intense as pain but will bring him a strange tranquillity."

"Will he be loved, Goddess?"

"Yes indeed. Many hurt minds will find his Poems purest balm. There is no Poet who will be so deeply taken to heart – no Poet who will have a stronger claim to have changed men's lives ..."

"O happy man!"

" – and also no Poet who will be so easily and so frequently mocked."

"Alas! How can this be?"

"I hear two voices," said the Muse, drawing aside to speak privately as if abashed by the proud humility of the shade of the Future Poet, "one is of the ocean; it speaks the storm-cloud's thunderous melody. Now it roars, now murmurs with the changing sea, now bird-like sings, now closes softly in sweet slumber. The other voice is of an old, half-witted sheep which bleats articulate monotony, and indicates that two and one are three, that grass is green, lakes damp, and mountains rocky."

"You hear two voices?" said Our Hero, bemused. "Where?"

"Unfortunately both voices will come from this same Greater Poet," whispered the Muse.

"How can this be?"

"In this incarnation you will have a most unusual mind – a mind which is somehow at once the circumference and centre of all that you feel or know. All things that you will see and feel will melt into you, as cloud mixes with cloud, and will mingle with your being. And so, uniting the outward world insolubly to the world within, you will become considerably uninviting to those who are moulded in a different frame."

"Alas!"

"But you will scorn them, as they scorn you."

"Is that a *comfort*?"

"Both your strengths and weaknesses will protect you. You will be sure that on all matters *you* are right. You will seem to see only what you want to see – which will be only, perhaps, yourself. You will seem to avert your eyes from half of human fate. Nothing will daunt the positive assertion of your own opinions."

"You spoke of weaknesses and strengths. But I hear of no strengths!"

"Yours will be a truly individual mind which will new-create all you see in a new manner, and refine these new creations, combining them by a master-spirit's law. Without your depth of feeling and your strange visionary power, your sense would lack its vital warmth and peculiarity. The weight and sanity of your thoughts and sentiments will be won, not from other minds, but from your own meditative observations, which will be fresh, and have the morning dew upon them. Together we will make audible a song of truth profound. Your language, too (though often borrowed from the Noble Poet of the Great Sublime), will seem not learnt, but native. A clear, intense apprehension of your mind's work will make alive the things that mind works on, wakening thought in pure sense of being."

The Muse returned to the table of Greater Poets of the drab Northern Isle and spoke to the assembled company:

"Ah, pale ghosts, rejoice! for never will such a voice be conveyed to your dull but troubled land. He will speak, and loose your hearts in tears. His clear and feeling eyes will open yours again. Rejoice!"

The shade of the Greater Poet in whose honour this oration had been made seemed strangely dissatisfied:

"Great Spirit, Majesty Divine, you have given me praise for intending to reflect faithfully in my poems the appearance of things and the feelings of human nature. I would fain hope to do so. But a Great Poet ought to do more than this; he ought, to a certain degree, to rectify men's feelings, to give them new compositions of feeling, to render their feelings more sane, pure, and permanent; in short, more consonant with Nature, that is, of course, with Eternal Nature, and the great moving spirit of things. He ought to travel before men occasionally, as well as at their sides."

"Indeed, indeed he ought," said the Muse, quite taken aback.

"I would sing," said the shade of the future Poet, "of truth, of grandeur, beauty, love, and hope; of blessed consolations in distress; of moral strength, and intellectual power and most, most of all, of joy."

"Certainly, certainly."

"I would arouse the sensual from their sleep of death, and win the vacant and the vain to noble raptures, while my voice proclaims how exquisitely the individual mind is fitted to the external world; and how exquisitely, too, the external world is fitted to the mind."

"Why yes, yes, of course."

"Come to my aid, prophetic spirit that inspires. Bestow upon me the gift of genuine insight, so that my song may shine in its place with star-like virtue, shedding benign influence. Let all pure thoughts be with me; and may thy unfailing love guide and support and cheer me to the end! For I must tread on shadowy ground, must sink deep, and ascending aloft, breathe in worlds to which the heaven of heavens is but a veil. All strength, all terror – not Chaos, not the darkest pit of lowest Hell – can breed such fear and awe as fall upon us when we look into our minds, into the mind of Man, my haunt, and the main region of my future song."

So prayed the shade of the Future Poet in holiest mood and seemed to gain all that he asked and more, for the Muse replied in tones of apparent humility:

"Friend of the wise, and teacher of the good! Great WORDSWORTH, I receive your prophetic prayer into my heart – thoughts all too deep for words! – the pulses of my being beat anew whenever I hear your words, my comforter and guide, rekindler of the joy of life, strong in thyself, and powerful to give strength!"

"Lamp of Light," said Our Hero aside to his Muse, "you will love this man particularly?"

"In his youth, at first, when ..."

"But then you will desert him too?" asked Our Hero, apprehensively.

"In his youth he will know the very spirit of joy and Nature", said the Muse with tears in her eyes. "In honoured poverty his voice will weave songs consecrated to Truth and Liberty. But he will desert these for public duty, and leave those who loved him to grieve – to grieve that, having been such, he should cease to be."

"Your grief is for more than this?"

"My grief is for my Poet and for all mortals. For where will my Northern Isle again find this Poet's healing power? Others will teach them how to dare, and to steel their breasts against fear; others will strengthen them to bear – but who, ah! who, will make them feel?"

31. A Prince of Song

The Muse now gestured towards the shade of a tall wild-bearded figure in a broad-brimmed hat and a long cloak, half-obscured by his own tobacco fumes, and half-slumped before several empty bottles of fortified wine.

"In some ways this will be your most successful incarnation," said the Muse (to Our Hero's mild surprise). "This Greater Poet (though as you see, no aristocrat) will be made a Lord, and when he dies the whole nation will go into mourning."

"He will flatter and pander to the multitude?"

"No, he will not strive for popular applause, but will seem naturally attuned to the heart-strings of his audience. He will seem to wield the most haunting measure ever moulded by the lips of man in the Northern Isle. I will teach him a magical art which will turn all the sorrows of life into a soft music played on the inner ear of the mind."

"He will resemble the Greatest Roman Poet, VIRGIL?"

"So it will be said. (But I should tell you that the same will also be said of *every single one* of my Greater Poets.)"

The Muse led her pupil towards the table and bowed low.

"Future Poet! I bow in homage to the mastery which will be yours in song, O soft, sweet, slow historian of the human heart! To you the laurel-leaves belong by right, to you, my love and my support. Great Heir of the riches of the whole world's rhyme, inheritor of Greek and Roman treasure, and of the subtle grace of my gentle Moralist, and the golden fire of the Greatest Poet, O Singer, in whom all singing ages converge — may this, the youngest (and oldest) of the poetic choir, snatch a gleam of flying splendour from your soul to make his work illustrious!"

"Mirror of Grace, Great Lady," replied the shade of the Greater Poet, "I know nothing; I can only trust that good shall fall at last — far off — at last, to all, and every winter change to spring — so runs my dream. But what am I? an infant crying in the dark; an infant crying for the light, and with no language but a cry. Often I long to crawl into some still and silent cave, there to weep and weep and weep my whole soul out to thee. And sometimes I hold it half a sin to put in words the grief I feel; for words, like Nature, half reveal and half conceal the Soul within. But for the unquiet heart and brain there is *some* use in measured language; the sad mechanic exercise, like dull narcotics, numbing pain."

Our Hero was not much elated by this discourse, and his sense of disquiet was increased when, looking up, he saw the brow of his Muse darken with (what he took for) prophetic gloom.

"As this Poet's own King Arthur will pass across the mere, serene and calm, rebuking grief and tears, so will this Prince of Song, great TENNYSON, depart and leave his land in dark. But there will be none to mourn — none who can wield his magic brand of song."

"O Muse, I do not understand one word you speak."

"After this Greater Poet there will follow a long, dark time during which you will make only a few melancholy songs and dull-glittering fragments."

"Alas! why should this be?"

"Partly because in you incarnations at this time you will forget (or choose to ignore) the virtues of your great forefathers; partly because the great popular success of this last Poet and the power of his verse will make the inhabitants of this Northern Isle suspicious of popularity and of verse."

"Suspicious of verse? Prophetic Spirit, how can this be?"

"Woe to the inhabitants of this Northern Isle!" said the Muse trembling to the point of incoherence. "Terrible, terrible will be this time!. Do not look in the Mirror!."

(Our Hero's eyes automatically disobeyed. But he soon drew back as his gorge heaved.)

"Humanity will be beaten down in a great wave of brutality, followed by a tide of cant and a crippling distrust of real emotion. Your sons will suffer from an excessive and irresistible infatuation with the Lesser Poets, and, neglecting almost all the Greater Poets, will be stupidly proud of their inability to make use of their inheritance. They will therefore be unable to sustain anything more than a few striking images, a short poignant song, or a few rhythmical grumbles about life's lesser miseries. Our Arts will be an embarrassment to them. In their sullen hearts they will prefer mere prose – prose! Above all they will be terrified of pleasure – crushed by a deep fear of joy and art. They will have an over-faith in the uncertainties of the Lovers of Wisdom and Truth, and in the certainties of the Men of Power. They will distrust all Music, all grandeur of generality, all dignity of assertion. There will be a revolt from the foul cellars of the Temple of Poetry and a super-domination of the critical over the creative faculties. All they will crave is emotional hygiene and ideological or philosophical purity. I am weary to think of it."

The Muse ceased, momentarily sick at heart, it seemed, and revolving in her mind the woes of this Dark Time. Our Hero was distressed by his Muse's outburst – particularly since, after his glance in the Mirror, he was prepared to half-believe what she said. But he was comforted when the shades of Greater Poets, the Lords of Highest Song, having whispered for a while among themselves, turned to him with gestures of welcome, honour and encouragement. The Muse smiled as Our Hero, to his great joy, was included as one of their number and sat and drank and spoke with them (but about what, or to what effect, he never would reveal).

"Enough, enough," said the Muse all too soon, "I have much to teach and you to learn."

Book Two

The Arts
of Poetry

BOOK TWO: THE ARTS OF POETRY

Part One:
Living Words

32. A Poet's Playthings

"Celestial Patroness, do not forsake me in my hour of need," cried Our Hero (the Soul of all future Poets) as the Muse and her pupil floated softly out of the Temple of Poets and lay for a while on a restful cloud, rosy with the light of rising suns.

Whether a day and a night had passed in the Temple of Poets, or whether Time had been suspended, Our Hero did not know. He was both exhilarated and wearied by the visions he had seen and gazed deep into the morn-lit eyes of his Heavenly Instructress. He was dazed, amazed, appalled, yet strangely happy. The Muse seemed lost, for a while, in contemplation of herself and her own glories.

"Will these things, Celestial Muse, come to pass?" he asked at last. "Is my fainting soul to undergo such sorrow on the earth – and to suffer such unbearable joy? Am I to triumph even in that dour Northern Isle? Hard indeed is this to believe; harder to understand."

"Is not this abundant recompense, Soul of all Poets, for what was lost?" said the Muse. "You have beheld the glorious shades of my progeny – my very *own* dancers, my *own* musicians, my *own* painters, my *own* thinkers, my *own* law-givers, my *own* men of power – your glorious future selves, our famous sons, Lords of Future Song."

"Heavenly Goddess, I am but a man, and as I am a man I cannot fathom this matter. I have seen those you say are my future selves. I have heard of their glories and their Fame. But I cannot see *how* such things of which you speak may be done with words alone. I saw none of my sons dancing or singing. Few seemed to be priests. You *called* one a prince but none appeared to be kings. Teach me, Chief of Nine, teach me as you promised, to dance and sing and paint and think and pray and give laws, for my former assistants have shown me I can do none of these things."

"Fear not, my Chosen One, for though the road is long, and the way hard, I will show you the dancing and painting and thinking and praying and legislating peculiar to Poets.

You must study by day and meditate by night, for if you do not learn my Arts the past will be obliterated and the future will never be."

"Why must I study? Can you not inspire my heart – simply, directly, instantly?"

"My Arts are indeed useless to one who does not already know them."

"Quite," grunted Our Hero.

"But I can only visit those who have studied my Arts. Only those I am already with can learn from me. The ground must be prepared for the seed. The tower must be built where the lightning is to strike."

"Chief of Nine, speak to me in words that I may understand." implored Our Hero, blinking at the sun.

"Yours (despite present appearances to the contrary) is the soul of a Poet."

"So you say, Celestial Being, so you say."

"When I reveal my ultimate mysteries you will respond instantly, rapturously."

"I will, Heavenly Spirit, I will, I *will*."

"But in every age and in every land in which you find yourself reincarnated, you will have to work – you will have new words to learn and new customs to study."

"But I will learn these things *naturally*. I will learn these things on my earthly mother's knee."

"Only I can teach you, My Child, to make POETRY from what you learn on your mother's lap."

"Why so, Prophetic Spirit?"

"Because in every land, the arts and workings of Poetry are various, though the Laws of Poetry are universal."

"How can the laws be the same when the workings are different?"

"As the wheat-field may be watered by a channel cut from a river-course or from buckets carried by slaves, so the ends and ways and purpose of Poetry are constant, but the means by which they are achieved may be utterly different. You must therefore prepare yourself by learning my General Laws; which can, however, only be understood by a *minute* and *prolonged* study of *particulars*."

"I was afraid of that."

"Do not be downcast. You already know that which it is essential to know."

"I do?" asked Our Hero, searching the face of his fair Instructress.

"Let us consider this matter. What is it that you know beyond other men?"

"Nothing, my Muse. I only know that I am ignorant of all things."

"Leave such cleverness to the Lovers of Wisdom and Truth."

"I know much suffering ... and I have known some joy."

"As other men and women?"

"As other men and women – and more so. I have known the joys and sorrows of performance and composition."

"I have been following your recent incarnations with some interest, My Child. Which parts of your Grand Ceremonies did you most enjoy?"

"I suppose, more and more, it was the ·Grand Oration – the part, alas, that my audience liked least."

"You enjoyed the Oration even more than arranging the dancing of nymphs or contemplating the reproduction of crocodiles?"

"Lamp of Light, First of Nine, Heavenly Goddess," began Our Hero, gathering himself together and trying hard not to blush, "it is certainly, irrefutably the case that the subtle employment or deployment of a vocabulary of some distinction, the modest display of ravishing terms and honeyed metaphors, the wise disposition of narrative, the artful intermixture of digressions have been, in some measure, a comfort to me in my trials upon the face of yon gleaming globe and ..."

"Quite, quite. Arranging words (however hamfistedly) gives you joy."

"Arranging words has brought me to my present unhappy pass."

"And what are words?"

"Words are sounds."

"Only sounds?"

"Words are gestures sometimes – or paintings, or marks, on stones or in clay or on pieces of wood, or arangements of flowers, or knots in coloured thread, or ... "

"If words can take all these forms, what *are* they?"

(Our Hero looked and felt more than usually blank.)

"Words, My Child, are a means of colouring, translating, picturing, embodying, expounding, expressing, arranging, aggrandising, communicating, trapping, stilling, moving or creating THOUGHT. Do you understand me now?"

"No, Great Goddess, no – alas. I understand nothing."

"Where is the difficulty?" asked the Muse, feeling her pupil drifting away from her.

"Heavenly Patroness, you speak of THOUGHT, but the Lovers of Wisdom and Truth demonstrated that I was utterly, constitutionally, incapable of *thought*, that the words I use are the contradictions of *thought* – and they were, I fear, quite right. In daily life my words leap from my mouth before my thoughts have formed. All too often, *had* I thought, I would have been silent. I am always saying what I do not mean and what I would wish *not* to have said. I reveal what I would have liked to have kept secret and hidden. And even in my most solemn Orations, my words seem to run away with themselves: one word pulls another along with it against my will. Some of my words do not seem to come from my *thought* – my brain, my mind – but to leap out of some deep, unknown, uncontrollable part of me. Heavenly Goddess, many of the words of mortals are involuntary expressions – groans or giggles or blasphemies or cries – of joy or of pain."

"So then, what are mortal words, My Chosen One? What ARE words?"

"For we mortals words are felt as little pieces of human experience – arbitrarily selected – and human feeling perhaps – fragments of human life maybe – voluntary and involuntary expressions possibly – inter-actions between the inner and outer worlds, I suppose."

"Language, my Chosen Soul, shows us Man," said the Muse imperiously. "It springs out of the most retired and inward parts of mortals and is the IMAGE OF ITS PARENT, THE HUMAN MIND."

"And the human body?"

"If you say so, Dearest Mortal. Shall we say the human *soul*? No mirror renders a man's real form or secret likeness as truly as his words."

"Or as untruly. We mortals, Lamp of Light, can lie."

"If you insist. But you will agree that your pleasure in arranging words is a pleasure in arranging and re-arranging little pieces of human experience – true or feigned?" (Our Hero nodded unconvincingly, shaking his cloud.) "Let us see the words from the barren Northern Isle so that we may know the souls of their parents, those philistines. Let us learn the pleasures of arranging their words so that they dance and sing – so that we may learn the pleasures of discovering, knowing and re-ordering the Human Soul."

"Can words do *that*?"

"Inevitably."

(Our Hero nodded furiously, looking and feeling blanker than ever.)

33. The House of Words

The Muse led her Poet to a neighbouring cloud from which the morning sun revealed the large prospect of a vast edifice. Muse and Poet, hand in hand, drifted gently towards a spacious balcony on the sunny side of this building (if it might be called a building, for it was a shapeless agglomeration of chapels and antechapels, alcoves and niches, vestibules and halls, bowers, galleries, cellars, follies, and outhouses without number). As they alighted they were faced by two portals – one regular and open, the other ornate, trellised and dark.

"This is the House of Words," said the Muse. "All the words that ever were spoken come here and mingle with those that will be spoken in times to come. Here they live, re-live or pre-live the lives they have had, do have or will have on the lips of mortals. Immediately below us is the chamber known as the Great Slough – the repository of all the human sounds to be uttered in the dour Northern Isle. Before you are two portals – the Portal of Sound and the Portal of Sense. Listen and look."

Our Hero inserted his head a little way through the Portal of Sound but quickly withdrew, squirming with revulsion. He felt faint.

"I have never heard such cacophony, such a babble. Let us leave this hubbub of words."

But the Muse held him firmly, unrelenting.

Our Hero, holding his hands tightly over his ears, looked timidly into the Great Slough. As his eyes became accustomed to the half-light, he began to discern, far below him, a mass of indeterminate shapes, writhing, spluttering, crawling, coughing, shuffling, gasping, waddling, cooing, stumbling and squawking. He had never seen such creatures. Some seemed to have no life of their own but to stick like burrs to other word-creatures. The larger or longer were segmented like insects. Some had tentacular roots. Many had long shadowy tails of association. The venerable tails of the eldest creatures were so lengthy they were lost in the dark. There seemed to be a constant egress and ingress from the Great Slough to other chambers of the House of Words. He could make out *some* distinct kinds or species of word-creatures but most seemed to be strange ungainly hybrids, reproducing like aphids and dying like flies: endlessly parting and conjoining, and then again parting. Some seemed to be born, to flutter and to evaporate even as he watched.

"These are word-creatures, my Poet: hard words, long words, lost words, winged words, foul words, short words, kind words, words of hate, words of love, words of peace, words of war, truthful words, lying words, deceitful words, guileful words, evil words, rude words, taboo words, sacred words, easy words, profane words, nonce words, comic words, ungainly words, soft words, smooth words, strong words, weak words, loaned words, learned words, borrowed words, invented words, stolen words – the debris of human experience, the flotsam of life in a Northern Isle."

"So many! So various! I had not known there were so many. O terrible world that has such creatures in it!"

Our Hero gradually loosened the pressure on his ears, closed his eyes, and began to mark individual sounds amidst the howling din.

"Listen, Dearest Pupil, what do you hear?"

"I hear forty or fifty different sounds, Heavenly Being, all revolting. I hear the usual human sounds of joy and sorrow, hope and fear, love and hate, rejoicing and lamentation – but they are ugly, ugly, ugly! This language, Celestial One, is clotted and clogged with consonants. The words are clipped off at the end – often into short, sharp, snips of sound. Plosives plop, push and plunge, permeating the darkness. Vowels prowl in foul crowds and few are true or pure. They seem to be the product of a horrible mingling of species. Many seem to have decayed and lost parts of themselves. These creatures refuse to accommodate themselves to each other as they would in any decent grammatical language. *Must* I really work with these ... these things of *darkness*?"

"It is true they are not pretty – but you must acknowledge them as your own. You, Soul of all Poets, were and will be the originator, preserver and restorer of the principles of language. The earliest words were yours alone. In every age you will re-purify the language of your tribe. But the original, fresh, pristine words breed on the lips, and in the minds of ordinary un-inspired mortals and bring forth a progeny that is weak, imprecise, unsuggestive, and, as you say, ugly, ugly, ugly."

"Lamp of Light, will I be able to make such ugly things beautiful?"

"Yes and no. No word (not even the first fresh word) is truly beautiful in itself – any more than a human tooth, or piece of skin, or bone or flesh is beautiful in itself. The beauty comes when they are *joined* – when they are given (or assume) form and feature, life and soul."

"Celestial Patroness, did I not join together more than a few words when I lived on the earth below?"

"Yes, Soul of Future Poets, but without fully knowing my Arts. You have not yet forged those mysterious bonds that hold words together for all time. Your mixtures of words have been forgotten. They come here to the House of Words and dissolve into their elements or mingle with weak, uninspired word-creatures."

"But some of my Orations were much appreciated – for a while."

"That was because of the solemnity of the ceremony which held the parts temporarily together, or because of the noble efforts of My Sisters's progeny – the skill of the Dancers, of the Lovers of Sound and of Colour and Form."

"But my words will not always be forgotten – will not always fall apart?" asked Our Hero plaintively.

"The sand heaped by one flood", said the Muse grandly, "is scattered by another, but the rock always continues in its place. The stream of Time which washes away the flimsy texture of most speakers, passes harmlessly over the adamantine bonds which will join the words of my Greater Poets each to each."

"How can this be done with *these* creatures?" said Our Hero, pointing into the Slough. "I have never seen or imagined anything so unstable, so mutable, so volatile, so fickle as these monsters – these creatures of a dour Land."

"You can see the enormity of your task – and the grandeur of what you may achieve. You will master even these materials. My mysterious Arts will teach you to join words so that they will seem to contain within themselves the reasons why they *are* as they are and not otherwise. You must teach your words to dance and sing so that they will find the passes of the human mind and inform the human Memory where they will become immortal. Try the Portal of Sense."

Our Hero turned to this Portal. As if in a dream, he seemed to live through the whole lives of generations of men and women of the Northern Isle in an instant. When his clouded senses cleared, he discovered that he knew and recognised the strange words as if they were those his own mother had spoken. Everything was altered. The hall below him was in complete silence, still as the interior of a Pharaoh's tomb. The weird creatures had vanished. In their places he saw (or seemed to see) pictures of things and of actions, past, present and future. He had a distinct impression of emotions, sensations, and ideas floating in the still air. He was aware of many varieties of loving and hating, various kinds of chair and bed. He also received a general idea of Love and Hate, and general notions of what a chair and a bed might be. For some time he compared his impressions of the two Portals, of Sound and of Sense.

"Lamp of Light, I see I was mistaken. When I heard only sound, I confounded laughter and tears, joy and sorrow, hope and fear, effort and ease. Sounds I took for suffering were really those of love; those which then seemed the expression of elegance, now convey a cold chill of infinite contempt. There is nothing to be learned from the mere sounds of language. I will remain here forever at the Portal of Sense."

"In all speech," said the Muse, drawing herself up to her considerable height, "words and sense are as the body and the soul. The sense is as the life and soul of Language without which words are dead. But sense is wrought out of experience and knowledge of human life and actions. You must listen very carefully at *both* Portals because you must note exactly *what* is said and understand precisely *why* it is said – and *how* it is said. In order to comprehend the nature and variety of the human passions, as they exist in all lands and at all times, you must first appreciate the *precise* tones and colours with which those passions are expressed in one time and place – in SOUND."

"I must? I must study these terrible creatures?"

"The words of different ages, nations, tribes, like all living creatures, have various ways of conducting themselves – various ways of con-joining and of walking for example. Before a Poet can dance in any language, he must first learn how the language may be seen to walk when it is about its own business. You *must* learn the colour and the weight and the grace of every sound and of every word. You *must* understand the effect of every word-creature in combination with every other word-creature until you have familiarized yourself with every mode of discourse. *Then* you may begin to be a Poet."

"I cannot believe that the Great Art of Poetry can depend upon such petty knowledge," said Our Hero (resisting a temptation to giggle).

"It is certain," said the Muse imperiously, "that without such petty knowledge, no man can be a POET; that FROM THE PROPER DISPOSITION OF SINGLE SOUNDS RESULTS THAT HARMONY WHICH ADDS FORCE TO REASON, AND GIVES GRACE TO SUBLIMITY, WHICH SHACKLES ATTENTION AND GOVERNS PASSION."

"All that by mastering sounds?" said Our Hero incredulously.

"All that and more – much more. By studying the arrangement of human sounds you shall penetrate the mysteries of the human heart and peer deep into the abyss of the Human Soul."

"So you have said, Lamp of Light, but I cannot believe that empty sound can have such power."

"EMPTY sound! My Pupil, you have much to learn."

34. A Creeping and a Crawling

With a firm hand the Muse turned our recalcitrant Hero towards the Great Slough.

"Look and listen carefully at the Portal of Sound! Find me some WORDS amongst the writhing mass!"

"These monsters, Celestial One, seem so often to be swallowing each other's tails that it is hard to be sure where one word-creature ends and another begins, but I think I hear and see some globules, or gaggles or agglomerations of sound which might, perhaps, be WORDS."

"Let us summon and examine them, my child. (At our command, all words are winged words.)"

At the Muse's call, four word-creatures, raising themselves from the morass, fluttered to the Portal, and, settling for an unsteady moment on an inner ledge, slithered onto the balcony outside. Our Hero took a quick backward step as they writhed at his feet, aimlessly blinking, mindlessly bleating.

ROSE-ie DARNS-in GOLD-in MORN-in

"Do you, Dearest Pupil, notice anything similar about these creatures?"

"The front segment of each word-creature is larger, heavier, than the back," answered Our Hero reluctantly. "Why is this, Lamp of Light?"

"They were so formed by the muscles and tissues of men and women – by the lips, and tongues, and diaphragms, and throats and lungs of mortals in a Northern Isle. It is your first business to make these word-creatures *dance*. What should concern you most", said the Muse, attempting a hint, "is the way they *move*."

Our Hero decided to try his best. The lesson might then soon come to an end.

"As far as I can see, in crawling, these creatures seem to take one great STRIDE and one short step. The first part of each of each creature seems to have more energy, or more weight, or more breath, or more muscles, or longer legs than the following weaker part." Our Hero looked around him, blinking and bedazzled. "But those over there, Lamp of Light, seem to crawl on some other principle. They seem to be a slightly different kind of organism," said Our Hero, shuddering as some more words were summoned to the balcony where they lay basking and barking weakly in the sun.

sal-UTE a-WAY bi-COS a-RISE

"These word-creatures, O Teacher Divine, have their larger segment to the rear and seem to creep with one short step followed by one long STRIDE."

"And these?" asked the Muse signalling to some slightly longer word-creatures which, instantly obeying, spread themselves on the balcony before Our Hero, waddling and wailing obligingly.

ex-AC-ted to-MORR-ow PO-et-ry GLOR-i-us

"These curious creatures seem to drag their slow lengths along with little tottering steps leading up to, or following, a great muscular STRIDE. They have one fat segment, with short squirming segments in front or behind. Great Lady, I have seen enough. May we now leave?"

"Do not be so dismissive! In this language, the way a word walks is one of the most important things about it. If you were trying to speak this language, but mistook the walk of your words, even if all else were correct, nobody would understand you. Would you like to see some of the very smallest word-creatures?"

"If I must."

At the Muse's call, the balcony was covered with a swarm of little gasping, coughing words. Our Hero squinted disapprovingly as they hopped out of the Slough like fleas.

for a oft to ov and by in tha so

"Heavenly One, it is hard to be sure, so closely do they cling to other words, but it seems that these pathetic single-segment creatures take or make a weak little step all on their own – but every so often, one of them swells up and takes a giant hop, or even a STRIDE."

"As in this group?" asked the Muse, smiling secretly to herself and summoning some word-creatures, which crawled over the ledge of the balcony like so many ants.

and TEN LOW WORDS oft CREEP in ONE DULL LINE

"How can any of these revolting metamorphoses be of interest to one who is to be a Poet?" asked Our Hero, unable either to contain himself or to see anything of interest in these little words.

"Come, come, my child, have patience," said the Muse quickly, sensing her pupil slipping away again. "Now show me any group of joined WORDS which you can make out among the hubbub of the Slough. Any swarm of linked WORDS which seems to have form, life, energy or direction will serve. You must listen very hard and you may take your time. The best words to examine are those formed by men or women who cannot help it – when they are speaking in *passion*."

"Very well, Goddess, if you *insist*," said Our Hero, listening hard. "I think I can hear what I take to be the sounds of children, or adults in anger perhaps, in ecstasy or in misery, making these noises with great rhythmical emphasis – over and over again –

i-wann-a-die i-wann-a-die die die

dont-crie-my-love my-love-my-love dont crie."

"Can you see how this pack of words moves – as a pack?" asked the Muse gesturing imperiously towards the first of the creatures with her feet as they poured through the Portal of Sound whimpering, whining, wailing and howling together.

i WANT to DIE i WANT to DIE DIE DIE

"These slobbering, moaning things, Heavenly Being, move by alternating the size of their paces:

step STRIDE step STRIDE step STRIDE step STRIDE STRIDE STRIDE."

"Is the pattern, *absolutely* regular, my child?"

"No, the creatures seemed to pause after the fourth stride," said Our Hero, separating some of the words from the others (also with his feet, but gingerly)

... i-WANT-to-DIE // DIE DIE.

"The word-creatures of the Great Slough," said the Muse happily, "the sounds that make up this language, often stand still or pause."

"Far too often for my liking," mumbled Our Hero.

"Ah, My Poet, the things you will do with the well-managed Pause! (But I digress.) What else do you notice?"

"The last 'DIE' was the largest or strongest or noisiest of all. It blew itself up. It took a long striding pace. It seemed almost to grow a new tail:

... i WANT to DIE // DIE DIE-IE-IE-IE."

"Yes, you see again that these tricky little word-creatures sometimes swell themselves up with self-importance; at other times they huddle themselves into the smallest possible space. In this language, words made up of a single segment can take either short modest steps or great, proud STRIDES. Now, listen closely! How does the second speaker respond to the first?"

"With these horrifying noises, Great Muse:

DONT crie my-LOVE / my-LOVE-my-LOVE / dont-CRIE-IE-IE."

"Does anything strike you as *odd* about these creatures, my Child?"

"They walk in and out of the pattern established by the first group of creatures, Lamp of Light:

STRIDE step step STRIDE step STRIDE step STRIDE step STRIDE ..."

"The *variety* of the ways that words may walk, my Poet, presents you with many difficulties, but also with numberless, mysterious, *wonderful* possibilities."

"Wonderful possibilities? Heavenly Being, why must I attend to such numbingly obvious or blindingly trivial things? Sound, I still maintain (though respectfully), is merely sound – empty, arbitrary sound."

"How often must I repeat myself?" asked the Muse with flashing eyes. "A Poet *must* work with the sounds of his native tongue. He MUST! (Although in some of your incarnations in the Northern Isle you will, naturally enough, feel tempted to try almost any other language – even a dead one.) A Poet must walk before he can run, and run before he can dance. He must discover the underlying Laws of the language. You have already perceived three principles on which to go to work. You have seen that these word-creatures are composed of segments of different shapes and sizes which (particularly when the speaker is in a state of passion) form regular (but variable) patterns of steps and STRIDES – or STRIDES and steps. And you have heard the Pause – you have heard my beloved Pause."

"Empty sound," said Our Hero (to himself).

35. Words That Walk

The noon-tide sun glinted on the towers and bowers of the House of Words. Our Hero began to spend longer and longer at each Portal. He adjusted his eyes to the gloom of one Portal and the blinding light of the other. He acclimatised his ears to the hubbub of Sound, and accustomed his mind to the starry silence of Sense. Slowly and reluctantly, he began even to half-enjoy himself, and resolved to do (more or less) as his Muse required.

"These words, Celestial Goddess, are the most wild, unruly creatures I have ever seen. I cannot *begin* to imagine how they may be properly patterned, let alone used to penetrate the human heart, order the human soul. I am both perplexed and intrigued."

The Muse smiled.

"You, Soul of all Poets, must make these creatures do your bidding: walk as you want them to walk: trot as you want them to trot: stop when you want them to stop, and then stand, promptly to attention, at your command."

"Such a command is beyond the power of mortals! It is impossible to harmonize or control such a cackle of sound – so *many* shades, varieties and colours of sense."

"Can you make out, amongst the hubbub, any group of words, any fragment of speech, which seems to be moving as one being moves, to be forming a pattern, to have shape, purpose, direction, life?"

Our Hero peered deep into the pit of words. Eventually, amongst the inchoate mass, he made out a group or gaggle of words, that seemed to come together to inform an airy, living shape. The Muse, watching her pupil's eyes, called the word-creatures he had chosen. With a cry like that of gulls, a long swarm of inter-connected words flew from the Portal of Sound, prancing, cavorting, and flexing their muscles, as if happy to see the light of the sun. Our Hero, trying to be dutiful, marked the

characteristics of each from his position at the Portal of Sense. But then, as the words emerged and buzzed around his head and his ears, he saw, or thought he saw, the image of the shape of a proud, contemptuous, eloquent man form and un-form before him. He shivered slightly, without knowing why.

"What an ear you have, my Poet!" said the Muse, smiling broadly. "I could not have chosen better myself. Please note how superbly these words run together and how masterfully they employ my beloved pause."

Our Hero, obedient to his Muse, divided some of the word-creatures into little sub-groupings: first a tiny flock of minute word-creatures:

as if we were

and then a pack of longer words:

villains / on necessity //
fools / by heavenly compulsion, //
knaves thieves and traitors / by spherical predominance //
drunkards liars and adulterers / by an enforced obedience of
planetary influence //
and all that we are in evil in /
by a divine thrusting on ///

"It is true, Celestial One, that these words seem to have more life, and direction than others I have seen. When these creatures pause for breath, that pause seems to mark a little block or unit of sense. And they *do* seem to arrange themselves in something like a pattern – a simple pattern consisting of two parts – a shorter and a longer. But the pattern is irregular – both the longer and the shorter parts expand with each section of sense."

"You learn well, my Chosen Soul."

"I do not understand these words. They are something strange. I gather that there are a number of names of various kinds of people – 'villains', 'fools', 'knaves', 'thieves', 'traitors', 'drunkards', 'liars', 'adulterers'. These are balanced by a number of words for ideas and forces – 'necessity', 'compulsion', 'predominance', 'influence'. The words for ideas have other words attached to them which seem to give them colour and precision – 'heavenly', 'spherical' 'planetary'. The relation between the words for people and the words for ideas is suggested by a series of those horrid little one-segment creatures – 'on', 'by', 'in'. But what that relation is I do not know."

"Let us inspect these words closely," said the Muse, dragging Our Hero away from the Portal of Sense and forcing him to sink to his knees and to bring his eyes close to parts of the slithering gaggle on the balcony. He shielded his eyes, fearing in particular the little jumping words.

"Goddess, I am not sure if these words are peculiarly ugly or peculiarly fine. I notice that the first half of each part of the pack contains a predominance of large-segmented, striding creatures:

VILL-ains ... FOOLS ... KNAVES, THIEVES and TRAIT-ors ... DRUNK-ards, LI-ars, and ad-ULT-er-ers ...
and that the second half contains a predominance of little tottering steps:

on ne-CESS-it-y ... by HEAV-en-ly com-PUL-sion ... by SPHER-ic-al pre-DOM-in-ance ... by an en-FORC-ed o-BEDE-i-ence of PLAN-et-ary IN-flu-ence ....
but in the last sense-section, this pattern is reversed:

and ALL that we are EV-il in/
BY a di-VINE THRUST-ing ON."
"Can you guess why the words are arranging themselves like that?"

"According to what I learned from the Portal of Sense, Lamp of Light, the ruler, or master, of this piece of sense is this group," said Our Hero pointing to some words at the front of the pack;

we make guilty of our disasters /
the sun, the moon, and stars,

All the rest of the words merely repeat, expand and exemplify this thought."

"My child, you sound doubtful."

"When I stand at the Portal of Sound or watch them here on the balcony, I seem to see the words cavorting, leaping and gambolling as if in wild enjoyment of their own life. I suspect that the reason for these words living in this group is to give a form to the speaker's contempt for human superstition – and his extended relish of his own contempt."

"What do you mean by 'the speaker', Dearest Mortal? A player? A dancer?"

"The Image of some Being created or suggested by these word-creatures. The pattern of pauses and long and short segments is a reflection of his voice and his muscles moving rapidly and easily with a series of sounds which he can load with the colours of his mind – a derision which mounts with the volubility of syllables. I have the impression that the more little word-segments he produces, the more he enjoys – and the less he believes."

"So the sound and shape of these words is as important as the sense?"

"Heavenly Goddess, I concede – THE SOUND IS PART OF THE SENSE: THE SENSE IS PART OF THE SOUND," said Our Hero (momentarily convinced). "The walking and squawking of the creatures at the end of this pack remind me of some kind of tune – a dry song of derision.

An-AD-mir-a-ble e-VA-sion
of-WHORE-mast-er MAN,
to-LAY-his-GOAT-ish DIS-pos-I-tion
to-the-CHARGE-of-a-STAR!"
Our Hero watched, speechless with admiration, as the pack of words re-assembled themselves and re-entered the Great Slough through the Portal of Sense in exactly the same order in which they had left. He saw (or thought he saw) the image of a proud man curling his lips as he curled his

LIVING WORDS: WORDS THAT WALK

syllables; turning his body as he turned his words. He heard, half-heard (or thought he heard) a terrifying sneer of absolute contempt which was also a dance of delight:

This is the excellent foppery of the world // that / when we are sick in fortune / often the surfeits of our own behaviour / we make guilty of our disasters / the sun / the moon / and stars // as if we were villains / on necessity // fools / by heavenly compulsion // knaves / thieves / and traitors / by spherical predominance // drunkards / liars / and adulterers / by an enforced obedience of planetary influence //

and all that we are in evil in / by a divine thrusting on /// An admirable evasion of whoremaster man / to lay his goatish disposition / to the charge of a star ///

"I cannot believe," said Our Hero at last, "that these words will be spoken by an ordinary man. How can I learn the natural workings of this language if you direct my attention to examples which bear all the marks of Your Presence, Heavenly Being?"

"It all depends on what you mean by '*natural*'," said the Muse with a wild laugh.

36. Dancing Words

The Muse and her Poet reclined on the balcony of the House of Words in the shadowless heat of the day. Our Hero had been impressed by the words he had just seen and heard, but continued to resent his teacher's unrelenting attention to minutiae. The Muse was pleased with the progress of her pupil but was ever wary lest he regress.

"You have seen words run hand in hand. Now let us make them *dance*!"

"I can now perhaps appreciate," said Our Hero reluctantly, "how the words of this language might be said to walk together, and I think I may one day understand how they may be made to trot and to march in decent order, but I cannot for the life of me guess how such an ungainly waddle, however spirited in its parts, could be transformed by me into anything which could properly be called a *dance*. How, Celestial One, can I emulate the light-foot graces of the dancing girls with these ponderous, jerking, joking word-creatures?"

"Through the Portal of Sound you can hear some children chanting. Listen to their noises. Let us catch their words and examine them closely."

The words of the chant circled upwards, fluttered through the Portal of Sound, and circled Our Hero's head, murmuring:

TWINCK-ul-TWINCK-ul-LITT-ul-STAH /
OW-ai-WUN-dar-WOT-yew-AH.

"My Pupil, what sort of patterns do you hear there, and how are they marked?"

"The pattern (if that is what you *insist* on calling it) is formed, I suppose, by a more-or-less regular alternation of STRIDES and steps."

"How can you know there is a pattern?" asked the Muse.

"It is marked," answered her recalcitrant pupil, yawning, "by the repetition, in various ways, of the same or similar sounds or groups of sounds."

"Such as? Such as? Wake up, My Chosen One!"

"Among the first group of words –
TWINCK-ul-TWINCK-ul-LITT-ul-STAH
the first two strides begin with a 'TW'; three of the short steps are made up of 'ul', and in the middle I see and hear several 'i' sounds. In the second group –
OW-ai-WUN-dar-WOT-yew-AH
two of the strides begin with 'W'. (Is this what you want me to notice and to say, Celestial Patroness?)"

"Indeed it is. Do the two groups have anything in common?"

"Both groups of creatures," continued Our Hero dutifully, "have the same pattern of steps and STRIDES and the same 'AH' sound as their final segment – a sound that seems to me to be somehow more open or longer than most others – a pattern which seems to have the effect of joining the two groups together, and marking them off as more separate and equal units than seems to be the general case in this dreadful language. I am mildly impressed, I suppose."

"Good, good." said the Muse rapidly, "Does that affect the movement of the group, as a group?"

"It seems to me that there is perhaps a greater difference between the steps and the STRIDES of this group than I noticed when I was watching ordinary accumulations of word-creatures. The three 'ul'steps, for example, in the first group are given hardly any weight at all – they are pathetic little half-creatures; but the larger segments jump higher than usual. I am mystified."

"Mystified, my child?"

"When I heard and saw those strange moaning, mutating words which you showed me first, and when I studied the march of proud contempt you showed me just now, the vigour, the muscles of the words seemed to come from the passions of the speakers. But these words seem to move *by themselves* – and in a way that is more lively and rapid than those I saw before."

"You have made two profound discoveries, my Chosen One."

"I have?"

"First, that the bond between word-creatures of similar sounds or similar segments is stronger than that between others. In this language, the head, stomach or tail of one creature may chime with the head, stomach or tail of another. Further (and even more importantly), when they chime in this way the word-creatures begin to *prance* – the difference between steps and strides becomes more marked, more vigorous, more sprightly, more regular."

Our Hero's mind suddenly emptied.

"And what, Great Muse, is the significance of that?"

"All the significance in the world. You yourself said that the words assume the rhythms of passion without the motive power of a passionate speaker – real or imagined?"

"Yes, I did say that."

"And do you suppose they would prance even if spoken by a parrot or some kind of talking *machine*?"

"I suppose they would."

"Once joined in this way, then, the word-creatures become independent of the joiner, of the speaker. THEY DANCE THE DANCES OF PASSION (as you say) BY THEMSELVES. The passion-pattern is *intrinsic* to the word-creatures. This you must concede. See how they go!"

"I concede, Heavenly Goddess – but cannot regard such an observation as a great discovery. I can still not see any point or purpose to such petty knowledge. Please may I return to the Portal of Sense?"

Our Hero was half way there before his Muse gently restrained him.

"Not yet, My Child. I am going to show you a more complicated and more wonderful dance of word-creatures."

"Dance? Are those children's words *dancing*?" asked Our Hero, staring after the word-creatures in disbelief.

"You must realise that a Poet's dances are not quite like those performed by your friends the players."

"(No friends of mine.)"

"Your business is not only to make the words dance themselves. You must make the minds of your audience dance – as your words take a hold on their Souls."

"Take a hold on their souls? Only Sense could do such a thing."

"To do this, you must take the fragments of pattern which, as you have seen, exist in the ordinary language and arrange them so that the pattern comes to seem more regular, more ordered, more vigorous than it ever does in speech. If you do this well, my Poet, the hearers of your Poem will *feel* your words as a spectator – and even as a participator – feels the patterns of bodily movement of a dance – as an irresistible force."

"They will?" asked Our Hero, full of unbelief.

"They will! Listen now, and watch the creatures I have chosen! What is the pattern? What are the features which distinguish these wondrous sounds from the generality of word-creatures in the Great Slough?"

The Muse, smiling secretly to herself, called her word-creatures to the balcony, a well-ordered, muscular pack.

WOR / he-SUNG / is-TOIL-an-TRUB-bul / ON-ur / BUT-an-EMP-tie-BUB-bul / NEV-ah-END-ing / STILL-beg-IN-ing / FITE-ing-STILL / an-STILL-dest-ROY-ing / if-tha-WURLD be-WURTH-thy-WINN-ing / THINK-o-THINK it-WURTH-en-JOY-ing.

"Are not these *fine* words, My Chosen Soul?"

"These word-creatures behave in an extraordinary fashion," said Our Hero, genuinely surprised as the words hopped happily before him. "The first thing I noticed, Chief of Nine, was that there is a predominance of STRIDE-step patterns –

ON-ur, NEV-ur, FITE-ing

and, as in the children's chant, there is much repetition of chimes, of similar sounds at the beginnings, middles, and ends, heads, stomachs and tails of words."

"Which sounds, My Pupil? Look minutely!"

"If you *insist*, Heavenly Instructress. There are many chimes – TRUB-bul / BUB-bul, beg-IN-ing / WINN-ing, TOIL / TRUB-bul – to such an extent that almost every sound has its echo, its chime, somewhere else in the gaggle – WOR, WURLD, WURTH, WIN, WURTH – or – IO, OY, OI, – or – UB, UB, UL – or – EM, EV, EN, – or – ILL, IN, ILL, IN. Is my attention sufficiently minute, Lamp of Light," asked Our Hero cheekily, once again resisting a temptation to laugh.

"This patterning," said the Muse, patiently, approvingly, "this chime-directed dance of words, becomes much clearer when the words are heard with understanding. Position yourself mid-way between the Portals. Listen again! See if you can see how these word-creatures mark out their dance."

The words hung for a while over our Our Hero's reluctant head, then entered his ears and found the passes of his mind. Somehow he heard a story of a musician singing a strange, haunting but vigorous song about war to a great conqueror seated besides his beautiful concubine, Lais, at a grand banquet in celebration of a famous victory.

He felt the energy of a dance – but whether it was a dance of sharp contempt or of sweet delight he knew not.

War, he sung, is toil and trouble;
Honour but an empty bubble;
  Never ending, still beginning;
Fighting still, and still destroying:
  If the world be worth thy winning,
Think, O think, it worth enjoying.
  Lovely Lais sits beside thee,
  Take the good the gods provide thee.

"I concede, Heavenly Muse," said Our Hero, recovering at last, "that these words seem *somehow* to suggest, or seem *somehow* to follow, an underlying pattern or rhythm *something* like that of a dance. The steps or figures of the dance are marked by similar sounds, yes, and by patterns of pauses. My mind is *somehow* carried out of itself – or made to dance along. And yet, when I move away from the Portal of Sense and look at the words, I see no dance. I see only a string of word-creatures crawling as word-creatures always crawl. These are a little more sprightly, perhaps, but that is all. I am once again *mystified*."

37. Sweet Singing

It was now long past noon. The shadows were lengthening across the roof (or roofs) of the House of Words. The gentle roar of words issuing from the Great Slough below reminded Our Hero of the moan of doves in immemorial elms, or the murmuring of innumerable bees. Baking in his niche, he longed for the cool of the Muses' Garden. Even more he longed for quiet. But to his lessons there seemed no end – no end to the words which the Muse called for his scrutiny from every corner of the Slough.

"We have seen a dance of words, My Poet. Now we must learn to *sing*."

"Heavenly Instructress, for all that you have shown me, I cannot begin to imagine how these words could emulate in any way all those miracles the musicians perform with sound."

"This is a language in which some of our sons will compose some of the sweetest songs."

"I can believe that it would be easier to sing in almost any other language than in this babylonish dialect – this mess of words."

"Why do you say that, my child? Why do these words irritate you so?"

"A musical language, Celestial Patroness, would be a language in which a singer might love to perform. Most of its words would end in vowels, which would allow the voice to expand and finish a musical phrase with ease and purity. But many of these word-creatures from the Great Slough have tails which end in a contortion or strangulation of the vocal chords – 'NNGG' or 'FFF' or 'VVV' or 'THHH'. How could any singer sing 'cough' or 'enough' or 'truth' or 'live' without reducing his audience to laughter? How can I sing, Lamp of Light, how can I possibly sing while biting my lip, or with my tongue clenched firmly between my teeth?"

"Any other complaints, my Poet?"

"I certainly have. The words in the Great Slough end much too often with buzzing, hissing sounds. How can I sing of 'streaMMZZ' or 'sciZZUZZ?'"

"Indeed, how? That is the mystery ... and the mastery."

"And so many vowels from the Slough seem not to be pure sounds at all (least of all the word 'pure' – or as it is spoken 'PEE-EW-uh')."

"Still more objections? My Poet, is there no pleasing you?"

"This language is so full of consonants that it seems a buzz, a bark, a snarl, a hiss, a growl, a snort, a whinny, a grunt, a bleat, or a howl, rather than any sound befitting the dignity of thinking beings!"

"But you must find those very words – 'buzz', 'bark', 'snarl', 'hiss' – *wonderfully* evocative of the creatures to which they refer?"

"Wonderfully evocative? Lamp of Light, I am afraid (respectfully I say it) that to me that seems merely *fanciful*. The inhabitants of the dour Isle may *think* that dogs bark and bees buzz but you, who know every word in every hall in the House of Words, must admit that other nations imitate animal sounds in very different ways."

"That is, of course, true."

"And to say that those words are evocative is far from saying that they are beautiful or musical."

"Perhaps. But your studies at the Portal of Sense will have taught you that words may suggest sounds different from those which they actually make – that mortals will think they hear doors slam and dogs growl when they hear no such sound? May not a similar deception ... "

"*Deception!* I thought as much."

"A device by which (by universal consent) the sound of a particular musical instrument is evoked by a particular arrangement of words?"

"Heavenly One, I doubt it."

"We will see. What, for example, do you make of this group of words?

The double double beat of the thundr'ing drum

Surely you hear the drum beating in the repetition of the consonants and vowels?" asked the Muse.

"Perhaps so, but I hardly consider the drum a musical instrument," said Our Hero snobbishly. "And as you have yourself admitted, the words do not actually sound like a drum. The sound is not the same – nor nearly the same."

"Very well, My Chosen One. You would, I hope, call the bugle a musical instrument. Listen, listen well to this group of words as they fly through the Portal:

Blow, bugle, blow, set the wild echoes flying,
Blow, bugle; answer, echoes dying, dying, dying.

Surely, surely, My Child, you hear the echoing bugle-call in those lines?"

"I fear, O Muse, I hear nothing of the kind. I am not given the quality of the sound; only, perhaps, some of the effect of distance and repetition. Were it not for what I gather of the sense of the word 'bugle', the rest of the creatures might, for all I can tell, refer to a horse whinnying or a dog barking in the distance."

"But you *must* agree," said the Muse, restraining her impatience, "that the repetition of the word 'dying' would not occur in ordinary speech, and, given the general sense, that it goes some way at least towards imitating the echoing and fading resonance of a bugle call?"

"I suppose so, Heavenly Muse. But it is almost as if the poet has exploited the very *unmusicality* of the language. 'DY-ing' might be thought of as a word beginning in something like a musical note and ending in a mere noise. It is clever, I suppose, to be able to suggest musical fading by such unmusical means."

"A little less sarcasm, my Pupil! You are conceding something important! You are conceding that, by exploiting

the parts of English speech which are roughly analogous to musical notes, and by setting them off with subtlety against those parts which are positively unmusical, a Poet can evoke sound which the mortal mind inevitably associates with real music. Listen and attend to my next group of word-creatures – a lovely sweet-souled pack."

Sing ye, sweet angels, alleluia sing,
That all the woods may answer and your echo ring.

"I suppose," said Our Hero, having studied these creatures quizzically, "I suppose I can hear the angels' song in the word 'alleluia' – sandwiched as it is between the strangulated 'NNGS' and buzzing, hissing sounds. But these words are cheating."

"*Cheating*, My Poet?"

"For the really musical word, they have joined with one from beyond the Great Slough altogether. Secondly, 'alleluia' is a word which is, I gather, sung far more often than spoken. Indeed, as far as I can tell from the Slough, it is never spoken at all," said Our Hero, proud of his obduracy.

"What do you deduce from that?"

"It is still very much a matter of the poet *telling* me that he is talking about music. I would not know that any of his words were musical if he had not *told* me that I should think of them as such. When I look at them, or hear them one at a time, I see and hear only the usual ugliness of word-creatures from a Northern Isle."

The Muse, feeling her pupil once again slipping away, redoubled her efforts.

"If you persist in such literal-mindedness, you will never learn anything, my child. Some Poets in the Northern Isle will create musical effects or impressions when they are not evoking real music at all. I will now call up for you a wonderful evocation of the music made by falling water ..."

100

"(I fear that my erstwhile friends, the musicians, would consider the idea, that falling water makes music, degrading to their profession.)"

" ... from a Poem in which a nymph is lamenting that her beloved, who loved only his own reflection, has drowned and been turned into a flower."

The Muse turned her reluctant Pupil towards a cloister in the Great Slough by which sounds from the Temple of Poetry waft to the House of Words. At her call the light-winged creatures swooped towards Our Hero. Despite all his efforts to fight them off, he felt the creatures creeping insidiously into his mind. To his surprise the shapes that formed in his brain were not of nymphs and fountains, but the image of a short stocky figure with a mountain belly and a rocky face. And when the image spoke there was little of the musicality of intonation which Our Hero expected. The Shade of the future Poet recited his composition, dwelling on the sense of the words as if they were quite separate from him — as if they were more true and lovely than he could ever hope to be himself.

Our Hero was astonished and confused by these words. He shook his head, determined to free his mind of them. With a struggle he maintained his opposition to his Muse.

"The repetition of the word 'drop' is effective, I *suppose*. But it seems to be another clever trick. Falling water does not make a sound like the word 'drop', but foolish listeners have been conditioned into thinking that it does so."

"You *must* feel that the fourfold repetition of an identical sound helps to re-enforce the lovely effect," said the Muse desperately. "Is it not wonderful that the word 'drop' is here both a verb of action and the name of a globule of water ... or of tears."

"But the word 'drop' isn't in itself a beautiful – nor even a sad – sound. Is only comes to seem so in this poem because I imagine a singer repeating the word over and over again and dwelling on it with the loveliness of real music."

"Do the sound and shape of the words not contribute at all to this loveliness? Come, let us inspect them."

At first Our Hero thought his Muse would shake him – so strong, so firm, so sure was the grip of her hand as she led him to the Portal. Resistance, he knew, would be pointless. He surrendered his will and his mind. And then he saw, or thought he saw, the word-creatures dance a beautiful, slow and solemn dance. And he heard, or thought he heard, a song which was at once a plea and a lament. The creatures, no longer vile, seemed to dance in lovely pairs, sure-footed, even-footed, keeping perfect time with delicate variety. The sounds, no longer ugly, seemed to chime with soft accord. And then he wept.

SLOW-SLOW fresh-FOUNT keep-TIME with-MY
salt-TEARS
Yet-SLOW-er-YET o-FAINT-ly GEN-tle SPRINGS
LIST to the HEA-vy PART the MUS-ic BEARS
WOE weeps out HER di-VIS-ion WHEN she SINGS
DROOP HERBS and FLOW-ers
FALL GRIEF in SHOW-ers
Our BEAUT-ies ARE not OURS
O I could STILL
Like MELT-ing SNOW up-ON some CRAG-gy HILL
DROP DROP DROP DROP
Since NAT-ures PRIDE is NOW a WITH-er'd
DAFF-o-DIL

SLOW-SLOW fresh-FOUNT keep-TIME with-MY
salt-TEARS

"At last, My Chosen Soul, you see that *something* comes to seem beautiful by means of this group of words?"

"Yes, *something* does. But I still think these words would have to say with the flowers: 'Our beauties are not ours'."

38. Soft Music

Our Hero, in the full glare of the afternoon sun, positioned himself midway between the Portal of Sound and the Portal of Sense. The Muse brought him cool water to drink and various fruit to taste. His spirits revived. But the Muse was relentless.

"Come, come my Chosen Soul, you stand on the foothills of Poetic Knowledge. Now, I have summoned a fragment from a play by that man who will be (despite himself) your most famous descendant. A great and sensuous queen calls for music:

Give me some music; music, moody food
Of us that trade in love ...

Would you agree that these word-creatures are not evoking any particular instrument or specific natural sound, but are, by their sounds, giving a general impression of the kind of languorous, melting music this queen wants to hear?"

"I would agree, First of Nine."

"You would agree also, would you not, that all the 'oooo' sounds contribute *superbly* to this lovely effect?"

Our Hero laughed.

"Certainly, Heavenly Being, but is it not also the case that without the *sense* of the word 'moody' the 'oooo's would not work to the same purpose; that these creatures make no sense when they are *only* sounds – no sense at all?"

"That is also the case," said the Muse (sensing acquiescence).

"And would you not in turn agree that these creatures make sense by reminding us mortals of a languorous music that we have heard ourselves?"

"Reminding you?" prompted the Muse happily.

"If I had never heard the musicians playing music like that to which this queen is alluding, her words would have no effect on me at all. These creatures, I still maintain, are not intrinsically musical. So I still do not see how you can say that these words have been made to sing. All poets can do, it seems to me, is to *trick* the audience into remembering the music made by musicians. It seems to me that this music of poetry has more to do with the Imagination than with the ear."

"At last, at last, you have discovered the true point of what I have been saying all along. Now I will summon the words of one of my favourite Poet-musicians."

The word-creatures came floating and drifting and soaring and swooping from the Slough. Our Hero welcomed them into his brain. He saw (and thought he recognised) the image of a figure in a long black coat come striding along the galleries of his mind, nervously fingering his long black beard. With a slight gesture of self-disparagement, the image began to recite, mouthing out his hollow 'oe's' and 'ae's' with slow, deep-chested music. Curiously, although the image of a shade of the Future Poet spoke only fifty words, those fifty words seemed to fill the whole hot afternoon:

There is sweet music here that softer falls
Than petals from blown roses on the grass,
Or night-dews on still waters between walls
Of shadowy granite, in a gleaming pass;
Music that gentlier on the spirit lies,
Than tired eyelids upon tired eyes;
Music that brings sweet sleep down from the blissful skies.

"My Pupil, you have found (or you *should* have found) that your mind was filled with the *sense* of music, even though the Poet has nowhere attempted to evoke its *sound*."

"Yes, this poet has positioned and arranged his words and controlled their associations in such a way that I become somehow conscious of the ways in which emotions and physical sensations affect my mind like music. I am given pictures instead of sound, and sounds instead of ideas."

"Now it is my turn to be lost," said the Muse, laughing. "Explain, little mortal! Tell me what happens in your mind."

"The words 'sweet', 'soft', 'still', 'shadowy', 'gentle' and 'blissful' describe both the effect of music and the effect of a wide range of circumstances in which my body and my mind interact with the world around me, evoking the sensations of both touch and sound."

"Is it the case, Dearest Pupil, that the sounds that the word-creatures make, or that the physical sensation of saying or hearing these words, contributes to this effect? Look hard at these creatures."

MUS-ic that GENT-lier on the SPIR-it LIES,
Than TI-red EYE-lids u-PON TI-red EYES ...

"I can see that we have there an extraordinary concentration of repeated and similar sounds. It seems to me that the two processes – of saying and of hearing – come very close together here – that *hearing is a kind of saying*."

"Hearing is a kind of saying? Explain again, little mortal!"

"I find it hard, while hearing these words, not to remember or imagine what they are like to speak aloud, or what they *might* be like to speak aloud. I seem to hear them with my tongue and lips and throat. I seem to hear these long-breathed, deep-chested, lightly aspirated sounds with all the force of bodily sensation." He paused. "But these sensations provide an analogy to music, rather than the thing itself."

"Must you *insist* on the thing itself? Can you not see how my Poets will make an unheard music of the mind?"

"As far as I can see, poets will give the impression of having heard a piece of music by giving their audience ideas and images which are analogous to those which arise in the mind while attending to a piece of music. By slightly exaggerating and delicately re-arranging the sound patterns of language, they will seduce the mind into believing that it is hearing song."

"Well done, My Child, you will make a Poet yet! And can you see that in doing this, the Poet is penetrating the human heart?"

"No, this I do not see. Poets, so far as I can tell, merely deceive, trick, bamboozle and beguile the human brain by seducing the bodily senses. It is all an *illusion*."

39. Stories in Song

It was late afternoon. Our weary Hero looked askance at his Muse, beautiful beyond dreams, powerful beyond terror, wise beyond imagination – but also something of a bully, and not, perhaps, entirely to be trusted. There was, it was clear, a price to be paid for her unrelenting affection.

"Come, come, my Chosen Soul, 'illusion' and 'deceit' are hard words for my mysterious Arts – Arts which will harmonise a harsh tongue and fill a barren land with dance and song."

"Dances and songs of the human mind, perhaps," said Our Hero cautiously.

"If you insist, my child, I will not demur – for, in making such a remark you are conceding that the Mind of Man is something you understand. Now I will show you a set of words where one of my Poets demonstrates with supreme mastery the various songs and dances at his command."

As the flying words entered his mind, Our Hero heard, or thought he heard, four stories – the story of Zephyr, the gentle west wind, the story of a storm-beaten shore, the story of the mighty hero Ajax hurling a rock in battle, and the story of Camilla, a warrior maiden riding zestfully to war.

Soft is the strain when zephyr gently blows,
And the smooth stream in smoother numbers flows;
But when loud surges lash the sounding shore,
The hoarse, rough verse should like the torrent roar;
When Ajax strives some rock's vast weight to throw,
The line too labours, and the words move slow;
Not so when swift Camilla scours the plain,
Flies o'er th'unbending corn, and skims along the main.

"I am impressed by these creatures, Lamp of Light", said Our Hero, anxious to please. "These words make clear to me (what ought perhaps to have been clear before)

– that the particular sounds chosen for repetition are of the utmost importance, and that the way I recognize the pattern – even the sound pattern – is determined by the sense of the words."

"Very good, little mortal. Did anything strike you in particular?"

"I notice that each part of the pattern (except the last) has the same number of syllables (ten), and that each part is felt as a separate unit or group or line of word-creatures."

"What is the pattern? What happens in your mind?" asked the Muse with real curiosity.

"Within each line, there is a predominance of step-STRIDE sub-patterns. And each pair of lines has a word with a similar sound, a chime, at the end."

"What effect does this word-pattern have?"

"This overall shape works in two ways: it binds the creatures together, and it draws attention to minor differences between them. So, although there are many little variations within the lines and from line to line, I can see that the different creatures work *together* as a pack. They do so as if they had leapt into this pattern of their own accord."

"You have made another important discovery. (For some mysterious reason, most of the Poetry composed in the Northern Isle will have something like the general shape you describe.) What is the relation of the pattern of sound to the pattern of sense?"

"It looks to me as though this Poet has used words that dance off the tongue to suggest images that dance in the mind. Hearing, seeing, saying become one process."

The Muse beamed happily.

"One process? As with the unheard music of my last example?"

"Exactly so, Celestial Being. When I say the word 'soft', I can hardly distinguish what the word means from what it feels like to speak. In his first two lines, the Poet has used far more 'S' sounds than would be usual in speech:

Soft iS the Strain when Zephyr gently blowS,
And the Smooth Stream in Smoother numberS flowS

As I speak or hear these lines, I feel that both my vocal chords and my mind are being soothed by smooth,

Here a number of word-creatures have come together words which are hard to pronounce comfortably – 'loud', 'surges', 'lash' – and, in the next line we have three STRIDES in a row – HOARSE ROUGH VERSE – which are like an *obstacle* to the regular flowing pattern of alternating steps and strides."

soft sounds requiring little effort. In both lines, too, the words walk into a more and more regular step-STRIDE pattern:

and the SMOOTH STREAM in SMOOTH-er
NUM-bers FLOWS

which suggests a regular movement to my mind, of precisely the same kind as that which the verse describes – water flowing gently, strongly, steadily."

The Muse gazed upon her pupil contentedly. All was proceeding according to plan.

"Is the whole passage like this? What happens next in your mortal mind and mortal frame?"

"Exactly the opposite is true of the next two lines.

But WHEN LOUD SURGES LASH the
SOUND-ing SHORE
The HOARSE ROUGH VERSE should LIKE the
TOR-rent ROAR

"An obstacle? Mortal, explain!"

"As I say these words, the very effort required to pronounce them from my whole mouth and throat seems to suggest the roughness and energy of the torrent beating the shore."

"Are you sure, My Poet?" laughed the Muse. "Can mere *empty* sound (as you are fond of saying) suggest *touch* and *force*?"

"Yes, in the next line I have to open my mouth wide to pronounce the vowel in 'vast'. This makes clear that the syllable is a STRIDE:

when A-jax STRIVES some ROCK'S VAAAST
WEIGHT to THROW
The LINE TOO LAB-ours, and the WORDS
MOVE SLOW ...

So we have three strides in a row, giving me the impression, again, of obstruction, and suggesting the mass of the rock. In the last line of the passage there are two extra syllables, and the line quickly settles into a

LIVING WORDS: STORIES IN SONG

regular and increasingly marked step-STRIDE pattern, so that, although the line of creatures is longer, my mind is given a clear impression of gathering momentum and lightness."

not SO when SWIFT cam-ILL-a SCOURS the
PLAIN

FLIES o'er th'un-BEND-ing CORN and SKIMS a-
LONG the MAIN

Our Hero, feeling he had done well, relaxed.

"Well done, My Poet. You have shown me that you have *some* idea of how my Poets will make their words sing stories in the human mind."

40. The Poet Chooses His Words

The shadows were lengthening on the House of Words. The Muse, elated, produced from somewhere an enormous hieroglyphic amphora.

"Now we are ready to choose some living words to keep and to play with – now you have grasped the Great Principles by which you may choose your words."

"No, My Muse, these great principles elude me."

"Where is the difficulty? Have we not seen that the words Poets use carry their meaning and force their value into the heart by deploying sound, and by inspiring the music and dances of the mind?"

Our Hero was tempted to acquiesce, and yet, despite himself, his words of opposition burst forth.

"But, Heavenly Being, in our attempts to produce an effect on the mind like that produced by musicians, we poor poets must use a tainted medium."

"Tainted? Why so?" asked the Muse.

"The musicians have invented instruments which produce lovely sounds, entirely different from anything ever heard in Nature. Even when their instruments are human vocal chords, these are made to behave in a way very different from the way they behave in ordinary speech. The tiniest part, the smallest note of music is thus both *invented* and *beautiful*. But we poets will have to use words which our profession has *not* invented. And these words, as we have seen, are not intrinsically beautiful – far from it."

"So, Dearest Charge, we agreed from the start. Why do you still hate them so? Have I not shown you some beautiful combinations of words?" asked the Muse, almost hurt.

"Most mortal words, most of the time, are used to lie, or to conduct trivial transactions. How can I make a work of beauty out of a medium that is normally used to threaten, to argue, to cajole, to persuade, to seduce, to deceive, to disguise, to palliate, to scowl, to sneer, or to wound?"

"Your distinctions, My Pupil, are false. You have seen (or should have seen) that the words which my Poets will use bear no more relation, when in their hands, to the words which the world uses, than do the notes of the musician to the chirping of birds, or to the buzzing of bees. Just as a musician transforms noise into musical sound, so the Arts of Poetry metamorphose the words of the world into the *Songs of the Soul*."

"How can this be, Majesty Divine? We have already agreed that as far as poetry is concerned, sound alone is next to nothing."

"That is not *quite* what we have agreed," said the Muse quietly, feeling her pupil, once again, drifting away from her.

"A Poet who used these sounds but ignored the meaning and associations they had acquired in the world would not be understood. As far as I can see, poets *must* use the words they hear spoken around them in everyday life – as they are spoken, and as they are meant."

The Muse sighed.

"My Pupil, is it not true that the number of words which men and women actually *use* in talking to one another is very much smaller than the number of words which they know, can guess at, or can imagine the meaning of?"

"That is certainly the case, Lamp of Light."

"It is for this reason that a Poet can use words seldom heard on the lips of his contemporaries, and still be understood."

"I suppose, Heavenly Muse, that *may* be true."

The Muse floated down into the Slough and quickly returned, grinning wildly, with a few peculiarly loathsome word-creatures – which (to Our Hero's astonishment and disgust) she put to her lovely lips.

"You would agree, Dear Charge, that the words which people use in everyday speech are very much tied to the ongoing situation and present moment in time in which the interface of their locutions occurs. No way is the street credibility of words maintained if the problem is viewed holistically. Semantic slippage is the dominant experience.

Communication occurs in post colloquial discourse modulation protocol for user status enhancement."

"Heavenly Goddess, I don't think I followed that ..."

"No, I hope *not!* That is how people in the Northern Isle will speak for a few months many millennia hence. But even *they* will not understand these words a few months later," said the Muse, spitting out the already dead words with mild distaste. "This is why Poets – who speak to all ages – *must* use a vocabulary which belongs to no particular time, but which reaches long into the past and far into the future."

"Into the past? Into the future? Goddess Divine, I am confused."

"Well, surely it is easy to see how a Poet might use words which reach into the past? Poets know that the best words sometimes carry a little of their own history with them."

"Their own history, Heavenly Muse?"

"On some occasions, a Poet will use a particular word chiefly because that word has been used on countless previous occasions to adorn or beautify a certain (otherwise apparently insignificant) action or object. Let us find some of these."

The Muse, amphora in hand, floated down deep into the Great Slough, picking up dark word-creatures here and there. Our Hero remained resolutely on the balcony. She returned happily, like a child with an apron full of flowers.

"At other times, My Poet, you will use a word in a way which reveals that you know that word's parentage, origin, or meaning in another language. Shall we add a few of these?"

"Old word-creatures will, I suppose, be easy enough to find. But I still cannot see how poets will be able to find words which speak to the future."

"That will be very easily done. Because mortals will get a pleasure from Poems which they find nowhere else, they will be prepared to work very hard and think very

long. A Poet may so arrange his words that an old word will be quite clearly made to take on a new meaning. Let us find some suitable materials."

Again the Muse dived to the depths, laughing happily to herself.

"Or, a Poet may borrow words directly or indirectly from a foreign language."

Off she went, skittishly. Into her amphora - which seemed bottomless - went ALLELUIA and PHOEBUS amongst a mass of borrowed words. "Or, very occasionally, a Poet may even make up a word from scratch."

"How can this be, Heavenly One?"

"Because listeners (in the hope of pleasure) will attend so carefully to Poems, they will both understand and remember a Poet's new words and phrases. If those listeners are themselves Poets they will use those words and phrases in their own Poems. And so the words and phrases will be passed on to the future. Sometimes a word or phrase will pass into the spoken language, and be used by men and women who are quite unaware of its source – unaware that they owe it to you."

"I can see the likelihood of that. But surely what you say can only apply to parts of poems? A poet who went in for too much of the kinds of transformation and invention which you describe would soon lose his audience. His poems would be unintelligible, and his audience would be unable to see their bearing on human concerns. A poet can, surely, only attempt the effects you describe in brief flashes, if he is not to to seem merely eccentric?"

"You are right, My Chosen One, when you say that the Poet cannot invent or transform too many words or meanings too quickly. But the Poet's Art is also, as we have seen and will see, one of careful combination and selection, and it is as much by *combining* and *selecting* as by inventing and transforming that the Poet creates a language different from that of the ordinary men and women of his time."

"What are you saying? Poets invent their own language? Impossible!"

"They will invent their own *mixture*. Every language has different categories of vocabulary and expression which are used for different purposes. Teachers use one set of words, and shepherds another. Let us find some good specimens of each."

This time Our Hero was dragged along when the Muse plunged into the depths. The morass of the Great Slough was not quite as revolting to his sensibilities as he had feared it might be, when surveying it from above. It was much easier to distinguish the various species of creatures one from another. His Muse busily sorted them into heaps – some here, some there. RUSSET, HOUSEWIFE, CANDLE, in one pile. LEUCOTHEA, SACRED, ADORNED in another.

"Notice, My Chosen One, that mortals use one set of words when they are being serious in public and another when they are being familiar at home. We will select some of both species."

"Why do I need these things?" asked Our Hero, noticing some particularly disgusting specimens: YONKER, PRANCING, ORIENT, GUSHING.

"There are some occasions on which brute force is appropriate, and others which necessitate elegance and delicacy."

The words HURLED, GLORIOUS, GOLDEN, SILVER disappeared into the amphora.

"On the other hand," said the Heavenly Instructress flinging some words over her lovely shoulder with gay abandon, "words too familiar or too specialised cannot easily be used by a Poet." (At this point she discarded some of the words she had gathered.)

"Why not? Are not familiar, every-day words those which my listeners might *feel* most intensely?"

"The everyday associations of words are hard to overpower. Mortals do not easily receive strong impressions

or delightful images from those sounds which they hear on trivial or coarse occasions," she said discarding more word-creatures. "And words which are too strange draw that attention to themselves which they should transmit to things."

More word-creatures were thrown aside.

"Your task is to *combine* words from all these categories so that they are no longer the exclusive preserve of any."

"Why may I not use words that are my *own* preserve?"

"A Poet must speak for *everyone*. You will take some of your words from the language of the tavern, some from the language of various trades and professions, but most from the language of the Poets who preceded you. Let us find some of these – the best words of all."

"Why do we want these long-tailed horrors?" asked Our Hero peering into the writhing interior of the Muse's amphora where he say the word creatures, HARBINGERS, MORN, PHOEBUS, EASTWARD, GOLDEN MAIN, and EMPYREAN cavorting together.

"They are absolutely *essential*. By keeping old words alive in their poems, and by borrowing words from each other, Poets will be able to invent a language which makes sense, but which was never spoken at any one time on the face of the earth."

"NEVER spoken?" asked Our Hero, with mounting incredulity.

"Come, let us now find some more phrases and words from the work of some of your future predecessors – some truly Poetical words."

"Lamp of Light, would it not be better for me to find words for myself?"

"Certainly not! You will use your predecessors' words because they give a general aura of age, wisdom and beauty to your work, also because they express, or may be *given*, a meaning which you cannot find anywhere in the language spoken around you."

"But I can not see how a poet can avoid producing a discordant chaos, a messy jumble of words which do not cohere. You say that poets have invented a new language for themselves. But it sounds to me as if they speak no language at all. Tearing a word from its natural place would seem to me to be the surest way of killing it."

The Muse looked into her amphora like a good cook contemplating her bubbling pot.

"We shall see, Soul of my Soul, we shall *see*."

41. A Poet's Grammar

Evening was turning imperceptibly into night. Our Hero (to his great regret) could no longer make out the features of his Heavenly Instructress. But he felt the warmth of her presence through the darkening air.

"A Poet, My Chosen One, uproots words in order to plant them in a different, and more fruitful soil. These words in my amphora are *living* words, or potentially living words – words which, joined one to another, may live forever. Just as in a well-arranged garden each plant seems to set off and enhance the beauty of all the others, so in a Poem all the words seem to grow in beautiful harmony from the same soil."

"I can see, Celestial Muse, that a transplanted flower might bloom as never before. But how can I make *words* live simply by transplanting them?"

"Since a poet chooses his words as much for their song and their dance as for their meaning – or regards their song and their dance as *part* of their meaning – and joins them together by new means and in a larger pattern of song and dance, both the meaning and the sound of the words seem to every listener to be quite different from the sound and sense which they bear in everyday speech."

"Both the meaning AND the sound are different?"

"The sound is different, because the sense is not the same."

"The sense is not the same?" asked Our Hero, suddenly floundering.

"Poets' words belong to a different order of sense – they flower and bloom with glory of meaning."

"A different order? Glory of meaning?" asked Our Hero, now completely at a loss.

"Is it not the case that mortal life is far more *wonderful* and more *terrible* than human beings are ordinarily able to say?"

"Oh, it is, Heavenly Goddess, it is."

"And is it not the case that the words of ordinary speech *lie* – lie by implying that mortal life is easy to comprehend and easy to live?

"That is also true."

"The sounds of my Poets' words *must* be different from the sounds of speech because the sense is not the same – because the sense is so much *larger*. And the sense is different because the sound is so much more *deliberate*. Return to the Portals of Sound and Sense. Listen to some sentences in ordinary speech."

The Muse called forth some words which appeared to Our Hero to be unusually ugly – even by the standards of the Great Slough.

(condescendingly) You're a SWEET little thing.

(cantingly) I am RELUCTANT to commit myself just now.

(coyly) Wine always makes me AMOROUS.

(officially) We must apologise for the slight DELAY.

"Now listen to a fragment from a future Poem – a fragment which will be dear to the hearts of following future Poets. It concerns the first man and woman who are imagined to have lived on earth," said the Muse, scanning the Great Slough for the desired words. "The Poet is describing the great love between the two, and telling how each of them finds completion and happiness in the other." (The words obeyed her signal and floated or flew or swam through the liquid air towards Our Hero's ear and mind.) "The woman," continued the Muse, "yields to the man with

> ... *modest pride,*
> *And sweet reluctant amorous delay.*

You will have noticed, My Poet, that some of the ordinary, ugly, lying, spoken words we heard just now are repeated in that little piece of verse. Is it not the case that, used as this Poet uses them, the words neither *sound* the same nor *mean* the same as when you heard them in everyday speech?" asked the Muse with self-conscious aplomb.

"Heavenly Being, I can see that the way in which this poet has arranged his words suggests many kinds of connection between the words which they would not otherwise have had."

"Good, good, but how and why?"

"The patterning of sound leads me to connect words which normally cannot be joined. The effect is to reinforce, extend or *exalt* meaning – even to produce a new meaning."

"New sounds: new meanings, good, good. Explain yourself!"

"Every time I say these words over to myself, I find myself speaking more slowly. The particular combination of vowels and consonants causes me to dwell on each word-creature – and as I do so, I become more and more conscious of its depth, or weight, or fullness, or pleasure of meaning:

> ... *with MOD-est PRIDE,*
> *And SWEET re-LUC-tant AM-or-ous de-LAY."*

"Good. But explain why, mortal!"

"I do not normally think of reluctance or delay as sweet, or of pride as modest, or of amorousness as reluctant, or of delay as amorous. But the way in which the poet has linked these creatures with sound ('reLuctant deLay', 'sweeT relucTance') allows me to see that, in his story, the woman is fully conscious of her own dignity and beauty, but entirely without egotism, or anything else which might make pride a sin, and that her delay is a flirtatiousness entirely without calculation."

"So you see, do you not, that – even in terms of sense – the very means by which the words are connected one to another are *quite different*, in this poetic fragment, from those which are employed in the everyday language?"

"Yes, Lamp of Light. In ordinary speech each word tends to have a single job to do. We mortals have names of things, we have words which tell us what those things are like, words which tell us what those things did, and words which tell us how they did it. But in our little fragment of verse, though the words 'sweet', 'reluctant', and 'amorous' are, strictly speaking, adjectives, words which tell us about the thing 'delay', they seem to me, as I hear them now, to have something of the quality of abstract nouns and of adverbs – of ideas and of human ways. As you suggested, the mortal mind, in attending to this fragment, is invited to entertain new entities – sweet reluctance and reluctant amorousness for example, and the poet is also indicating that the woman in the lines is yielding sweetly, reluctantly, amorously."

"So you see, a Poet's word-connections are more fluid, living and flexible than the grammar and sense-expectations of everyday speech."

"This seems to be so, Goddess. In this fragment, the poet is combining words in a way that never was before, using a grammar that never was before, to describe a love that is unique and ideal. But I cannot tell how it was done."

"In composing and listening to them, poet and listener enter into a complicity. By offering his words as a Poem, the Poet is offering the promise of a distinctive and rich kind of pleasure. In order to get that reward, the listener is prepared to allow the Poet's words an unusually unimpeded passage to every corner of his mind."

"So it *seems*, Heavenly Muse."

"And do you *now* see that the proper disposition of single sounds results in that harmony which adds force to reason and gives grace to sublimity, which shackles attention and governs passion?"

"I have seen force given to reason, and grace given to sublimity: my attention has been shackled and my passions governed – but I am still unwilling to attribute all this to *sound*."

"If sound and sense are not entirely separable – as we have seen they are *not*," (Our Hero nodded) "then to discover the perfect form of human sound is also to find the perfect form of human sense." (Our Hero nodded in pretended comprehension) "And, since the perfect form is that which finds the paths through the human mind, then the proper disposition of single syllables is also the penetration of the human heart. The movement of Poetic word-creatures mirrors the movements of the human mind when set in motion by interaction with the outer world."

"Perhaps I see some of this (darkly)."

"Do you *now* see the force of what I said to you, when we first came here to the balcony of the House of Words, that the pleasure you Poets will take in arranging these words (and the pleasure the listener will take in hearing them so arranged) is a pleasure in having human experience arranged, re-arranged to produce new combinations of feeling – more sane, pure, permanent feeling?"

"Lamp of Light," said our weary Hero, seeing the sun descending below the horizon, "I do not doubt the veracity of what you are claiming, but must admit that my weak and mortal mind is not yet entirely convinced by your words – neither by their sense nor by their sound."

Part Two:
The Poet's Dawn

42. A Poet's Inheritance

Our Hero and his Heavenly Instructress, hand in hand, stepped on to a passing cloud, and so returned to the Muse's floating Garden. It was the time when weary bodies close their eyes in balmy sleep and soft repose. The wind no longer whispered through the trees. The early stars in silent order moved across the sky. The Muse led her pupil from the edge of her garden, and laid him down on a grassy bank. He had been bored and exhilarated, elevated, depressed, excited and wearied by his long lessons. And although he longed for rest, a substantial doubt oppressed his mind.

"You have shown me many marvels, Celestial Being, but there is still one important question for which I *must* have an answer before I sleep."

"Only one?" asked the Muse, disappointed.

"You have told me many times that poets inherit their arts and words from one another, as a child inherits parts of his mind and his body from his ancestors."

"I have."

"But you have also shown me that life and language are constantly and irreversibly changing."

"I have."

"*Surely*, in each new incarnation I will be living in a completely different world from that of my ancestors, and will have new challenges to face and new problems to overcome?"

"Indeed you will."

"How then *can* the work of my ancestors, however much it may delight me, be of more than limited and passing use? And if I *do* want to plunder the word-hoard of a previous life, how *can* I do so in a new body and with a changed tongue? Should I not find words of my own?"

The Muse laughed.

"MANKIND IS EVER THE SAME, AND NOTHING IS LOST OUT OF NATURE, THOUGH EVERYTHING IS ALTERED."

Our Hero looked into the face of his Instructress with real pain.

"Alas! I do not, cannot, understand."

"The ever-changing forms which make up the surface of life," said the Muse patiently, "can never express *all* that Man is or might be. In the normal heat of living even the ablest mortal may not comprehend *all* the conditions which have governed, do govern, and will govern, human life. It is the business of my chosen children to compose according to an essential, eternal human nature which is hidden from view by the ever-changing face of things."

"I understand less and less. How can something essential and universal be *hidden*?"

The Muse gathered herself to her full height.

"Poetry *never* preoccupies itself with the surface of life, though it may use the idioms and objects of every-day life as a means of expressing its deeper truths. For this reason, my Poets have *much* more essentially in common with their fellow Poets in other ages and of other tongues than they do with the ordinary men of their own place and time. For this reason, my Poets have more use for each other's words, pictures and stories than they do for those they find living (and dying) around them."

"Great Spirit, I find this hard to understand; harder to believe."

"Have patience, My Child! I will show you how my Poets, over five centuries – over twenty-five generations – in our Northern Land, will depict an event in Nature which has meant much to men and women in all ages. (It once meant much to you.) It will often happen that, in a long

Poem, a Poet will lavish his art on imagining that moment when night gives way to morning. Listen to my Poets' Dawn! You will learn how and why my Poets use each other's words. And if you attend *very* carefully, you will see that, between them, these especially living words obey all the Laws, and display *all* the Arts of Poetry."

43. Stories of the Morning

Our Hero was not overjoyed to hear that there were more lectures to come. It had been a long day. He felt absolutely no inclination to be cooperative.

"I find it hard, Prophetic Spirit, to believe that any poets will make poems about the dawn. I don't think that there is much to say about it. It is hardly a gripping subject for future song. After all, what happens?"

"Well, what does happen, little mortal?"

"Do you *really* want me to answer that question?"

"Indeed I do."

"Well, the dawn occurs every twenty-four hours; a large orange globe appears over the horizon. The intensity of light increases considerably ..."

"Yes, and ...?" said the Muse, patiently, caressingly.

" ... and some plants distend their reproductive and light-sensitive parts."

"And ...? My Chosen One, what else?"

"Moisture is observed to have collected on plants and on the ground – but it soon disappears."

"And ...? What do you know about this moisture, my child?"

"This moisture is believed – by some people – to be beneficial."

"Anything else?" said the voice of the Muse in the dark.

"Not really, Heavenly Being. Oh yes, male domestic fowl – and other birds – make the characteristic cries of their kind."

"And ... what causes the dawn?"

"It has been long known that various large bodies in or above the sky are responsible for these changes in the perceived environment."

"Yes, yes, go on ..." said the Muse, pressingly.

"And, Celestial Being, I get out of bed," said Our Hero, dreaming of sleep.

"And ...?" asked the inexorable goddess.

"And ... nothing."

"Nothing?" asked the Muse, astonished. "If that was *all* the dawn meant to you, you would not be My Chosen Poet. You would not even be a human being! You would be one of those gods that one Roman Poet will imagine banqueting away in their heaven without the slightest interest in what happens on earth!"

"Why do you say that, Great Muse? I was trying to be accurate."

"Because that thing in your head – if there is anything there at all, which at the moment I am inclined to doubt – is a human mind, and the human mind can never see only one thing at a time. It can never see anything without speculating about it. Human beings see by speculating."

"Are you sure, Lamp of Light? I think I just see – with my eyes."

"The process of speculation uses all your available mental faculties in such quick succession that everything seems to be happening at once – and to be happening so completely that it is hardly noticed. If you *could* notice you would find it thrilling."

"I would?" asked Our Hero, staring idly at the early stars.

"Human bodies and memories, and conscious and unconscious hopes and fears tell you mortals much more about the dawn than those facts which you *think* you have simply observed. For a human being, the dawn is not a collection of phenomena such as you gave; it is a wonderful *story*."

"Wonderful, wonderful," murmured Our Hero, yawning.

"Human beings, inspired by me, will tell many stories about the dawn - the story of Boötes ..."

"Who?"

"Boötes, the great charioteer of the sky; and the story of Phoebus ..."

"Fibbus?"

"Phoebus, the handsome sun god – and the story of Eos, the beautiful saffron-robed dawn-goddess, cursed by Aphrodite the love-goddess with a constant and insatiable longing for young mortals ..."

"(That sounds more interesting.)"

" ... and the story of Phosphor, the planet Venus, which appears just before sunrise; and the story of the circling hours which guard heaven's gate, and the story of Leucothea, the ..."

"Please, Mirror of Grace, I cannot take in all these strange names at once!"

"All these old stories will be used, when hymning the dawn, by the Poets you saw in the Temple. But the Poet's Art – your Art – is to do more than merely *tell* stories about the dawn, however wonderful. You have to make the sun *rise* in the mind of the listener. Poets will enjoy comparing themselves to a god summoning up and shaping matter out of Chaos. A Poet who has mastered his Art can summon up a whole world with a few effortless words. 'Let there be dawn,' says the Poet, and dawn appears."

"It does?"

"The Poets' dawn will be a dawn which is not like any dawn which ordinary mortals have ever seen, but it will be a dawn which they instantly recognise."

"How can something new be *recognised*?"

"Because poets please by providing the mind with a more beautiful, shapely and coherent idea of the subject than could be perceived by any onlooker's brain from the phenomena alone. The beauty, shapeliness and coherence are produced by selection and recombination of *living* words – pieces of encapsulated human experience ."

"By *lying* you mean. I have heard all this before."

"FROM POETRY A LISTENER NATURALLY EXPECTS (and from good Poetry always obtains) A VIEW OF THE WORLD MORE BEAUTIFULLY ADORNED THAT THAT WHICH HE INHABITS," shouted the Muse – whose patience was, after all, not inexhaustible.

"But my (former) friends and colleagues, the painters and sculptors, showed me (to my great sorrow) that I could neither see, nor make others see. They had eyes for things I did not even know were there."

"The business of a Poet is not to record specific and particular details for their own sake. Poets do not count the streaks of the tulip or list the different shades in the green of a forest. In a Poet's word-pictures, we are shown only those prominent and striking features which will bring an object or a person or a scene into another's mind."

"By 'art' you mean, as usual, a set of tricks and lies?"

"Exactly. A painter touches the imagination of the eye with images for the eye. A Poet has to touch the same imagination, but without the use of visual images – by words alone."

"That is not possible!"

"It is *essential*," said the Muse, speaking rapidly, her eyes flashing. "Your Arts are these: never work on any one sense at a time. Evoke the illusion of sight (as the illusion of music) by recalling the memory of sound; the sensation of taste by the memory of touch; the impression of light by the memory of weight. Do it in innumerable ways and in ever-changing combinations. Keep the minds of your audience in a whirl of perpetual confusion."

"Goddess Heavenly Bright, this sounds as dishonest as all your other suggestions. Why can I not simply list the visual impressions which most strike me, truthfully, and leave it at that?"

"Because you mortals can only understand what you see when eye-impressions are mingled with other sense impressions, and when both are connected by Memory and by sound. You will often want to describe things which cannot be seen – either because they have never actually existed, or because they are too large or too small for the eye to comprehend. Catch familiar things in old words: combine them in new ways. You will make your audience see a world which can only exist in the mind."

"This is all very well, Illuminator of all Darkness, but I was rather hoping to get to grips with reality – *for a change*."

44. *Human Dawns*

Our Hero and his Muse lay on the grass beneath the sliding stars and the silvery moon. The moment of sleep had passed, but sleep retained its attractiveness as an idea.

"Celestial Patroness, why cannot poets simply talk about what they know – about what it feels like to get up on a cold morning after a long night of long lectures for example?"

"They will, of course. Behind every Poet's evocation of the dawn will lie a recollection, implicit or explicit, of what the morning means in terms of purely human activity. Listen! I will show you one."

The Muse opened her amphora, releasing a pack of words which circled in the darkness.

The time when early housewives leave the bed,
When living embers on the hearth they spread,
Supply the lamp, and call the maids to rise,
With yawning mouths, and with half-opened eyes.

Our Hero listened *almost* as attentively as his Muse desired.

"I can see, Chief of Nine, that the poet here has *tried* to make us see the dawn by selecting only those details that can be seen and heard within a house. It seems fine to me."

"But most of my Poets will much prefer to see the morning as both human and more-than-human."

"Why, Great Lady?"

"They will do this, because they will be trying to convey in their Poems the connections perceived by the Human Imagination between what happens at the dawn, and the deepest desires, pleasures, hopes and fears of humanity."

"Please explain."

"They will be trying to convey the full human significance of the dawn while describing the full glory of what happens in the skies as the sun bursts forth, bringing light to a dark world."

"Is there not a danger of cutting Nature down to human size?"

"No, My Poet, it is a more a matter of elevating mankind by testifying to the capacity of the Human Mind to comprehend and embrace natural processes of extraordinary *grandeur* and *vastness*."

"O Muse, I am lost. Grandeur and vastness are beyond my capacities."

"The gods have not set limits to the capacity of the human mind to develop, or project, or intuit on the strength of a very little experience. The Poet, who is (despite present appearances) an exceptionally conscious and self-conscious human soul, conceives of the dawn as a moment of great emotional significance. The Poet understands the phenomena by imbuing them with the pleasurable significance which they have for the human mind."

"He does *what*? He understands by *imbuing*? Lamp of Light, I am in the dark."

"So while some Poets – like the one whose word-joinings we have just heard – will sometimes tell of a purely human dawn, and other Poets sometimes about a more exclusively heavenly dawn, the more difficult (but also more common) device is to mingle the two so cleverly that mortals see both at once. Listen! I will show you a Poetic Dawn created almost entirely out of the most common and everyday materials. Listen!"

The Muse again shook her amphora. Our Hero heard, but could not see, the creatures as they flew happily towards him.

Night's candles are burnt out, and jocund day
Stands tiptoe on the misty mountain-tops.

"These words," said Our Hero, once again trying more-or-less to please, "lead my mind from the homeliest of details – candles flickering, as their wax is nearly all melted away – to a picture of the starry sky imagined as a town full of candle-lit windows, and then finally bring on the day, standing like a merry giant (or grand goddess) among the morning mists on the mountains. The light spring in the walk of the word-creatures gives this giant a light spring in his step."

"Calling one thing by the name of another, as here 'stars' are called 'candles', the simplest of poetic devices ..."

("Or tricks.")

"... is the source of almost all Poetic ideas – and of a great many living words. In this description of the dawn, the morning, just for an instant, walks out and *does* something. It also feels, and expresses its feelings in gesture, appearance and movement. Is it not *wonderful!*" said the Muse, laughing as she returned her words to the amphora – all except two – RISE and MOUNTAIN – which scuttled away in the grass and the dark.

45. Morning Larks

As the Muse continued to lecture her pupil on the beauty of the poets' dawn, the moon in a flood of glory burst through the scudding cloud. The Muse, who had no need of sleep, was warming to her subject, but Our Hero found it difficult to keep his mind or his eyes open.

"I can see, Celestial Being, *some* connection between those two dawns, but neither seems *dependent* on the other. The first poet wanted to do one thing, and the second quite another. It looks to me as if poets will say what they want to say, or will say what the time requires or demands, and they will say it in their own words."

"Poets (as I have told you before, and will tell you again) who write for their age and their age alone, and in the language of their age alone, will have little chance of lasting."

"Yes, you have said that from Poetry a listener naturally expects, and from good poetry always obtains, a view of a world more beautifully adorned than that which he inhabits. But might not such *adornment* be a contradiction of truth?"

Instead of answering, the Muse reached deep into her hieroglyphic amphora.

"In my Poets' world, the birds that herald the dawn will be LARKS, MESSENGERS or HARBINGERS of day. The ROSY MORN, or the MORNING STAR, will OPEN (or OPE) the GOLDEN GATES of HEAVEN, and the GLORIOUS SUN, SOL or FIERY PHOEBUS, will RISE (or ARISE) in the ORIENT, or over some EASTERN or EASTWARD HILL. He will SMILE, SALUTE (or RE-SALUTE) the day, and send his BEAMS or STREAMS or RAYS of LIGHT to GILD the OCEAN (or the GOLDEN MAIN), STRIKE the MOUNTAINS with BRIGHT, GLORIOUS or EMPYREAN LIGHT, and DRY the SILVER DEWS that ADORN the plants like PEARLS or GEMS."

Our Hero stared for some time at the group of creatures his Muse had selected. They were not easy to assess by the light of the silent moon.

"Celestial Patroness, I must confess, this prospect *appals* me. I don't want all my poems to be dull with repetition and artificial with contrivance. Will my sons be able to think of nothing else to say, no other words to say it in? (I knew there was nothing interesting to say about the dawn.)"

The Muse looked at her pupil in something very like disgust. It was some time before she regained her composure and her patience.

"My Poets will be quite happy to select the same words for depicting the dawn which had been used by their predecessors because, as I have been *trying* to explain, the Arts of Poetry, like other human arts, are passed on from generation to generation. The efforts of your early incarnations will be forgotten forever, but the Arts of Poetry will not progress, evolve or improve after the days of the first Poems to be continuously remembered through human history."

"How can this be? In many human skills, mankind can be seen to be constantly improving on an initial barbarity."

"There is no such thing as a trial Poem. A Poem is a Poem or it is not. If is is a Poem, all my Arts will have been used. The words will dance and sing together in perfect harmony. I have told you that the first poems to be remembered will contain all the Arts of Poetry developed to their absolute perfection."

"How *disheartening* for late-comers!"

"Not at all. As I have said before (and now doubt will have to say again) it will be *invigorating* and *inspiring*. The first native Poet who will be continuously remembered in the dour Northern Island will invent, discover or otherwise gain possession of the complete Art of Poetry. When you inhabit his glorious mind and body ..."

"(As I remember his shade, he will be short and fat.)"

" ... you will assemble all the elements which later Poets will use when writing about the dawn, and you will shape them into a harmonious whole."

"I will, Prophetic Spirit?"

"You will start with the LARK, which you will instantly transform into a court official or squire, preparing for the entrance of a great lord. Your lark will come busily, as a herald or MESSENGER of the coming day, and sing an elegant song of greeting to the morning or MORROW. Your sun will be seen as a vigorously active young nobleman, Lord PHOEBUS. It will be as if he leaps out of bed with a laugh. Then you will turn him into the heat and LIGHT of the sunbeams or STREAMS, drying the greves or foliage, wet with the night-dew. The master-device in any description is to enliven the inherited elements with one or two fine strokes of freshly-telling observation — or something, anyway, that is made to seem fresh and new. By this Poet, the listener will be suddenly made to consider the precise quality of light reflected in a dew-drop suspended beneath a leaf. Listen carefully!"

The Muse waved her hand over her amphora and over the heap of words writhing in the grass. It was too dark to see anything clearly, but Our Hero heard (or thought he heard) a voice — a voice as light and grave as any voice he had ever heard:

> The busy larkë, messenger of day,
> Saluteth in her song the morrow grey,
> And fiery Phoebus riseth up so bright
> That all the orient laugheth of the light,
> And with his streames dryeth in the greves
> The silver droppes hanging in the leaves.

Our Hero found he had nothing to say. The Muse stroked him gently on the arm.

"Over three hundred years after this passage is first heard on the earth below," she said delightedly, "you will tell the same story in another incarnation, and will hardly wish to change a word of the description — so nearly timeless and perfect will it seem. Rouse yourself a little and tell me why."

"The perfection (if that, Heavenly Muse, is what it *is*) has been produced by delicately combining the patterning of language with the patterning of pictures. A line of word-creatures is given to each new thought: one to let me see the messenger-lark, one to hear her song of salutation, one to show Lord Phoebus rising from his bed, one for the whole East laughing with the light, one for the dew in general, and one for the silver drops themselves."

"Well done, little Poet! In a later incarnation, when you again tell this story, you will keep this basic pattern, even emphasise it, by playing with head-chimes ('Beams so Bright') and adding details, with their associated patterns of sound. Your second sun will Renew the Rose, Lick the Leaves, and Dry the Dews. Listen!"

(A more rapid voice was heard in the gloom.)

> The morning lark, the messenger of day,
> Saluted in her song the morning gray;
> And soon the sun arose with beams so bright
> That all th'horizon laughed to see the joyous sight:
> He with his tepid rays the rose renews,
> And licks the dropping leaves, and dries the dews.

"At first," said Our Hero happily, "I thought that the patterning here was mere decoration. But it is — isn't it? — a musical arrangement to express *joy*! I was sorry to miss fiery Phoebus, but I suppose this poet will want to delay the high-point of interest until we come to the word LAUGHED. He loves the thought of the sky laughing."

"How do you know that, my bright little mortal?"

"It is the thought which gives life to the whole."

"Yes, and it is a surprise which has to be carefully prepared. It seems to be a law that the human mind can only normally tolerate a certain number of monosyllables at a time. It then seeks relief, relaxation or direction in a longer word with a clear rhythmic shape of its own. Both my Poets will exploit this little law by leading up to the phrase in which they depict the sky laughing by a sequence of little steps across a line ending (with beams so bright / that all ...)."

"The second poet also lengthened his line by adding an extra word-creature (JOYOUS) to extend his sense of the *wonder* of the spreading light and of the fancy that the pleasure which he has is shared by the sky itself."

"Yes. Yes! So you see that *POETRY does not change*. Many of the words are the same, and where they are not the Arts are identical."

"Perhaps. But I cannot believe this is a fair example, Great Muse. This is not true recreation, merely repetition. The later poet simply will not be able to think of anything original about the dawn."

46. *Messengers of Day*

It was midnight, but warm, in the Garden of the Muse. She returned some of the word-creatures to her amphora, leaving others to hop on the ground. MESSENGERS OF DAY, GOLDEN RAYS, LARKS, LAUGHING, BRIGHT, LIGHT, and various ROSY things joined the misty MOUNTAINS and RISINGS which had escaped from her second set of words. To these she added GLORIOUS, BLUE, MAGNIFICENT and several kinds of CLOUD.

"You are right, my Pupil, but only in degree. Many Poets will borrow from this Father of Poetry. (That is why he will *be* the Father.) But borrowing is not theft. Consider this little group," said the Muse, picking up MESSENGERS OF DAY. "There is no law to say that these messengers *must* be larks. I will show you the powers of these creatures, these miraculous messengers at their plainest. Listen!"

The Muse waved her delicate hand once over the words on the ground, and once over her amphora. Immediately the little creatures leapt into poetic order:

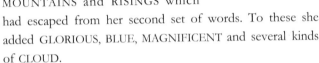

Yon grey lines
That fret the clouds are messengers of day.

Our Hero, liking the look of the words, decided to be, once again, helpful.

"Lamp of Light, I can see how *that* was done. The poet who will arrange those words will see morning clouds embroidered with a pattern of grey lines. His mind will connect these clouds with a phrase he has heard before, and with liveried heralds announcing the arrival of the Lord of the Day."

"Good. I will show you another lovely metamorphosis effected by MESSENGERS OF DAY. In this case, my Poet will be more interested in the *effects* of morning light and the *sequence* by which various parts of the horizon are transformed by different colours. But he will use the *same* word-creatures," said the Muse waving her lovely hand, triumphantly, happily.

... the rosy messenger of day
Strikes the blue mountains with her golden ray.

"Yes, I see that the MESSENGER OF DAY has here become the light itself – and has almost the power of a goddess."

"The Poet's subject when writing about the dawn is, as you have noticed, his joy and wonder, real or imagined – whether he is telling another's story or describing a daybreak which he has seen himself."

"I am confused, Bright Goddess. Sometimes you say that poets will only be able to see what other poets will see before them. Now you speak of poets seeing for *themselves*."

"Your distinction is false. My next set of words will be joined one to another by a Poet who, from time to time, will feel, as you feel now, oppressed by the weight of example accumulated by your predecessor-selves, but most of the time he will realise that it is *by means of them* that he is able to speak at all."

"And he will say exactly what they said?"

"Not quite. He will pride himself on having his eye on the object whenever he writes of Nature. But his mind will inevitably turn to his predecessors as much as to what lies before him when he attempts to convey his wonder at the dawn."

"Why '*inevitably*', Heavenly Goddess?"

"Because, *as I keep telling you*, Poets can only see through the spectacles of Poetry."

"You have indeed often told me this, Lamp of Light, but I have never understood why it should be so."

"If ordinary mortals habitually perceive in the world around them only what other people have taught them to perceive (as they do) then the Poet's eye follows the patterns of perception opened up by his predecessors in his Art. When this Poet describes the morning, he will see it as a pomp, almost a royal procession. For him, too, the world will seem to feel happiness. He, like my last example, will be interested in BRIGHT light on MOUNTAINS. He too will enliven the inherited elements in his description with a detail that seems to be freshly perceived. He will notice, as it were for himself, the way in which the morning sun sheds heavenly empyrean LIGHT, revealing the mountains shot through with different hues of reflective rock."

At the command of the Muse, a slow and stately train of creatures emerged from the amphora and with steady movement joined the words in the grass to form long and stately sentences, stretching over several lines. Our Hero's answering inner voice moved in a sustained and solemn sweep as he heard them.

Magnificent

The morning was, a memorable pomp,
More glorious than I ever had beheld.
The sea was laughing at a distance; all
The solid mountains were as bright as clouds,
Grain-tinctured, drenched in empyrean light

"The wonder and the joy of these words (or of this poet)," said Our Hero, listening to the words flying in the dark night, "strike me as quite different from that of either of the two groups we heard just now (though I will concede that I see some similarity of phrase and idea)."

"Can you not see, my child, that the new word-creatures give life to the old – and the old to the new?"

"Perhaps I half-see."

"What interests you most in these words?"

"The sea laughing, I suppose."

"And have we not met that LAUGHING before?"

"Yes, Majesty Divine. Yes, it was another of the Father's creatures."

"Do you now see?"

"Now I see (but darkly)"

THE POET'S DAWN: RISINGS

47. Risings

Our Hero lay gazing at the moon high in the heavens, and the sky powdered with stars. The Muse drew closer in the dark to keep her pupil warm through the long night, for she *still* had much to teach and he to learn.

"The process by which the human is connected with the more-than-human is, like all Poetical Processes, reversible."

"Reversible?" asked Our Hero, yawning with incomprehension.

"As you can clothe the created world in the language of Humanity (you will remember that we saw the sea 'laugh' like a human being) so Human Beings may also be described in the language of the heavens."

"The language of the heavens?" yawned Our Hero.

"Some of the loveliest paintings of women in Poetry will join them with the sun, the moon and the stars."

"How, Bright Goddess, can a woman be joined to the stars?"

"You must understand, My Child, that living words should make such connections easy – even natural. My Poets will, for example, find infinite possibilities in the words RISE, ROSE, ARISE, applying them sometimes to the sun, and sometimes to mortals, wakened by the sun."

"Another cheap trick?"

"Let us see," said the Muse, ignoring him and rummaging in her amphora. "Here is another very short group of words collected by the Father of Poetry in the Northern Isle, among which we can see this verb-creature, ROSE, working hard. This Poet will tell a story in which the main events are set in motion by the attractions of a young girl. He will need to focus attention, quickly and purely, on her beauty and grace, and the power on men of that beauty and grace. He will hit upon an idea so simple that it hardly seems to be Art at all:

Up rose the sun, and up rose Emily"

"This is not *poetry*, Great Goddess, but the plainest of plain statements. Two things happen. The sun rises. Emily rises. That is all."

"Yes, but the word 'AND' between them disguises an *extraordinary* mental leap (or series of leaps) on the part of both Poet and listener."

"Are you, in your infinite wisdom, now about to tell me that 'and' is one of the extraordinary living words which your poets will discover?"

"In the first place, you must concede, little mortal, that there is a *causal* relationship. Emily rises *because* it is morning. But there is more to it than that, is there not?"

"Yes, O Muse. As I hear the line, the two actions appear to happen simultaneously. Two bright and glorious objects, warming to the heart, rise in view."

"The compliment to Emily is surely all the more exquisitely delicate for being *implicit*? How would it have been if the Poet had said – 'Up rose Emily, bright as the sun, and as fair'?"

"The point of comparison would stop there, with brightness and fairness, O Muse."

"But in its simpler form, Emily rises like a goddess, with all the shinning attributes of a glorious sunrise?"

"Perhaps, Celestial One, perhaps; but the rising of the sun and the rising of Emily are entirely different matters."

"Does not the very plainness of the statement leave your mind free to speculate about both situations and the connections between them? You might, for example, imagine the sun throwing aside its bedclothes, or Emily's bright, radiant nakedness."

"Indeed I might, Great Lady," said Our Hero, smiling to himself.

"Such suggestions, if they are present, would be touched or tinged with comedy, as is the very blandness of the parallelism itself. This device will be used again and again, until one Poet will deliberately over-topple the comparison into full comedy. Listen to my next group of words where the sun comes to wake a beautiful girl asleep in her curtained four-poster bed. This girl, Belinda, is not only *as* beautiful as the sun, she is *more* beautiful (or so my Poet will pretend). The sun (or SOL) approaches her softly, gently, timidly, and sends his beams (or RAYS) in trepidation, knowing that, when Belinda opens (or OPES) her eyes (rather than the gates of heaven), she will outshine him in brilliance and lustre as the night is outshone by the sun. Listen!" cried the Muse, with her habitual wave towards the amphora, invoking poetic words in the dark.

Sol through white curtains shot a timorous ray,
And oped those eyes that must eclipse the day.

"Later in the same Poem, the girl having risen (at noon) sails out on the silver river in an elegant barge. The dawn has been GLORIOUS in many of these passages. Belinda, at this moment is *more* glorious than the sun as it RISES over the sea, spreading its BEAM. Listen!"

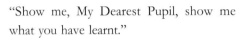

Not with more glories, in th'etherial plain,
The sun first rises o'er the purpled main,
Than issuing forth, the rival of his beams
Launched on the bosom of the silver Thames.

"Show me, My Dearest Pupil, show me what you have learnt."

"Gladly, Goddess. This poet divides the action into two pairs of lines or couplets. In the first couplet, the sun's *rising* is described exclusively in phrases which present no vivid picture to my mind, but give a general impression of grandeur and beauty. *Something* glorious rises over the main, the great sea. I do not actually see (or even half-see) anything until the second couplet. There the river itself assumes some of the brilliant femininity of Belinda, who remains, throughout, unseen (though not unappreciated), like some mysterious goddess of the sky."

"Good, good! We are progressing. Now save the creatures, ISSUING FORTH, for me. I have further surprises in store."

48. The Dance of the Sun

The Garden of the Muse was full of sweet night smells. Every bush and tree seemed to be competing to fling their scents into the cooling air.

"Are these creatures – ISSUING FORTH – living and poetical words?" asked Our Hero, sleepily, incredulously.

"Indeed they *are*, my child. Many Poets in the Northern Isle will believe that the life of their language consists largely in its verb-creatures and in other words of action; words which tell not only what is done, but how it is done, and in what *spirit*. Let me find some of these," said the Muse reaching deep into her amphora for some verb-creatures: COMETH FORTH, GUSHES, HURLED, THROWS, closely followed by PRANCING and DANCING. As they fell on the grass, or among the flowers these creatures began, instantly, to con-join with the escaped words that already lay there: GOLDEN, HEAVEN, PHOEBUS, DEW, BEAMS, BRIGHT, MORN, CLOUD and STAR.

"In my last example, as you noticed, my Dearest Pupil, the Poet did not need to *say* that his sun-girl moves with the grandeur of a queen or goddess in procession. The idea is incorporated in his saying that she ISSUED FORTH. Words of power are needed because when a human is linked with the sun, and the sun with a human, the poet's words must evoke the *force* of his new creation. A sun/girl must behave in a way that is both like and unlike a girl and a sun separately. This again is one of the recurrent devices, (or tricks, as you would say) of my Poets when depicting the dawn. They work their trick by connecting the movement of the sun across the heavens with various human movements."

"But, Lamp of Light, the sun and humans do *not* move in the same way. We humans, after all, cannot fly."

"It is the effect on the heart of an onlooker that provides the common denominator. Does not the Human Heart leap up to behold the gracious movements of youth and beauty's pride?"

"It does, Goddess, it does indeed," said Our Hero (feeling old).

"I will now show you, My Pupil, this connection between the movement of a proud young mortal and the progress of the sun. I will show it to you as it will appear in the language of the Northern Isle – but this form will be a rendering of a much older Poem – a Poem which (I am happy to say) you will write quite soon ... (well, within the next millennium perhaps)" said the Muse with a smile. "Listen!"

> *... the sun*
> *Which cometh forth as a bridegroom*
> > *out of his chamber*
> *And rejoiceth as a giant to run his course.*

"Heavenly Instructress, I see how this con-joining was done. The strength and power which I as a mortal know most intimately is that of a strong man, conscious of and glorying in his might. For a human being the sun's strength *must* seem similar, and the sun *must* similarly glory in its own irresistible progress. Am I right, Instructress Divine?"

"Indeed, you are, my Dear One. But the possibilities are not yet exhausted. The words of my next Poet will allow his audience to see a god, a bridegroom and the sun *all* at once. They will make you see both the dancing of the young man and an orderly, stately and vigorous movement of heavenly bodies beyond and behind the dancing. Listen and behold! The Poet will convey this loveliness of move-ment in verse where the various elements – consonants, vowels, phrases and cadences –

seem themselves to move in an ordered, gracious dance, which mirrors the stately and energetic motions of the planets."

> At last the golden oriental gate
> Of greatest heaven gan to open fair,
> And Phoebus fresh, as bridegroom to his mate,
> Came dancing forth, shaking his dewy hair,
> And hurled his glistering beamës
> > through the gloomy air.

"What an energetic sun, My Muse!" said Our Hero, trying to please. "These are indeed words of power placed in positions of power."

"Positions of power, my child? Explain!"

"The creature, HURLED, forms the first striding segment in its line of words, and this (co-operating with the sense) causes it to take a firm hold in my mind. I seem to see Phoebus dancing forth, hurling his beams."

"Yes, the word DANCING seems to have (for mortals) a vigour that ISSUE lacks. Word-creatures of the *utmost* power and grace are needed to bring forth the more-than-human-humanity of this sun-god."

"I am almost ready to concede that DANCING FORTH is a living phrase – a phrase that can live various lives in various poems."

"My Poets will use both halves of the phrase – DANCING FORTH. Here, first, is one who, surprisingly, took the word FORTH rather than DANCING. The expression of wonder which my Poets will associate with the dawn is not always one of unalloyed joy. Here are the words of a Poet who will use the common elements, but the transforming alchemy of his Art will produce a different compound. Listen!"

> When the first matin-song hath wakened loud
> Over the dark dewy earth forlorn,
> What time the amber morn
> Forth gushes from beneath a low-hung cloud.

"I see, Heavenly Muse, that this poet's lark will perform the morning offices in a bleak temple cloister. His earth before day-break is dark with dew and forlorn. The burst of morning light seems more like a sombre rain storm pouring water down on the earth than the rays of a bright furnace."

"Just as this Poet stresses the gushing of the morning light, so Poets generally will lavish much art on imagining the precise action performed by the first breaking of light in the morning. One Poet, wanting to express his pleasure in a May morning, will make the MORNING STAR come DANCING from the EAST, leading the months of spring."

The Muse shook some words from her amphora to the grass where they joined with BRIGHT, STAR, and EAST.

> Now the bright morning star, day's harbinger,
> Comes dancing from the East, and leads with her
> The flowery May, who from her green lap throws
> The yellow cowslip and the pale primrose.

"Here," noted Our Hero, "May THROWS the flowers from her lap (as in the earlier passage the sun, shaking his DEWY hair, HURLS his BEAMS through the air). The strong verb-creature, THROWS, coming at the end of its line causes the whole pack to pause in momentary emphasis before the thing which is being thrown so vigorously is named."

"Yes, my child, and that vigour has comic possibilities.

My next Poet had likened the sun to a young man or 'younker' whose mother, or lover, lets him out in the morning to prance across the heavens."

See the morning opes her golden gates
And takes her farewell of the glorious sun:
How well resembles it the prime of youth,
Trimmed like a younker, prancing to his love.

"Again I can see, Bright Goddess, that the poet's art has been to make his crucial word of action tell the longest story. PRANCING is what horses do as much (or more than) men," said Our Hero, laughing. "This young man has groomed himself almost like a young stallion pursuing a filly. The poet seems to me to have worked his trick with a smile – both at the *felicity* of his own art, and at the young man he is writing about."

"That seems likely. These creatures are the work of a young man and will be written with a smile at the felicity of the words (by a slightly older Poet, a mature master of his art) about the bridegroom Phoebus which we heard just now. Do you see now how and why my Poets, your sons, will use each other's word-creatures – the truly Poetic and living words?"

"Heavenly Instructress, I think I begin to believe you."

"At last, my Chosen One, at long, long, last."

49. The Gates of Light

The Muse and her Poet lay still beneath the star-filled sky. Our Hero was not sure whether he was indeed becoming convinced by the words in the amphora, the lessons of his Instructress, or whether he was merely succumbing to the weight of her will. The Muse, delving happily in her amphora, and among the flowers and the grass, re-selected some LARKS (again), PHOEBUS (again), DEWS (again), ROSY and MORN (again) and (yet again) ARISE. To these she added with peculiar care HEAVEN'S GATE, GATES OF LIGHT and two heavenly COURTS.

"An individual Poet will always be able to con-join these wonderful word-creatures in a way that has never quite been used before."

"How can this be? There must be a limit to the possibilities."

"Just as you, My Pretty Poet, may have inherited your great-aunt's eyebrows and your grandfather's nose, and still think your face distinctively your own, so a Poet with a particular job to do finds himself selecting at one time one element from the store of words available, and at another time some other. But he is still entitled to call the end-product HIS Poem."

"He is?" asked Our Hero, relaxing among the night-flowers.

"Indeed he is. Listen now to a brief story of just one of the poetic words or ideas from the last combination of word-creatures which we encountered — the GATES of heaven and of LIGHT. This GATE will be one of your most popular and successful inventions or discoveries. You have just heard of the morning opening her GOLDEN GATES. And you heard, before, that the golden oriental gate of greatest heaven 'gan to open fair. One Poet, needing a song where a lover bids his lady sweet arise, will imagine that the LARK (rather than the morning) is the opener of the doors of the sun's great

palace, He will see his LARK flying up until it sings outside the very gates of heaven."

At the wave of her hand some word-creatures con-joined and took to the air.

Hark, hark, the lark at heaven's gate sings,
And Phoebus gins arise ...

"Celestial Goddess, I see that Phoebus himself RISES up just as he did for the Father of Poetry in the Northern Isle."

"Not *exactly* as he did. The permutations are inexhaustible, and the shades of colour innumerable. Listen! Another Poet, wanting particularly to draw attention to the beauties of the created heavens, will make the MORN a door-keeper to the GATES OF LIGHT."

The words from the amphora circled in low flight beneath the stars calling softly to ROSY to join them.

... morn,
Waked by the circling hours, with rosy hand
Unbarred the gates of light.

"Instructress Divine, substituting 'light' for 'heaven', to make THE GATES OF LIGHT, has the effect of transferring some of the colours and associations of HEAVEN to the light itself. Am I right, Great Muse? LIGHT becomes a king-like power — or a religious force?"

"That is so. My Pupil, this is *most* important! Now, here is the power of LIGHT at its simplest," said the Muse with a wave of her lovely hand.

Now rosy Morn ascends the court of Jove,
Lifts up her light, and opens day above.

"Heavenly One, all that this ROSY MORN has to do is to hold up her lantern in the palace of the gods and, behold, day begins."

"Listen again!" said the Muse, enthusiastically, and with mounting urgency. "By the next set of word-creatures, the dawn is imagined as Leucothea, a Greek sea-goddess, drenching or embalming the world with fragrant healing ointment. As the lark of the Father of Poetry

Saluteth in her song the morrow grey

so this Greater Poet will have his goddess 're-salute' the world."

The Muse waved her lovely arm: the lovely words moved in solemn procession towards our now-rapt, now-distracted Hero.

... Meanwhile
To re-salute the world with sacred light
Leucothea waked, and with fresh dews embalmed
The earth ...

Our Hero's mind wandered – but was not directionless. Was he dreaming or awake? What was it about these words that seemed to have the power of dreams to bemuse his mind?

"Is it that this Poet, O Muse, invests his lovely dawn with attributes carefully chosen to suggest that the bringing of LIGHT is a holy and beneficent ritual for the world, and therefore for mankind? Is that why he calls his light SACRED?"

"The sacredness which a Poet finds in the LIGHT of dawn has little to do with the sacredness of any one religion."

"How can this be?"

"Listen again! Our next Poet, like the last, will combine the religious vocabulary of two religions, the Christian religion whose founder will sometimes be described as the Light of the World, and the religion of the Greeks and Romans who often will portray the loves of their gods in near-comic terms."

The saffron Morn, with early blushes spread,
Now rose refulgent from Tithonus' bed;
With new-born day to gladden mortal sight,
And gild the courts of Heaven with a sacred light.

"This is all very strange!" said Our Hero, now almost entirely enthralled, enraptured, entranced. "These word-creatures seem somehow to move from sexual delight to SACRED light."

THE POET'S DAWN: EASTERN HILLS

50. Eastern Hills

It was now the darkest hour. Our Hero could hardly tell if his eyes were open or closed. Having passed beyond tiredness, he was inclined to be compliant. The Muse did not notice the passage of time: her pupil, she felt, was learning.

"You *must* understand, Dearly Beloved, that the living words which my Poets use are often religious but never religion."

"Lamp of Light, I do not follow. Religious but not religion?"

"Let us consider another set of word-creatures, another group of Poetical colours: EAST, EASTERN, EASTWARD, ORIENT, MORN (as a kind of goddess), and HILL."

"Can 'hill' be considered a poetical colour? I cannot imagine a plainer term, or (by your very own precepts), a word more *dull*," said Our Hero.

"We will see. We have (many times) heard that the MORN moves from one place to another. Where she travels from is usually the EAST, or, more poetically, the ORIENT. You have already heard of the ORIENTAL gate of greatest heaven and seen the morning star come dancing from the EAST. In another incarnation, noticing the rapid spread of light across the wave-tips of an eastern sea, you will turn MORN into a ship and a ploughman. Listen!"

Morn in the white wake of the morning star
Came furrowing all the orient into gold.

"That group of creatures – 'all the orient' – reminds me of the words of the Father of Poetry;

... all the orient laugheth of the light ...

but each creature seems to be recast, fresh and new, another and the same."

The Muse beamed delightedly.

"Can you tell how it will be done, My Chosen One?"

"Has my later future son has combined different worlds by transplanting words from two different areas of human life and feeling: 'furrowing' and 'orient'?"

"Exactly that! These con-joinings depend upon a peculiarity of the human mind. They exploit the reservoir of association that lies ready to be tapped beneath the most apparently mundane of words."

"I am lost. How can there be a reservoir of association in the *mundane*?"

"It is possible (as you should have gathered from the House of Words) to use the words 'east' and 'eastern' in an entirely commonplace way – ' his house lies to the east of the city'. But released from such a particular context, the same word can conjure wondrous worlds of mysterious riches."

"Please explain, Heavenly Instructress."

"Listen, my child, to another son investing the morning dew with the richness of the jewellery of the EAST, which is at the same time the richness of a bountiful harvest."

Now Morn her rosy steps in th'eastern clime
Advancing, sowed the earth with orient pearl.

"Great Muse, I would not have believed it possible to use both EASTERN and ORIENT in two consecutive lines. I also notice that this poet will use a strong creature for the travels of his MORN, the word 'advancing', and, like the last, will combine a word from farming, 'sowed', with a word of mystery and wonder, ORIENT. The effect is, I think, to increase the *mystery* and *wonder* of the morn-goddess."

The Muse glowed with satisfaction.

"But the god-like mystery and wonder of the dawn can be evoked (by an exceptionally gifted Poet) without any word or idea taken from a realm beyond everyday experience."

"How may this be done? Are you not now contradicting your *own* Laws?"

"Judge for yourself, Dearest Pupil! MORN can, for example, be a young villager, striding across the hills, and still have an almost godlike presence. And the lovely HILL need not be 'orient', merely 'eastward'. Listen!"

The Muse-conjured words echoed in the night.

But look the morn in russet mantle clad
Walks o'er the dew of yon high eastward hill.

"I am still not entirely convinced that HILL does not contradict you laws."

"Consider one last example, My Child. Almost all the Arts which we have been considering will be used together by this one small tribe of words. Listen! Attend!"

With a flourish the Muse called the creatures from her amphora and bade them con-join with STAR and LIGHT and FIERY PHOEBUS and EASTERN and HILL.

By this the northern waggoner had set
His sevenfold team behind the steadfast star,
That was in ocean waves yet never wet,
But firm is fixed, and sendeth light from far,
To all that in the wide deep wandering are.
And chearful Chanticleer with his notë shrill
Had warned once, that Phoebus' fiery car

In haste was climbing up the eastern hill,
Full envious that night so long his room did fill.

"Here, Heavenly Goddess," said Our Hero, pleased himself and anxious to please his fair Instructress, "the 'northern waggoner' refers to a constellation of stars twinkling in the sky, but is perceived (at least by me) more as the master of a heavy, trundling, covered cart pulled by lumbering oxen."

"What do you make of such a con-joining of disparate word-creatures?"

"Disparate they certainly are! As the constellation moves behind the pole star, this poet invites me to see his oxen and his waggon moving across the night sky towards morning."

"Do you see that the *daring* of the Art is, once again, in combining the technical word 'team' with the 'steadfast star' in the same line?"

"Yes, and the word 'steadfast' immediately gives the star itself a kind of *personality*," said Our Hero happily.

"And in this case, my child, a moral value, since the star is a guide to sailors, and, more than that, a symbol of fixity to all that in the wide deep wandering are," said the Muse, smiling sweetly. "The steadfastness of the star is a sign, for this Poet, of the god's benignity to the world."

"Its steadfastness, O Muse, seems to me to be captured in the steady movement of the verse, and reinforced by the various chime-patterns."

"Indeed it is, My Poet. In the last four lines, you will, I hope, notice that the Poet draws on all the traditional elements. His messenger of the dawn is, for example, the cock, Chanticleer, at once a homely and a famous and *wonderful* literary bird," said the Muse, smiling incomprehensibly to herself.

"And the impetuous haste of the sun god's chariot comes as a pleasing surprise after the lumbering waggon of the opening. The rapid movement of the sun in the heavens, the movement that occurs every day of every human life, is made fresh and accessible by the explanation that it is speeding *because* of the human passion of envy," said our Hero gaily. "The god is impatient at night's over-long occupation of the realm which he thinks is all his own."

"Do you now see, My Chosen One, that, in this, as in every single one of the word-groups we have looked at, the inherited words contribute to the inherited regularity of the dance, which is part of the Art by which my Poets combine the wildly disparate elements of their description into a whole? Do you now see that the patterning of sound and rhythm make the forged connections even firmer, and convert what would otherwise seem so many patches of light turbulence into a firm and strong *current?*"

"I think I see, Illuminator of all Darkness. The poetic current flows in time (even if it is only mental time and therefore imaginary time). The images and their associations form themselves in my mind in an ordered and stately manner which reminds me of a dance. Their sounds group themselves in a way which reminds me of a tune. Because of all this, the effect is one of *pondered wonder*, rather than a breathless gasp."

"Exactly. These are your Arts, my Chosen Soul, your inherited Arts – and your hereditary words. You have heard some few episodes in the Great Poem which all my Poets, like the co-operating thoughts of one great Mind, will build up from the beginning to the ending of the Human World."

"Great Goddess, something of this you said long ago," said our weary Hero. "Then I did not understand. Perhaps I follow a *little* closer now – but haltingly."

51. The Grandeur of Generality

There were some glimmerings in the east. The silver trees turned to dullest grey. Our Hero rubbed his tired eyes, looking at his Muse with blank unbelief. Would she never weary of her lessons? Never let him rest?

"Some Poets, my child, will of course devise quite different ways of describing the dawn from any that we have been considering. But most will seem to be working on common principles to a common end. They will agree that the essential need in a poetic description of the dawn is to convey the *Grandeur of Generality*."

"And what, Heavenly Goddess, is the grandeur of generality?"

"Though they will supply at least one detail of their own, not one of these Poets will present a dawn that is in any way peculiar. My Poet's dawn is not a dawn produced by freak meteorological conditions. Nor is it a dawn observed by some highly idiosyncratic individual. The grandeur of the dawn depends upon it being seen as a recurring phenomenon, and one which affects – or might affect – all mortals at all times. A Poet's sense of the wonder of dawn depends upon his realisation that he is witnessing something which has meant – or might mean – much the same to all humans in all ages (though, of course, mortals cannot know that without Poetry)."

"Is it for this reason that when poets write about the dawn poets will keep by and large to their ancestor's words and pictures?"

"Precisely for this reason. And it is for this reason that they will use each other's regular rhythms – as a means of inheriting *full humanity*."

"Full humanity?" asked Our Hero, suddenly lost.

"Precisely. The light that shines on you as you get out of bed each morning is not sacred."

"I suppose not, Celestial Being – particularly not when it disturbs the sacred bliss of sleep," said Our Hero, longing for rest.

Do you not see, my Poet, that the light which shines on you as you awake each morning only *becomes* a SACRED LIGHT when the beams that cause you to rise also bring light to the world, causing plants to grow and birds to sing, and when it is the light that has shone and will shine on mortals since the dawn of human time."

"So you say, Majesty Divine – and who am I to disagree?"

"Dawn, for mortals and for gods, IS as my Poets make it and not as you described it when you were pretending to be an insensible idiot or uncaring god. For mortals the dawn IS a sacred wonder. And my Poets will see it and make mortals see it by means of my Great Arts."

"They will, Mirror of Grace. How could they do otherwise?"

"Tell me now, My Child, what are the Poetic Arts to be used in the depictions of the dawn?"

"They are too many and too various to mention," said Our Hero, yawning behind his hand.

"An evasion, I think. Here is your catechism –

Will you see by speculating, by imagining and by telling or recalling stories?"

"I will. (I cannot do otherwise.)"

"Will you combine wildly different imaginings, speculations and stories?"

"I will. I will"

"Will you mingle observation of phenomena with the sensations which those phenomena prompt in you, as in all humans?"

"Daringly."

"Will you select and shape in order to make beauty?"

"Discriminatingly."

"Will you harmonize patterns of thought in patterns of language?"

"Instinctively."

"Will you conceive of cosmic processes in human terms?"

"Exceptionally."

"Will you attribute the human pleasure in phenomena to the phenomena themselves?"

"Naturally."

"Will you put your words of power in the places of power?"

"Forcibly."

"Will you release the reservoir of associations latent in common words?"

"Potently."

"Will you subsume all your details to the Grandeur of Generality?"

"Triumphantly."

"And will you do all this in a way that recalls the music of song and the vigorous patterns of the dance?"

"Inevitably."

"And in each and every one of these respects, will you follow the perceptions opened up to you by your predecessors in my great Arts? You will be the true inheritor of the words, and therefore of the souls of your Great Predecessors?"

"Yes, yes, by all means, yes."

"My Poet, you have passed the foothills of Poetic Learning."

"I have?"

"Indeed, My Chosen Soul, you have."

At that moment a large orange globe appeared over the horizon and the intensity of observable light in the garden was considerably increased. The plants distended their reproductive and light-sensitive parts. Moisture collected on the vegetation and on the ground. Some birds produced the characteristic cries of their species.

Our Hero saw larks, clad in the livery of messengers, singing at the gates of very heaven, and rosy morn issuing out, closely followed by fiery Phoebus in his golden chariot, who rose over an eastern hill and re-saluted the dawn. The god laughed, shaking his dewy hair, and dried the silver drops of dew that adorned the leaves like gems and orient pearls.

"Good heavens." thought Our Hero, "it is true – I *am* becoming a POET".

How can I live without thee, how forgoe
Thy sweet Converse and Love so dearly joyn'd,
To live again in these wilde Woods forlorn?

Part Three:
The Powers of Poetry

52. Calling New Powers into Being

Morning dawned fresh and fair in the Garden of the Muses as it floated between the House of Words and the Temple of Poetry. The warmth of the sun was softened by a light haze. The birds sang and the butterflies were out in force. Our Hero, who had not slept all the long night, nevertheless found his energies strangely restored. The Muse cradled her pupil's head in her lap and smiled down upon him with a warmth like the sun's. He in turn gazed up at his Muse with admiration, wonder, answering love (and a certain degree of native scepticism).

"You now know, My Poet, how to reply to those fools who said you could not dance or sing or paint. You have learnt to give your words the full force of Poetry: THE FORCE THAT GIVES LIFE TO DEAD MATTER; THE FORCE THAT GIVES SHAPE AND BODY TO THOUGHT AND FEELING; THE FORCE THAT CALLS NEW POWERS INTO BEING."

"Alas, Great Muse, I do not even understand what it is you *think* I have learnt.

"Have you not seen that when my future Poets tell you something, or describe something, you more than see it, you feel it too? It seems to have a palpable existence for you?"

"As if I had been present, yes; as if what the Poet describes were there to touch and to know," said Our Hero – with a slight smile of obedience.

"Can you not see that, from describing the real world in such a way that your audience see and feel it as if for the first time, it will be only a small and easy step to make them entertain the reality of a world which you have invented for yourself?"

"No, O Muse," said Our Hero, his mind suddenly blank.

"I tell you, you will make your audience *see* and make your audience *know* a world which does not exist – a world which can only exist in the mind."

"For a moment, Celestial One, I thought I was following along the deceitful pathways of your soul. But now ... but now I am again lost. It is one thing to remind an audience of what they already know: quite another to bamboozle them into believing a complete *falsehood*."

"Come, My Chosen Soul, come to the Fountain of Art!"

The Muse turned to her fountain and her pool. As Our Hero peered into the clear crystal water he saw (and thought he recognised) a shimmering tiny figure emerge or half-emerge from the depths.

"Here, once again, is the shade of ALEXANDER POPE, the little poet with the Magnanimous Soul. He will call some particularly delightful new powers into being. He will create a new set of gods."

"He will create Gods? Virgin Daughter of the Skies, are we not verging on blasphemy?" asked Our Hero, looking intently at the face of his Instructress.

The Muse laughed.

"These new gods will be the smallest immortal beings ever envisaged by the minds of mortals, creatures of the air, who preside over the lives, the dress and the fancies of female mortals in the very first flush of their womanhood. As he will imagine it, these little spirits will fly round in the lower sky, unseen but ever on the wing. They were once enclosed in the beauteous bodies of light coquettes, but (by soft transition having changed from flesh to air) now sport and flutter in the fields of the sky."

"It all seems most unlikely – the silliest stuff I have ever heard."

"My little Poet will make you *see* these creatures of his mind."

"He will?" asked Our Hero, with more than usual incredulity.

"He will call these new powers into being. A beautiful young girl (the one we met before, you may remember, rising at noon) will sail in a barge on the river Thames, accompanied by a host of these tiny creatures, these Sylphs. You will hear (and *see!*) the chief Sylph, Ariel, almost overcome by the weight of his responsibility. Begin!"

The small shade in the pool, with a voice as clear as a bell, but musical and soft, began:

And now secure the painted vessel glides,
The sun-beams trembling on the flowing tides
While melting music steals upon the sky,
And softened Sounds along the waters die.
Smooth flow the waves, the zephyrs gently play,
Belinda smiled, and all the world was gay.
All but the Sylph; – With careful thoughts
oppresed,
Th'impending woe sat heavy on his breast.
He summons strait his denizens of air;
The lucid squadrons round the sails repair;
Soft o'er the shrouds aerial whispers breathe,
That seemed but zephyrs to the train beneath.
Some to the sun their insect wings unfold,
Waft on the breeze, or sink in clouds of gold.

"What Arts of making has my little Poet used?"

"None," replied Our Hero, listening attentively to the words.

"None?" asked the Muse anxiously, fearing regression from her charge.

"None, Lamp of Light. The Poet has not told me much about what his little gods look like ... or what they *are*. He has given some hints about their military bearing by calling them 'squadrons', but he has immediately

counteracted that by drawing attention to the delicacy of their form, and the fluidity of their movements."

"Well, little mortal? How is it done?"

"By reminding me of some things I know already – winds, whispers, insect wings, light objects carried by a light wind, clouds, and gold."

"Any one thing in particular? What happens in your mortal mind?"

"I am invited to recall the way in which newly-metamorphosed insects hold out their damp, transparent, tiny wings to the warmth of the sunshine."

"Are these little creatures *exactly* like butterflies?"

"No, these little gods are lighter even than insects – light enough to be carried effortlessly on the lightest of winds," said Our Hero comparing the real forms of butterflies in the garden with the impression which formed in his mind in response to the words which came from the fountain.

Some to the sun their insect wings unfold,
Waft on the breeze, or sink in clouds of gold."

"Does this Poet remind you ONLY of what you already know?"

"No. I am also invited to see the impossible – *clouds of gold.*"

"What do you suppose the Poet might intend by that?"

"Perhaps the sun charges the air with light, making it bright, and somehow dense enough for these little spirits to sink into, as if it were water."

"Let us hear some more from the little shade."

Our Hero looked into the water. He thought he saw the future poet smiling below the ripples on the surface as he spoke his lines:

Transparent forms, too fine for mortal sight,
Their fluid bodies half dissolved in light.

"Now, Celestial One, I learn that these creatures are so fine that they cannot be seen by mortal eyes. They seem almost to get smaller and finer as the poet looks, as I look. They are dissolved in the very light which had been supporting them."

"Pray continue, great POPE," said the Muse to the pool.

Loose to the wind their airy garments flew,
Thin glitt'ring textures of the filmy dew:
Dipped in the richest tincture of the skies,
Where light disports in ever-mingling dies ...

"The Poet will still not tell me what his creatures *look* like, Heavenly Being, only that their clothes are finer than any material known to man."

"Have patience, my child. What does that suggest to you?"

"For an instant they almost became loosely-clothed girls in the open air ... but then my mind is filled with images of ever-changing colour – but these colours are not fixed and stable, but the unfixed colours of light itself. And then there is the strange idea of light 'disporting', of light enjoying itself in wanton play."

"Pray, let us hear a few more words," said the Muse to the affable shade in the pool.

While every beam new transient colours flings,
Colours that change whene'er they wave their
                                                        wings.

"Lamp of Light, I now see that this painting of wonderful, ever-changing colours and light, has, at the same time, been a strange kind of *joke* ..."

"A *joke*, little mortal? I do not see you laugh."

"... well, a painting of the ever-changing beauty of the bodies and minds of young girls."

"A painting of minds? Explain, little mortal!"

"The colours are as transitory as they are beautiful and as beautiful as they are insubstantial. My mind receives an impression of fluidity, invisibility, transparency, airiness and glittering filminess, but the words that matter are '*transient*' and '*change*' and '*colour*'."

"If these are the words that matter, my child, what follows?"

"These little god-like creatures," said Our Hero excitedly, "are compounded out of a set of impressions of the natural world and a set of feelings about young girls."

"Are these impressions disparate, or joined to one another?"

"They are *joined*. The force joining feeling, thought and knowledge, is *delight* – the Poet's delight, my delight – and the word-music of delight."

"And so, My Child, you can see the Arts with which Poets will paint the products of their own imaginations – how they will animate matter, embody thought, and call new powers into being?"

"By 'arts', you mean tricks, but I see none here. I will admit that I can see these airy spirits (more or less) and that my Imagination is prepared to accept them (while my reason rebels), but I am still unable to identify the means by which it has been done."

"Come, My Dearest, do not be obtuse. The first 'trick', as you call it, is to exploit the peculiar tendency of the human mind to discover (and to delight in discovering) similarities between any one thing and almost anything else – as in this example, resemblances are drawn between light and clothes, or light and liquid."

"Ah, yes," said Our Hero (doubtfully).

"The second trick is to attribute life (and pleasure) to abstractions or to inanimate objects – as by these words, beams are made to fling colour, and light is made to disport itself."

"Of course," said Our Hero (despondently).

"The third trick is to endow every part of the picture with movement, as here, every wing-beat affects the texture of light, and even clothes fly."

"Obviously," said Our Hero (desperately).

"The fourth trick is to make the painting for the imaginary eye also a painting of feeling – as here we are made to see the Poet's delight (and something more than delight) in young female mortals."

"Quite," said Our Hero (despairingly).

"The fifth and most important trick is to base your invention on a great animating Thought – a large general truth or perception about humanity and ..."

"Enough! Enough, Heavenly Muse! You have reminded me, once again, that no human being can ever be a Poet."

53. Can Poets Think?

For a time the Muse was silent. In the cool of the morning, Our Hero found himself drifting into sleep. A playful serpent slithered past in the dew-laden grass. Our Hero started, suddenly surprised.

"You talk of 'invention'," he began, "and 'new powers being called into being' and 'truth' and 'humanity'. You assume, Heavenly Goddess, that I am capable of thought."

"Why yes, My Child, all human beings are capable of *thought*."

"So it is said. But the more Arts you tell me are mine (or will be mine), the less I feel myself able to control and modulate the movements of my own mind. I am afraid that it *still* seems to me that these Arts are, at bottom, a series of trivial deceits played on the brains of my audience in order to produce facile and fleeting excitement."

"...devices to produce profound and permanent pleasure..." murmured the Muse.

"The Lovers of Wisdom and the Lovers of God were surely right. I have never been able to decide what I really believe or disbelieve. I cannot marshal an argument. I can hardly follow a train of thought."

"Without me, you can only be as other men are. But when I am with you..."

"When you are with me, Celestial Patroness, it is infinitely worse."

"Worse, my child? Why so?"

"In your presence, Mirror of Grace, thoughts (such as they are) come crowding in so fast upon me that I am hardly master of myself. My mind is filled with warring images and jarring sounds struggling for harmony. The Arts you are teaching me, the Arts of dancing and singing and painting in living words, cannot help me to THINK."

"With my Arts, O my Poet, you will sing songs of sense, paint pictures of wisdom, and dance the dance of thought. I will now release a group of words – another fragment of one of my favourite sung stories to come. The first woman has just suffered the first nightmare. The first Man is explaining how it is that her mind can play tricks upon her, against her will, particularly during sleep."

The Muse opened her amphora, allowing a troop of words to escape. They quickly arranged themselves in decent order, and entered the ear and brain of Our Hero – who was instantly transported to two places at once. He found himself in the Garden of Eden (where he beheld Adam, the goodliest of men, speaking with innate wisdom, quietly, tenderly, patiently, consolingly, to his fair Eve, her cheek flushed and wet with the first human tear). And he found himself, simultaneously, within the (suddenly spacious) interior of his own mind.

> *...know that in the soul*
> *Are many faculties that serve*
> *Reason as chief; among these Fancy next*
> *Her office holds; of all external things,*
> *Which the five watchful senses represent,*
> *She forms imaginations, airy shapes,*
> *Which Reason, joining or disjoining, frames*
> *All what we affirm or what deny, and call*
> *Our knowledge or opinion; then retires*
> *Into her private cell when nature rests.*
> *Oft in her absence mimic Fancy wakes*
> *To imitate her; but misjoining shapes,*
> *Wild work produces oft, and most in dreams ...*

"Does that seem to you to be a description of the workings of the human mind that might impress even the Lovers of Wisdom and Truth?"

"It might, I suppose. But my reason tells me that the words of poems are not dancing, that there is nothing to see, and that I hear no song."

"So the dancing and painting and singing are what this Poet calls 'imaginations', airy shapes without substance or reality?"

"Yes, that is exactly what they are; the airy shape of a dance, a mere imagining of a picture, and some mimicry of music."

"And is there the airy shape of a dance in the passage which we have just heard?"

"A very stately dance, where the word-pattern seemed to go like this:

ALL what we'a-FIRM/ and WHAT de-NY/ and CALL

our KNOW-ledge/ or o-PIN-ion

with the hint of an imagined tunefulness or chime, as in –

all ... call.

My sense that the dance is stately depends in part upon my recognising that weighty matters – all that we affirm and deny – are being discussed", continued Our Hero.

"So, while considering the weighty matters, your mind performs a stately dance, and in following the steps of the dance, you find yourself considering weighty matters?"

"It seems so. The stops and turns in the dance are also the stops and turns of the sense. The various sub-divisions of the dance are also the various stages of an accumulating thought (or story, or picture)."

"And what governs and directs your understanding of the dance?"

"I know not, Heavenly Muse."

"Is it your sense-impressions?"

"Perhaps."

"Or a wild imagination?"

"Possibly."

"Or Imagination ruled by Reason as chief?"

"My understanding is directed, Divine Being, by all these things at once. But I suppose I have to admit that the governing power is Imagination governed by Reason."

"Why do you say that?"

"I *imagine* Lady Reason (an abbess, perhaps, or a virtuous queen) retiring after a hard day's work

Into her private cell when nature rests

and my Reason, or my sense of how things are, *approves* of this imagining."

"Why?"

"Because it is very like what seems to happen as I slumber, give way to reverie or surrender to some ungrounded apprehension."

"Does the stately dance of the word-creatures help you?"

"Yes, Celestial Being, I imagine that Lady Reason walks as the words walk:

IN-to her PRI-vate CELL when NA-ture RESTS

and I imagine that that imagining aids the first."

"You are *sure* that these words are not like a dream, the wild work of uncontrolled fancy?"

"No. I must admit that these words are the opposite of wild work."

"What is the distinction?"

"The airy shapes are not mis-joined. On the contrary, they are arranged in a way that is, I think, *perfect*."

"The dance is not arbitrary, but deliberate?"

"So it seems. This first man, this Adam (and the Poet his creator), clearly has a mind from which Lady Reason has NOT retired. The airy shapes are doing her bidding."

"And thinking is the exercise of reason?"

"I suppose it is."

"But, according to this passage (which you said might impress a Lover of Wisdom), Reason is the governor of Imagination and Imagination is the interpreter of the senses."

"That is what the Poet said, and I am inclined to believe him."

"Then the Arts of Poetry, which order and arrange, which join and dis-join the airy shapes which the Imagination has created from the representations of the Senses, in every way resemble the exercise of Reason?"

"Celestial Muse, you seem to have convinced me (though I still cannot believe it) that POETRY AND THINKING ARE ONE AND THE SAME!

54. Images of Wisdom; Songs of Thought

The Muse and her Poet retired from the heat of the rising sun to the cool of the fountain's side. Our Hero breakfasted on grapes plucked from an overhanging vine and sipped pure water from a rivulet supplied by the fountain. He studied the ripples on the surface of the water, sparkling and dancing with the morning sun. His spirits, which had been thrown into confusion, revived.

"Do I understand you, Teacher Divine, to be saying that the Arts of Poetry are not deceits at all, but a distillation of the process of human thought itself?"

"That *is* what you understand me to be saying."

"But, even if this is true, I do not see that you have taught me anything to do with that process – that you have taught me knowledge or wisdom."

"My Poet, I have been teaching you nothing else."

"But I still know no more of the secrets of the Lovers of Wisdom than other men. They speak with understanding of the beautiful and the good. They have computed the circumference of the earth, and traced the movements of the stars. Hear my petition, Majesty Divine. Release me from the burden of your arts. If I do as you have bid me, all my days and all my nights will be spent in study, in ordering unruly words, and learning how to make them dance and sing and paint pictures in the mind. Let me know instead the ways of wandering stars, the depths of heaven above, and earth below! Teach me the various labours of the moon! Explain the eclipses of the sun! You, from whom nothing is concealed, name the force that draws out summer nights and shortens winter days!"

"Very prettily spoken, My Poet, but your petition is refused."

"Alas, I cannot see that, without such knowledge, my works will ever amount to anything that could be called a contribution to the useful knowledge of the world."

"USEFUL is not a word that comes unbidden to my lips. It is true that not one of your sons will contribute one jot to the '*useful*' knowledge of the world. Let that be clear. But do not be downhearted. You will have your own kind of knowledge and sense and wisdom."

"My own sense, knowledge and wisdom?"

"Danced knowledge, sung sense and images of wisdom. Let us consider an example. In times to come there will live upon the earth two great Lovers of Wisdom and Truth, Heraclitus and Pythagoras. They will teach (or will be believed to have taught) the following doctrines:

that all things are in constant motion

that fixed states are unknown in Nature

that all things suffer from entropy

that indestructible fundamental matter is

continually expressed in novel forms

that the passage of time is constant and inevitable

that continual change is a concomitant of the

perpetual passage of time

that each passing section of time alters the past

and brings into existence new events and objects."

"Those propositions, Majesty Divine, seem extremely probable."

"Let us now compare that account of the teachings of Heraclitus and Pythagoras with some words to be used by one of your sons in our Northern Isle, when recalling those teachings (with more than a little help from one of his Roman predecessors):

> *... Nature knows*
> *No steadfast station, but, or ebbs, or flows:*
> *Ever in motion; she destroys her old,*
> *And casts new figures in another mould.*
> *Ev'n times are in perpetual flux; and run*
> *Like rivers from their fountain rolling on;*
> *For time no more than streams, is at a stay:*
> *The flying hour is ever on her way;*

And as the fountain still supplies her store,
The wave behind impels the wave before;
Thus in successive course the minutes run,
And urge their predecessor minutes on,
Still moving, ever new: for former things
Are set aside, like abdicated kings:
And every moment alters what is done,
And innovates some act till then unknown.

"Now is there a difference between my bald summary of the Lovers of Wisdom and Truth's account of the flux of nature, and that given by the Poet?"

"Yes indeed, Lamp of Light. The Poet was far more *elegant* and *harmonious.*"

"May I press you on those terms? What precisely do you mean by 'elegant'? Do you mean 'decorative'?"

"Not just that. I suppose I am thinking, at least partly, of the dance-song the Poet has made his word-creatures perform."

"Such as …"

"Such as his description of times which

> *RUN*
> *Like RIV-ers from their FOUNT-ain ROWL-ing ON*

so that, when I say or think these lines over, I seem to remember or invent a song about Rivers, Running and Rolling on to the sea."

"Do you mean that this passage is an example of what was often thought but never so well expressed?"

"More than that, I think. Not only do the dance and the song of the words help me to imagine some of the ways in which time might be like a river, they help me to imagine what it might be like to *feel* that thought."

"Explain!"

"The eye of my mind is presented with a stream of pictures, or fragments of pictures; of the ebbing and flowing of tides, of fountains, of waves, of hours with wings, of the repealing of laws, of rivers, of figures cast in bronze and then melted down, of abdicated kings, of a great group of men desperately running and urging each other on."

"Are you given words, pictures or thoughts?"

"I am not conscious of a thought having been put into words, the words into rhythm and the rhythm into pictures – the thought, the ideas, the pictures and the words seem to be *inextricable* one from another."

"Is that what you meant when you said that the poem was 'harmonious'?"

"Yes, Heavenly Being, that was partly it. The pattern of sound seems to create an analogy for the pattern of images so close, so *very* close, that the sound seemed almost to become a picture:

> *The WAVE be-HIND / im-PELS / the WAVE be-FORE*

But I think that when I called the passage 'harmonious', I was also thinking (vaguely and indistinctly, the only way I ever think) that, just as each disparate part fits into the whole, so I am perturbed at the top of my mind and calmed at the depths – at the same moment."

"Perturbed and calmed at the same time? Explain!"

"It seems harmonious because it seems to compose, order and harmonise my thoughts and feelings as I listen."

"Were you *taught* anything by that group of words?"

"Yes and no. There was no new thought as such, but where your account of the teachings of Heraclitus and Pythagoras was couched in generalities which seemed true but which did not to touch me, the Poet's generality led me to think feelingly and feel thoughtfully of my own life and my own death."

"In what way, my child?"

"It made me think and feel at once that I am being carried helplessly down this river of time; that I am already some one else's predecessor; that I am old and in the process of being destroyed and set aside like an abdicated king; that I am already a former thing, and that there will be no remembrance of me."

"You alone, my Chosen Soul?"

"No, the poetry interested me because it connected the process of time with human life; with my life, and everybody else's life ... and death."

"I do not see you weep, my son."

"The poet was not downcast; nor am I, listening to his words. For though his subject is the destruction of all things, his song is, like time itself

still moving, ever new

a song of endless creation, timeless and immortal."

"Can we not say, then, that the elegance and harmony of the words is also an elegance and harmony of mind and feeling?"

"Perhaps we can. The elegance and harmony may be the result of a great many thoughts and feelings (which might, in other circumstances, fight bitterly against one another) co-existing in perfect equipoise and equanimity, just as the warring images and jarring sounds co-exist within the order of the verse."

"So the wisdom is in the music."

"Partly or largely, yes."

"Explain, my child, and elaborate."

"The calming undersong which I heard and felt (or thought I felt and heard) seems to be the expression of a comprehensive mind joyously contemplating the course of the world in which Time and Nature destroy in order to create, and in which every destroying minute brings something new into the world."

"There is, then, a *world* of difference between the mere statement of a doctrine and the poetic treatment of similar conceptions."

"Yes, Lamp of Light. The poem enables us mortals to dance out, and sing through, the teachings in our own minds and bodies, feeling ourselves to be taking part rather than merely agreeing."

"So my Poet was telling a different kind of truth from that of the Lovers of Wisdom?"

"Heavenly One, he was."

"But a Truth, nevertheless?"

"Possibly, possibly."

"Do you at least see, My Chosen Soul, how it is that Poets will make a distinctive contribution to human knowledge though not to the stock of human thoughts?"

"No, Celestial Muse. That I still do not see."

"Will you not admit that Poetry may be, as you say, '*useful*'?"

"Great Goddess, we must be using that word in different senses."

THE POWERS OF POETRY: A DANCE OF THOUGHT

55. A Dance of Thought

It was now past the morning of the day, and Our Hero was hungry again. When the Muse at last noticed this, a ripe melon fell in his lap. He chewed contentedly and spread himself among the flowers. But the Muse had no mind to let him rest.

"Perhaps," she began, "we could get some help from another of your sons-to-be."

The Muse turned towards the pool by the Fountain of Art. First a mist appeared, and then, out of the mist, came the figure of WORDSWORTH, rejoicing, as always, in the spirit of life, bare-chested, chanting at the wind:

> *... I have felt*
> *A presence that disturbs me with the joy*
> *Of elevated thoughts; a sense sublime*
> *Of something far more deeply interfused,*
> *Whose dwelling is the light of setting suns,*
> *And the round ocean and the living air,*
> *And the blue sky, and in the mind of man:*
> *A motion and a spirit, that impels*
> *All thinking things, all objects of all thought,*
> *And rolls through all things. Therefore am I still*
> *A lover of the meadows and the woods,*
> *And mountains; and of all that we behold*
> *From this green earth; of all the mighty world*
> *Of eye, and ear – both what they half create,*
> *And what perceive; well pleased to recognise*
> *In nature and the language of the sense*
> *The anchor of my purest thoughts, the nurse,*
> *The guide, the guardian of my heart, and soul*
> *Of all my moral being.*

"I can see that the mockery I have so far endured is nothing compared to that which I shall have to face in future incarnations. Tis Poet, Heavenly Being, speaks like you."

"But do you think he speaks sense?"

"I could not tell. He spoke in so grandly and so passionately that I could not always follow."

"Do you remember the lines where the Poet spoke of the things he loved:

> *... all the mighty world*
> *Of eye, and ear – both what they half create,*
> *And what perceive ... ?"*

"I remember, but do not understand."

"Would you not agree that the world you mortals know is made up of things that you think really exist and things which you imagine may exist – and that you are never quite sure which is which?"

"Yes, my Muse. We mortals are in a state of permanent confusion and doubt whether anything (including ourselves) can be said to exist at all. I myself sometimes have the strange sensation of existing only in the afternoon reverie of some middle-aged dreamer."

"And even with those things that you think probably do exist – such as mountains – your imagination is at least as important as your perception."

"I suppose so. I have never seen a whole mountain. Only aspects of a mountain. I guess the rest. And if it comes to that, I can never be absolutely certain that what I think I see (partial as it is) may not be a mirage, an illusion, an hallucination. But why are we speaking in such large and general terms, Lamp of Light? Our subject, surely, is *poetry*?"

"Because we are considering the playground, the stage, the theatre of Poetry, namely the Mind of Man, and, according to the Poet we have just heard, there is in the Mind of Man

A motion and a spirit, that impels
All thinking things, all objects of all thought,
And rolls through all things ... "

"And what might that be? (I must admit that this one one of the places I was lost.)"

"The dance and the joy of human thought, obviously."

"How can the dance and the joy of human thought exist in

...the light of setting suns,
And the round ocean and the living air,
And the blue sky...?"

"Do all these things exist outside or inside your mind, My Child?"

"Outside (surely?)."

"If you are watching the light of setting suns on the 'round' ocean in the 'living' air or in the 'blue' sky, are you perceiving, imagining, remembering, inventing or feeling?"

"I suppose, now you press me on the matter, that I am doing all these things. I do not *perceive* the ocean to be round. I *guess* that it might be so. I suppose the sky might *not* be blue, even while perceiving that it *is*. That the air lives is a feeling connected both with my guess that the air gives me life, and with my perception of it moving as the wind."

"So your mind and the natural world are constantly and inextricably mingling and overlapping?"

"Yes – *in my mind.* I think, in fact, that sometimes in the motions of my thought I more than half create the mighty world of eye and ear."

"Moreover, My Chosen Soul, although you do not think that your oceans and mountains and skies are mere invention, but have an existence which is genuinely independent of you, you nevertheless habitually assume that there is some sort of consonance between what is out there and what your mind is creating itself."

"That is true. I find it hard – impossible in fact – not to attribute delight to what is giving me delight, or sadness to what is making me sad. Take the light of setting suns, for example ..."

"Is the light of setting suns delightful or sad?"

"Both. It disturbs me and calms me at the same time."

"My little mortal, explain how you are disturbed and calmed at the same time."

"The peculiar light which signals the end of day and which lasts only a moment seems peculiarly beautiful. And my mind moves inevitably from considering the solemn beauty of a sunset to thoughts about the transience of life, all life, my life."

"So we agree, then, that all human apprehensions of the world are half-received and half-created?"

"We agree, Great Lady, we agree."

"I explained (at great length) when we talked of the dawn, that the very abilities of mortals like you to see any significance in the objects of the outside world resides in your irresistible tendency to tell and remember stories about them; to be constantly connecting them with, or seeing their elements repeated in, your own lives."

"You did, indeed, explain that – (at very great length)."

"Is it not the case that, for a mortal, every large thought is compounded of perceptions, imaginations, memory, inventions?"

"Every movement of my mind is accompanied by pleasure and pain, joy and sorrow or the memory of

THE POWERS OF POETRY: A DANCE OF THOUGHT

pleasure and pain, joy and sorrow."

"Elaborate, my child."

"Whenever I have leisure to be aware that I am thinking, the process and progress of thought is felt as pain and pleasure are felt. And my thoughts seem often to move of their own impulsion (in much the way this Poet describes) and to lead me I know not where."

"So you would say that there are two essential ingredients of your thought – an apparently self-generating movement and the sensation of joy and sorrow?"

"Yes, I would."

"And is it not your experience that things which posses acute feeling and dynamic movement *dance?*"

"Yes, that is, I suppose, one definition of what a dance is."

"But is it not also your experience that the dance of thought is over before it has begun: that as the mind moves from one place to the next it loses sight of its own footsteps?"

"My thoughts, if I have any, are momentary as a sound, swift and transitory as the lightning in the dark night."

"It follows from all you have been saying, does it not, that the only body in which human thoughts

Whose dwelling is the light of setting suns

could have full, permanent expression, could have, that is, full existence or being, would be in some kind of ordered *dance* – either the dance of bodily movement, the dance of colour, the dance of musical sound, the dance of forms, or the dance of words which is Poetry?"

"It seems to follow."

"And does it not follow that Poetry has, therefore and thereby, the utmost importance to the continuing life – the continuing existence – of Humanity itself?"

"Heavenly Creature, although I see you have shown me how human thought might sing and dance, I still do not believe that I possess or will possess important or useful knowledge."

"Offspring of my Dreams, have you understood nothing – *nothing?*"

"A little here and there, perhaps."

"Yours, My Chosen One, is the soul of a POET."

"So you say, Celestial Patroness. (So you *keep* saying.)"

"Listen then, Beloved Poet, all things will be revealed."

56. Poetry, Useful Knowledge and Truth

The sun was high in the heavens: all the shadows became foreshortened. The Muse seemed to be possessed by a fit of wild enthusiasm and would brook no interruption. Our Hero, supine on the grass and among the flowers (which seemed to spring anew even as the Muse spoke), was happy to listen to her voice. He was enjoying the grapes, the melon, and the sun.

"Let me explain again what I have already explained, so that you may know and feel all that it is necessary to feel and know – and so may become truly a Poetic Soul."

(Our Hero smiled compliantly.)

"Your knowledge, O My Poet, is the breath and finer spirit of all human knowledge: it is a deep and penetrating understanding of the mind of Man and the pleasures of the human mind."

(Our Hero grinned with disbelief. He had heard all this before.)

"It is a knowledge you possess intuitively and inwardly, and not outwardly and analytically," said the Muse, hurriedly.

(Her Pupil was pleased to hear this. It was comforting to know that he knew without knowing. It was what he had always hoped would be the case.)

"One of the things which you know is that, as far as the fullest and deepest apprehensions of humanity are concerned, there is no substantial difference between the world outside and the world within, between fact and fiction."

(Our Hero yawned happily. Despite all that had been said, he knew this was arrant nonsense. His mind began to drift.)

"You know that inner mental events are as powerful as exterior happenings, and that a dream may affect a day in your life more than anything which 'really' happens on that day – even though you know it was only a dream.

You understand with peculiar acuteness that when mortals say 'this is true', or 'that is a lie,' what they really mean is 'this is a good imagining' and 'that is a bad imagining'."

(As far as Our Hero was concerned, at this moment, full of melon and basking in the sight of the Muse, all imaginings were good imaginings.)

"You guess or imagine that mortals make sense of the world by guessing or imagining a whole on the strength of a few hints. That which seems to them to be true or good is an imagining which includes more observations, fits better with other lasting imaginings, than that which seems false or bad.

And good imaginings, you well know, are always accompanied by abundant pleasure – a pleasure which seems deeper and is more lasting than the pleasures of false or inadequate imaginings. This pleasure is as much of the body as the of mind: of the mind as of the body."

(The Poet stretched himself luxuriously.)

"Men understand the world in which they live, and their dealings with other men, by turning them into stories. They people their stories with invented personalities and imagined motives and significances. However, although men may *think* they can tell the difference between the stories they tell themselves and the stories you tell, in the eyes of the gods, the balance of truth may go quite the other way."

(Our Hero found the weight of his own incomprehension almost too much to bear. His head began to nod; his eyes to close of their own accord.)

"But the mortal mind, as you know if you search your own, is subtle. It is quite possible for a man to say 'this imagining is false on its surface but true in its core' or 'that imagining has an attractive outside but treacherous depths'."

(Our Hero gazed doubtfully through misty eyes at the fair form of his Divine Instructress, searching for treacherous depths.)

"The characteristic quality of what you mortals call 'truth' is that it is always found deeply and lastingly pleasurable. Poetry is a true, complete, and human form of discourse because it admits, and indeed rests its case on, the story-telling, the fictionalising, which is in truth (though you poor mortals may never admit it) an essential part of all human attempts to understand the world.

So when the Lovers of Wisdom tell you that all your works are lies, you may tell them that it is partly because they ARE, and declare themselves to be, LIES, that they may be considered the truest form — certainly the most human form — of discourse. Poetry makes palpable the very *process* of human thought."

(At this Our Hero managed to open one eye, and raise one eyebrow, briefly.)

"Moreover, since stories can take many forms, some of which seem to be true, but incompatible with others which seem equally true, Poetry offers a special kind of pleasure precisely because it *is* provisional, a pleasure which is not offered by those forms of human discourse which claim to be telling the truth, the whole truth and nothing but the truth. Mortals delight in the lie which is also true; the truth which is also a lie; the truth that is most true when most a lie."

(Our Hero mused happily on the delightfulness of this lie.)

"This knowledge will allow my Poets to reign as monarchs over all other practitioners of human wisdom — of wisdom about humanity. For they will not only show the path to wisdom, but provide such a sweet prospect of the path that any and every man will be enticed to enter and to journey on."

The Muse, at last sensing some lack of full attention from her pupil, attempted to elaborate:

"Imagine yourself on a journey through a fair vineyard."

(Our Hero obeyed effortlessly. He saw the grapes, the vine-trees ranged in rows.)

"The Poet is like a man who stands at the gate and gives you a cluster of luscious grapes, so that, full of the enticing taste, you long to pass further in and on."

(Our Hero, in his Imagination, tasted of the grape and entered further in and on into the vineyard of his mind.)

"The Poet does not begin like the Lovers of Wisdom and Truth, or the Men of Power, or the true Priest — with obscure definitions, fine points of law, or prayers of penitence and supplication. The Poet does not load the memory with doubtfulness."

(The Muse, sensing that something was distracting her pupil — who was, in fact, almost asleep — redoubled her energies.)

"Poetry, you must understand, is the IMAGE OF MAN AND NATURE embodied in pleasure. For a Poet (for you, My Beloved), Poetry comes easily. You compose under only one restriction, the necessity of giving unmediated and lasting pleasure."

(Again the Muse sensed some disbelief, some doubt, from her recumbent charge.)

"Do not consider this necessity of producing pleasure as a degradation of the Poet's Art. It is far otherwise. It is an acknowledgement of the beauty of the universe; it is a homage paid to the native and naked dignity of man, to the grand elementary principle of pleasure, by which he knows, and feels, and lives, and moves."

(The elementary principle of human pleasure seemed to Our Hero at this moment to consist mainly in slumber.)

"The pleasure provided by the Art of Poetry is the profound satisfaction which mortals feel when in the presence of what they believe to be the profoundest truth about themselves. For the object of Poetry is truth, not individual or local truth, not truth to the surface of life, but general truth – the truth of the moving soul of things. It is carried alive into the heart by passion, by pleasure; it is a truth which is its own evidence."

(Our Hero, despite himself, began to sigh gently.)

"My Poets will produce true imaginings of things – feelings, human relations, persons, creatures, buildings, monsters – which have never existed and will never exist in real life. You, My Poet, will produce another, fresher, fuller world, by making things either better than the world, or by making things quite anew – by creating forms such as never were in the world. A Poet is free to range the zodiac of his own wit."

(Our Hero was indeed ranging the zodiac of his own wit – in dreams. Unnoticed by the Muse, he had rolled over and given himself up entirely to slumber.)

"The pleasure offered by Poets' true imaginings will colour human feelings about the world as surely and as profoundly as their experience of the world mortals think of as real. Throughout history, men will base their own imaginings about what the world is like as much or more on the Poets' inventions as on first-hand-imagining-and-observation. When mortals ask themselves: what is man? what is love? what is heroism? what is human happiness? and other such questions, they will draw their sense of these things as much from our unreal and artificial creations as from the world they think of as 'real'. They will know in their hearts that our fictions are truer than the realities they perceive with their eyes and ears."

(Our Hero was in that state where the eyes and the ears send no messages to the conscious mind.)

"That is why your knowledge, O My Poet, is (as you would say) 'useful': it is the breath and finer spirit of all human knowledge. That is why Poetry is the first and last of all knowledge. Poetry is as immortal as the heart of man because it IS the heart of man." (A resonant pause ensued.) "Do you see? Do you agree? Are you listening?"

"Heavenly Goddess, I am very much afraid," said Our Hero, wearily bestirring himself at last, "that my mind, if I have one, was elsewhere."

THE POWERS OF POETRY: A DANCE OF AGONY

57. A Dance of Agony

The afternoon was long and warm enough to accommodate several such sermons from the Muse. Our Hero's only wish was that he did not have to pretend to concentrate. He decided to let the words of his Teacher float harmlessly over his head like the clouds. The Muse, however, had (as usual) other ideas.

"My Poet, my Chosen Soul," said the Muse, caught between amusement and annoyance at the regressions of her pupil, "Have you at least understood how the Arts of Poetry allow you to see into the Human Heart and how a proper disposition of single sounds results in a harmony which governs passion?"

"O Celestial Being, my mind seems not to have retained anything beyond the faintest glimmerings of how such things might be. How can non-musical sound govern passion? Surely it is in the nature of human passion to be incoherent, and perhaps to be heard only in moaning, and to be seen only in the distorted features of a ravaged face."

"The expression of extreme passion in Poetry will be, I must warn you, strange."

"In what way *strange*?"

"At no other time is the difference between Poetry and Life greater or more absolute; nowhere else is the artifice of your Arts more apparent. Let us take, for example, human suffering. In the House of Words there is a Bower of Sorrows. In the Bower of Sorrows there is a Chamber of Agony. Go there, if you dare."

Our Hero crossed the clouds and descended the winding steps to the Bower of Sorrows.

Slow and unsteady was his return. His face was pale and he trembled like an aspen in the wind.

"What did you hear?"

"O Muse, there are no words in the Chamber of Agony. All I heard were moans and howls and cries and groans. But they were not the moans and howls and cries and groans of human beings; they sounded more like the barkings of rabid dogs and the bellowings of wounded cows. And there was no distinction between the sounds. Those who suffer the agony of bereavement or betrayal make the same sounds as those whose arms hang severed from their shoulders, or those whose backs are breaking on the rack."

"So, what is the Poet to do when his story requires him to represent agony?"

"Obviously I must not think of harrowing my audience as I was harrowed in the Chamber of Agony, for my audience would leave (as I left) and never return. It would be unbearable."

"It would also be pointless, because there is nothing to be learned from groans."

"True. And if I attempted to follow the incoherence of real-life, you might justly feel that I was not fulfilling the task you have set me."

"I would desert you the moment you began to try such a thing."

"And yet, if I set about giving a coherent voice and form to such feelings, would I not be untrue to life? Would I not, once again, be *lying?*"

"Why yes of course! Have you understood nothing."

"Should not a Poet, perhaps, leave such matters alone."

"Nonsense! Let us hear some of the ways in which your greatest future incarnations will present agony and sorrow. I will show you a supreme and extreme example. An aged king – who has already suffered what there is to be suffered, who has broken or witnessed the breaking of every sacred bond, who has been betrayed and tormented by those who owed him most, who has learned how much more bitter than hell it is to have a thankless child – is grieving over the corpse of his daughter."

The Muse released a small group of sounds from her amphora. Our Hero noticed the voicing and tones of an actor, but as the words entered Our his soul, what he *saw* was an old man holding all that was left of his last hope and last love in his withered arms:

Howl, howl, howl; O you are men of stones,
Had I your tongues and eyes, I'd use them so,
That heaven's vault should crack; she's gone for ever.
I know when one is dead, and when one lives,
She's dead as earth...

... no, no, no life?
Why should a dog, a horse, a rat have life,
And thou no breath at all? Thou'lt come no more,
Never, never, never, never, never.

"What do you think of that?" asked the Muse, smiling brightly.

As the words of the actor, or the old king, or the future Poet, had been sounding, Our Hero had risen bolt upright in the grass. Now, considerably shaken, he stared at his Muse, aghast.

"How can you smile at such a moment? Have you no pity? Are you a goddess of stone?"

"Come, come, my child, that was a *fiction* – that was Poetry."

"That was human suffering."

"Such as you heard in the Chamber of Agony?"

"No, My Muse, this was *worse*."

"Worse?"

"In the Chamber of Agony, I heard only howling dogs and bellowing cows. This old man was a suffering human soul. It was as if agony had entered and taken possession of him, and shaped his whole being into expressing that pain, and nothing else. I heard the voice of pure grief, the true voice of human agony. I am *appalled*."

"Good. How was it done?"

"Done? You mean it was a trick?"

"I mean it was Art."

"No. No. No. Lamp of Light, I will never believe that! The violent simplicity of some of that language came close to the groans I heard in the Bower of Sorrows:

Howl, howl, howl...
... no, no, no life?
Never, never, never, never, never

Repetition always seems to accompany the expression human agony – there is endless repetition in the Chamber of Agony. But I do not, *cannot*, understand how you are able to talk like this, Heavenly Being. How can you speak so cooly about such burning sorrow?"

"Because I am the Muse of Poetry, and Poetry is an Art. You have noticed the wonderfully effective use of repetition. But what else do you notice about the sound-pattern of these creatures?

Why should a dog, a horse a rat have life,
And thou no breath at all? Thou'lt come no more ..."

"I suppose, Cruel Goddess, now you force me to think of it, that, after the first two, these words follow exactly the pattern you taught me long ago:

WHY should a DOG, a HORSE a RAT have LIFE,
And THOU no BREATH at ALL? Thou'lt COME no MORE ..."

But what difference does that make?"

"All the difference – all the difference in the world – all the difference between heaven and hell."

"I can't see that."

"Have you learned *nothing*? Consider these words again:

And thou no breath at all

Consider them just as word-creatures. What qualities do they have?"

"They are simple and ordered. Six little words dancing a slow dance of agony."

"Perfectly simple and perfectly ordered?"

"Yes; I cannot imagine how a syllable could be changed to advantage. They move with those sure-footed, even-footed pairs I saw before:

SLOW-SLOW fresh-FOUNT keep-TIME with-MY salt-TEARS."

"And are they beautiful?"

"Truly beautiful. And heart-breaking."

"But beauty gives pleasure, always gives pleasure? (Beauty is pleasure?)"

"Lamp of Light, I see where your remarks are tending. But I cannot consider these words on their own. What I heard was an old man's unbearable suffering."

"As in these words?" asked the Muse:

*I know when one is dead, and when one lives,
She's dead as earth ...*

"or, to emphasise the art, like this:

*I KNOW when ONE is DEAD / and WHEN one
LIVES /
She's DEAD as EARTH /*

is that where you heard an old man suffering?"

"While hearing those particular words, living that particular moment in my Imagination, I am certainly filled by a sense that terrible things have happened, and are still happening, to this old king."

"Only that, little mortal?"

"No; my mind is simultaneously on something else, a vision of the reality of the thing that we hide behind the words 'agony' or 'grief'. The old man suffering seems to recede and give way to something larger, I don't know what, but there is something in the inexorable tread, tread, tread of those short words beating the awful certainty into his mind:

*I know when one is dead, and when one lives,
She's dead as earth ...*

something there which ... I don't know ..."

"A kind of beauty? A form? An eloquence which can express the *reality* of agony as nothing else can in the world? Is there not something held *within* the form or created by the form? The whole is controlled – not by the old man, but by a higher intelligence?"

"Perhaps, perhaps, I don't know. It is just that I feel so sorry for this man, and so sorry for his daughter and for all men – and for myself. Oh my Muse, why is there such sorrow in the world? Why must I contemplate such agony?"

Our Hero broke down and wept, as he had wept long ago, like a beaten child.

58. *A Song of Grief (and of Joy)*

The Muse encircled Our Hero with a full embrace, rocking him gently to and fro, kissing his cheeks, his eyes, his tears.

"The law, my Child, is immutable. Man is born to misery, just as the sparks fly upward. But do not weep, do not weep, my Love, my Hope, for you are a Poet, and Poetry is joy; never more so than when it deals in sorrow. Poetry weeps such tears as angels weep, as I weep."

"I do not see how this can be," said Our Hero (weeping).

"Is it not *always a pleasure* for humans to make, to build, to create?"

"It is."

"And is it not a pleasure to dance?"

"Yes."

"And to sing?"

"Yes."

"And to know your own mind (the mirror of all minds) and to possess your own soul (the mirror of all souls)?"

"In my experience that has never happened, but I would imagine it would be a very great pleasure indeed."

"Then must it not be the greatest pleasure open to a mortal to make out of human misery a song of thought, and out of human grief a dance of the mind?"

"I suppose it must," said Our Hero (unconvinced).

"Let us consider some examples."

"Yes please, Great Goddess."

"I will call the shades of two of your future selves. The first will describe the moment that, in his story, – from which we have heard before – is the cause of all human woe. Eve, the first woman, has just come to Adam, the first man, bearing in her hand a bough from the one tree in the garden of Eden from which God has forbidden them to eat. Adam knows in the instant that all is lost, both for her and for him."

The Muse called the shade of JOHN MILTON, the Noblest Poet, who walked with great dignity from the dark of the cave, bowed austerely to the Muse, and began to recite with great precision and musicality of diction. As he spoke, his words entered the mind of Our Hero, who found himself once again in the Garden of Eden and saw Eve holding an apple-laden bough, her face flushed as if with wine, and saw the garland Adam had been preparing for her return fall from his hands and lie forgotten at his feet.

O fairest of creation, last and best
Of all God's works, creature in whom excelled
Whatever can to sight or thought be formed,
Holy, divine, good, aimiable or sweet!
How art thou lost, how on a sudden lost ...

... Some cursed fraud
Of enemy hath beguiled thee, yet unknown,
And me with thee hath ruined, for with thee
Certain my resolution is to die:
How can I live without thee, how forego
Thy sweet converse and love so dearly joined,
To live again in these wild woods forlorn?
Should God create another Eve, and I
Another rib afford, yet loss of thee
Would never from my heart; no, no, I feel
The link of nature draw me; flesh of flesh,
Bone of my bone thou art, and from thy state
Mine never shall be parted, bliss or woe.

"Will I compose such things," said Our Hero, smiling through his tears, "so full of sorrow, and so lovely?"

"Even this, my child."

"What a joy will it be to be such a Poet!"

"And to know such sorrow? (Your tune has changed.)"

"Yes; it will be a joy to know sorrow as this Poet will know it. I feel what Adam feels, know what Adam knows, while all in the Bower of Agony was incomprehensible, unintelligible, and what the old king said was too much to be borne."

"How is that? (You sing a new song.)"

"In order to make me feel what Adam feels, this Poet must be imagining, with *intensity*, what it might be like to be in Adam's position, while being himself in a state of enviable calm, of complete tranquillity, choosing the words of beauty and power with the care and the thought which turns sorrow into music."

"Music, my Poet? I thought you did not believe in the music of sorrow?"

"I heard music from that Poet, or from Adam:

How art thou lost / how on a sudden / lost ..."

"What kind of music, Dearest Mortal?"

"In that line of words I recognise the full weight of human sorrow, at the same time as feeling the full pleasures of poetry. The music makes me *know* what Adam feels (lost, on a sudden lost) as I can never know what another human feels in life, but it also makes that feeling beautiful and therefore bearable."

"Is it only the beauty that makes it bearable?"

"ONLY the beauty! No, the sorrow can be endured because it has been comprehended, understood, seen round and seen through, absorbed, submitted to a pattern ... or rather a pattern has been found within it, since nothing is forced. That is the beauty."

"Adam's beauty?"

"I hear the voice of a man, and of more than a man. I hear the voice of love and the sorrow of love itself."

"Explain."

"The man is there in the pattern of simple repeated phrases:

how lost ...
how lost ...
with thee ...
with thee ...
without thee ...
how forego ...
no, no ...

which resemble or represent the repetitions of agonised speech and the mental patterns of human love. But I am given more than a *representation* of feeling."

"More, little mortal?"

"I am made to know what Adam's love *is* in terms of his life – as his imagination sees the garden of Eden turning into a wilderness:

How can I live without thee, how forego
Thy sweet converse and love so dearly joined,
To live again in these wild woods forlorn?

And yes, before you say anything, Prophetic Spirit, that last and most beautiful line has the familiar entirely regular lovely pattern:

to LIVE a-GAIN in THESE wild WOODS
for-LORN"

"When speaking about the old king I mentioned a higher intelligence, but you did not quite believe me. Do you see anything of that here, my child?"

"Yes, I suppose I am conscious of two minds."

"Two minds, My Chosen One?"

"I am in the presence of Adam's mind, and that of his creator. I take in the situation entirely through Adam's words (as I listen I become Adam) but at the same time, I am also able to see more than he does."

"Explain."

"Adam sees things with a terrible clarity, which is also almost a confusion. He is at the same time sublimely, wisely, loving, and also almost foolish. (Eve is someone in whom the holy, the divine and the good 'excelled' in the past tense.) It is the poet who understands, who is both inside and out, comprehending a whole."

"Inside and outside, little mortal?"

"He is inside, feeling what Adam feels, and outside, considering what Adam feels and what Adam does in relation to the sum of things."

"The sum of things?"

"Yes. At this moment Adam is much *more* than a single man."

"Again you say 'more', my pupil. What do you have in mind?"

"Adam's sorrow is the result of great forces operating upon and within him. The poet has given him words of a power beyond the merely mortal:

... I feel
The link of nature draw me; flesh of flesh,
Bone of my bone thou art, and from thy state
Mine never shall be parted, bliss or woe.

Something is created and brought into being. I do not see merely a man."

"What, then, do you see?"

"I think I see Great Nature in action ... and feel it too."

"You do. You see and feel more than you know you know."

"I do?"

"Is the dance of grief that these word-creatures dance a different thing from the Poet's placing of human suffering in relation to the sum of things?"

"*The knowledge dictates the words; the words express the knowledge.*"

"Exactly, My Beloved, exactly!"

59. The Poetry of Sorrow

Again the Muse embraced Our Hero (though there was no longer cause). The tears she kissed were no longer tears of grief. They had turned (without altering) from tears of misery to tears of exultation.

"Now, at long last, My Chosen Soul, you know indeed what it is that you will know. You know how Poets will penetrate the human heart and peer deep into the abyss of the human soul. Now let us learn another story, and hear another Poet."

"Gladly, Great Lady."

"The noble shade of CHAUCER, the Father of Poetry in the Northern Isle, will now recite part of a speech from one of the wisest and most beautiful of love stories. A young Trojan knight, Troilus, has loved the lady Criseyde with a boundless and faithful love, a heart utterly true. She has been forced to go to the camp of his enemies. One day Troilus sees the brooch that he gave to Criseyde as a token of faith on some armour captured from a Greek, Diomede. He is forced to know what he had long feared: that all was lost."

From the pool came a short man with an other-worldly manner and a voice at once as light and as solemn as any heard on earth. As the words entered his mind Our Hero heard Troilus lament that Criseyde had broken her 'bihest', her promise, her oath, and that Diomede now provided the 'feste', banquet of the mind and senses that was once his to give. Our Hero heard Troilus speak of his confusion: that he had 'trowed' – believed, expected or thought – that since Criseyde 'nolde' (was not willing) 'in truthe to stonde', to remain fixed in truth towards him, she would at least not have 'holden him in hand', deceived him, played him along. And then Our Hero heard Troilus say that he simply was not capable of unloving Criseyde. She who forced him to endure such pain, who inflicted such suffering upon him, was yet the created being he loved most in all the world."

Then spak he thus, 'O lady mine, Criseyde,
Where is your faith, and where is your bihest?
Where is your love? where is your truthë?' he said.
'Of Diomede have ye now all this feste?
Alas, I would han trowed atte leste
That since ye nolde in truthë to me stonde,
That ye thus nolde han holden me in honde ...

... I see that clean out of your mind
Ye han me cast; and I ne kan nor may,
For all this world, within mine hertë finde
To unloven you a quarter of a day.
In cursd time I born was, weylaway,
That you, that doon me all this woe endure,
Yet love I best of any creäture.'

"That makes me cry," said Our Hero, "but it does not make me *unhappy*."

"How can that be, little mortal?"

"The mixture of words here is very similar to Adam's. There are hints of a simple human voice in the simple human question – '*where? where? where?*'

Where is your faith, and where is your bihest?
Where is your love? where is your truthë?

and again we have a list of attributes (faith, behest, love, truth) so that at the moment of loss we are made to know the value of that which is lost."

"And that makes you cry, my Dearest Poet?"

"Yes, but controlling and sustaining everything is a word-walk of subtle regularity and great beauty. Again, this man, this Troilus, is eloquent in his misery, but the voice that speaks is not the voice of a personality. It is verse which seems to be the direct expression of a clear pool of soul; gentle but terribly clear-minded:

> *... and I ne kan nor may,*
> *For all this world, within mine hertë finde*
> *To unloven you a quarter of a day*

He knows, and I am made to know, the full truth of his story.

> *... you, that doon me all this woe endure,*
> *Yet love I best of any creäture."*

"How then is the sorrow conveyed? By the story alone?"

"The sorrow is conveyed by the reticence of his word-creatures."

"What reticence?"

"They move steadily, surely, about their business without clamour of loud exclamation. They carry within themselves the sense of all the things Troilus does not say, no longer has the leisure to say."

"The sorrow they convey is the sorrow of what they do *not* say?"

"Just that."

"Does the Poet know suffering?"

"I cannot believe that this poet will not suffer, will not have suffered by the time he writes this. But, no, Celestial Muse, it is clear that the Poet is not himself suffering while composing or reciting, nor does he want us to suffer."

"Why not?"

"Something is created; something is made; a new power is brought into being. A sorrow is perceived by this creation with a clarity which real life never allows. A mind knows (really knows rather than being, as I usually am, merely *confused* by) sorrow. That which is created is infinitely pleasurable. We are made to see beauty, the beauty of the human soul, reflected in beauty of language."

"Reflected in, or created by?"

"The poet's power of language is also a power of human imagination. If there *were* such noble souls as Troilus's and if those souls could find a form of true and full expression, so would they speak. In Troilus, human nature has been improved upon."

"Would you concede, Dearest Pupil, that Human Nature could only be drawn – let alone improved upon – by a mind that comprehends Human Nature?"

"I can see no way of not conceding."

"And so, My Poet, what is it that you and I will do with human sorrow?"

"The poetry of sorrow is different from real sorrow by being more eloquent than sorrow, fuller than sorrow, larger than sorrow, freer than sorrow. The mind is widened, filled with a great expanse of thought."

"Is it still human sorrow, My Child?"

"It is a more-than-human sorrow, Great Lady. It is a sorrow without pain. Real sorrow destroys the mind. But for the Poet, sorrow, or the contemplation of sorrow, is something which enables him to make, to create, almost as a god creates."

"So that for the Poet sorrow is a joy?"

"It must be so, Heavenly Muse. And for the listener there is the endlessly repeatable pleasure of meeting these new children of humanity: great-souled Adam, gentle Troilus."

"You enjoyed meeting these Poets and their creations?"

"Lamp of Light, I cannot believe I will write such things – not in a million incarnations."

"In these two incarnations, My Chosen Soul, you will be indeed god-like – you will have a god-like mind and wield a god-like power."

60. The Laws of Poetical Creation

The shadows were now lengthening, as afternoon slipped into evening. The Muse and her Poet moved to a flowery bank, warm with the last rays of the sun. Our Hero, who had listened long, was tired and confused. Somewhere among the tangle of his impressions lurked the inkling of a suspicion that he might be approaching the edge of a great secret.

"Great and Lovely Lady, Heavenly Muse, Steadfast Star, I am once again lost, again drowning in a sea of thought. You seem to be saying that the pleasures which you and I will offer are identical with the pleasures offered by Nature herself, and that the Poet's makings are equal to the makings of the gods. But you cannot (of course) be saying these things. Such claims, O Celestial One, would be not only extravagant beyond the bounds of thought, but downright blasphemous."

"My Poet, My Chosen Soul, have you understood *nothing* I have said?"

"I have heard your lessons and marked them well, and at the time I conceded the truth of much that you said. but when I think about you words and their implications, I fear they will drive me mad."

"My Child, why do you say that?"

"Because the ability to distinguish between dream and reality, between fact and fiction, between truth and illusion is most precious to me, as to all mortals. When we loose this ability, or when it is taken from us by accident, deception or disease we go mad."

"Your belief that you possess such an ability is the greatest illusion of all."

"Alas, alas!"

"Have we not agreed that the abilities or capacities that matter are the capacity to tell a good story from a bad and to distinguish between levels of fictionality?"

"We agreed, but I did not understand (really, or fully – or at all)."

"Are the imaginings mortals receive from you equal or unequal to those which they invent for themselves?"

"You have said that mine are superior, but my feeling is that men will always prefer their own accounts of the world, since, whatever you say, they will consider them truer and more *useful* (if you will pardon the word) than mine."

"In practical and (as you say) 'useful' matters and everyday affairs perhaps mortals will prefer their own inventions."

"I am sure they will, Goddess."

"But, as you well know if you search your own heart, in their secret souls mortals delight in exercising an imagination very like that which you will exercise in your work."

"Yes, but I still think there is a difference between my idle dreams (mere fantasies) and the kind of Imagination I use in inventing stories."

"But the one depends upon the other."

"I don't understand."

"Is it not the case that the ordinary mortal capacity to invent stories is innate only as a *potential?*"

"That certainly has been my experience, Lamp of Light. I have met too many men and women who seem to have no call for stories at all."

"The realisation of this human potential depends on and is derived from you, Beloved – from your capacity to imagine well."

"Shall I be responsible for the Imaginations of all mortals?"

"You will. From you and only from you mortals will learn how to imagine and therefore how to live."

"Really?"

"Mortals will hear your stories in their cradles and live in them in joy."

"I don't understand."

"Is it not the case that, for a mortal infant, life is best when it is a series of stories? Their play and their playthings are stories? Their little past is a story? And their long future?"

"Perhaps so. But when I was no longer a child I put away childish things."

"Does not the man dream what the boy believed?"

"Certainly not," said Our Hero (lying).

"Come, come. Adult mortals will dream continually of things (such as perfect love or true heroism) which, my Poet, will exist in your creations, rather than in the world which men think is real."

"Everybody has day-dreams."

"But the dreams which you inspire are of no small importance in making and keeping your species human."

"My species is human because we never grow up?"

"That would be one way of putting it. Did you not find when incarnated on the earth below that, even in the practical world, when mortals call upon the experience which is stored in their memories, they allow themselves to confuse what happened in the world with what happened to the invented personages in your stories?"

"Sometimes ..."

"I tell you, many mortals will have long imaginary conversations with the creations of your fictions as if they were their own best friends. When it comes to the inheritance of the species, mortals will not find it possible to distinguish between what their ancestors *really* did and what you, my Poet, will *pretend* that they did."

"That I can easily imagine. My sense of the past of mankind has far more to do with old stories than with any study of the Laws or monuments."

The Muse sensed some agreement from her pupil at last. She stroked his cheek and ran her fingers teasingly through his hair.

"So you will accept that the past is made by Poets and the world equally?"

"As far as my imagination is concerned, yes, it is. I may not speak for other men and women."

"Of course you may. And now, Beloved, you must not rest there. For your powers (our powers) are greater than those that created the world."

"So you hinted before. But I don't see how that can possibly be."

"The information which the world presents to the senses is limited by the Laws which created the world, is it not? But you can make *anything* do *anything* – anything that can be imagined by the Mind of Man. The Laws of Human Imagination are more extensive and more flexible than the Laws of the world. You can make the past present and the present past. You can make one short point of time fill all remaining eternity. You can make things remote seem close."

"I can?"

"You can make the wonderful seem intimately familiar: can show humanity operating in circumstances to which it could never be exposed in the world."

"I can?"

"You will."

Our Hero would have believed the words of his lovely Muse if he could. Her promises were, after all, wonderful. But she seemed to be attributing powers to his mind which, search as he might, he could not find.

"Celestial Guardian, are you not exceeding the bounds of reason? I find most other people's fantasies unengaging, sometimes repulsive, often downright boring. Why should my inventions please and interest other men and women, and have such power to affect their imaginations?"

"The difference between you and other men, ordinary mortals, is that yours is the soul of a Poet."

"So you say; so you have said."

"And ordinary mortals are not visited or inspired by ME. They dream or invent for themselves and by themselves alone. They dream from their individuality, from that part of themselves which divides them from other men (a liking for melons, or very fat women, or very thin men, or crocodiles). When you dream, you invent, and you create, from that depth of soul which you share with mankind; the each in all, the all in each."

"I do?"

"Yes. And where you obey my Laws, other mortals cheat."

"They *cheat*?"

"They cheat."

"What do you mean? How 'cheat'? Did you not say (two minutes ago) that I could do anything I liked, when I liked, as I liked? Did you not say that I could make anything do anything that can be imagined by the mind of man; that I could make the past present and the present past; make one short point of time fill all remaining eternity; make things remote seem close; make the wonderful seem intimately familiar; show humanity operating in circumstances to which it could never be exposed in the world?"

"I said these things."

"And isn't that cheating?"

"No."

"Why not?"

"When I say you can make anything, there is one proviso."

"Which is?"

"You can make anything provided what you make is a POEM."

"Alas!" cried Our Hero, feeling his head spinning.

"And what, my Child, is a POEM?"

"You would like me to say: a song and a dance of human thought and human truth."

"Exactly. You must make the Mind of Man dance and sing; the minds of all men and all women dance and sing. The Mind of Man cannot be set in motion – or not for long – by materials uncongenial to itself. Your danced and sung imaginings must therefore be absolutely true; true in spirit, true in every particular – true to the moving spirit of things."

"But all this long, long while, through all the twists and turns of our long conversations, you have been teaching me to LIE."

"The absolute truth to which you must adhere, and from which you must never deviate, is not the truth of the world. It is truth to the Spirit of Man; truth to the constituents of the Human Mind and Human Soul."

"So, although the laws (as you call them) governing my creations are different from those governing the world, they are laws nevertheless?"

"Yes, you, My Poet, are governed by Laws – governed absolutely, despotically, tyranically. These Laws are as severe, as inexorable, as immutable, and as powerfully *creative* as those which brought the this circumambient universe into being. It is by means of these Laws that a new world leaps forth when you say, 'let it be'."

61. The Poet Discovers his Gods

The night sky was now cloudless. Our Hero looked down on the earth below. Over the whole half-world nature seemed dead. All things were hushed. The mountains themselves seemed asleep. In the Muse's garden the little birds were singing in their dreams and the sleeping flowers sweating beneath the night-dew. But the Muse denied rest to Our Hero's soul and sleep to his eyes.

"Heavenly Being, if I am, as you say, superior to the laws of the world, the boundaries of Time and the pressures of Place, that would make me a god."

"God-like, my child, merely god-like."

"This I can neither understand nor, Lovely Lady, entirely believe. The Priests came to me and told me that all my stories were blasphemies. They showed me that I knew nothing of the true gods at all. Even though I was not, perhaps, *entirely* convinced, it must be wrong to say that my knowledge and powers are superior to those of the gods they call true. If I were to make the claim myself, I would certainly be the main attraction at their next sacrificial bonfire."

"I am afraid, My Poet, that your relations with the Priests will always be fraught with difficulties both in practice and in principle."

"How, Majesty Divine? And why?"

"Despite themselves, the Priests will not be able to help using your arts to glorify their gods or adorn their sermons, just as they will use my sister's progeny to adorn their churches and to grace their chapels with choirs."

"And I?"

"While you, My Chosen One, despite yourself, will always be talking of their gods, and using the words they have invented to describe their mysteries."

"I will?"

"Indeed. Poetry, you must understand, is most just to its own divine origin when it administers some of the comforts and breathes some of the spirit of Religion. Nevertheless, Poetry and Religion are as far divided as any two things can be which co-exist in the human mind."

"Please explain yourself, Majesty Divine. I am lost."

"My Beloved, do you understand what the Priests mean when they talk of trembling in the presence of the gods?"

"Yes. When the statue in a temple begins to shake, my heart leaps, my muscles tighten, and I fall on my knees in sincere supplication."

"At such moments, does it matter to you if the statue is of the finest marble, worked by the most delicate sculptor's hand, or a crude lump of wood, battered and rotting with age?"

"It does not matter at all. Although I was once tricked into worshipping a wonderful sculpture, the moment I realised it was Art, my religious awe gave way to professional admiration and sensuous pleasure. In fact, if there *is* a distinction to be made, the crude lump of wood might enable me to concentrate with more pure and undivided attention on the power and will of the deity."

"Why is that, Dearest Mortal?"

"If I am admiring the statue, I am revering the Muse of Sculpture and forgetting the true god."

"So you would agree that, in true Religion, the state of mind of the worshipper has nothing to do with the beauty or ugliness of expression used in temples and ceremonies?"

"I am no more in awe of the god when the prayers are offered by the most beautiful singer, than when they are spoken by the oldest Priest in his cracked and croaking voice. It does not matter to me if the arrangement of the words in a prayer is ugly or beautiful; it is enough that they should be acceptable to the gods."

"Do the composers of prayers have to worry whether the words they use will capture the imaginations and move the passions of the members of the congregation?"

"No. It is enough that the congregation have come to worship, and that the prayers are directly and properly addressed to the gods."

"So you see, the Priests were right. They do not do not need our Arts. Their prayers are addressed directly to Omniscience and Omnipotence. A Poet is a human speaking to humans. In your stories, you try to make everything as *beautiful* as possible, in order to give your audience as much *pleasure* as possible. The Priest is chiefly concerned that his words should not contradict the laws and procedures which his gods have revealed or declared. When the Priests speak of their gods, they speak of truths which have been revealed to them and which are thus absolute, unquestionable and beyond decoration."

"But I think that, for my Poems to be at all true to what life seems to be – with all its wonder and its terror – they must include a perspective on human behaviour and on the human world which is more than *merely* human – which does not assume that humanity is necessarily the centre of all things. (And I, Celestial Guardian, have never felt at the centre of anything)."

"Is it not a strange and wonderful thing about the mortal mind that it can imagine the existence of beings – gods or spirits – who view the human condition in a way which mocks the very act of Imagination which has created them in the first place?"

"It does seem strange and (as you say) *wonderful*."

"What kind of gods do you desire, My Chosen Poet?"

"I think that when I am composing my Poems I will want to include many different gods from many different lands."

"Yes; you will invent comic gods, gods who make love to mortals, gods who threaten their peers, gods who act and speak with total inconsistency, and gods who *do not know* who really rules this universe."

"That I can well imagine. If I put gods into my Poems I will *never* expect my audience to *believe* that my gods behave exactly as true gods might behave."

"Why not, Poet of my Dreams?"

"My gods will not be the product of *belief*, they will be the result of my allowing my imagination the freedom to speculate about pleasurable possibilities. The will be invitaions to my auditors to enjoy the pleasures of speculation."

"And an essential part of that pleasure for your audience will be the knowledge that your gods are NOT true. If your audience were trembling in awe and supplication, their minds would not be free to enjoy the ever-changing play of light which your fictions will shed on the world. It is by telling delightful lies, by creating pleasurable and provisional fictions, that you and I will reveal the workings of the great and infinitely various power which rolls through all things. And do you now see why Poetry and Religion are at opposite poles?"

"Not entirely."

"Priests require worshippers to believe that the gods are not the products of human imagination but exist as absolute facts. Such belief makes pleasure irrelevant – or worse, distracting, diminishing. For you, for me, *mortal pleasure alone is sacred*. Pleasure is our business:; our true religion. You will delight in imagining divine beings and will encourage your audience to share your delight in those imaginings. You will give mortals the peculiar pleasure that comes when they seem to see the world they live in as if for the first time, and recognise there the glorious gods of your invention – recognise creatures of delight with delight – in delight."

62. A Mystery

It was the time when witty Poets say that Phoebus sinks into the bed of the sea-goddess. All the world glows rosy red as she blushes, snuffs her candle, and draws the modest curtains of the night. Our Hero and his Muse, side by side in the long grass, talked softly, opening their hearts, as the garden lay all open to the stars.

"Chief of Nine, it still seems to me that everything you have been saying shows that I can do nothing without your aid; and you, I am more and more sure, are a Great Goddess. No Poem that will last could be written by a man who was *merely* a man. Poetry is not, like reasoning, a power to be exerted according to the *will*. No man who is merely a man, can say 'now I will compose poetry'."

"No, indeed. The greatest of your incarnations will not be able to say it. The will and the conscious portions of your nature are neither prophetic of my approach or my departure."

"But if my Poems celebrate you, will they not then be acts of worship – a homage to a goddess, paid with due reverence, by a man who has become more than a man by the grace of being favoured by your visits, and (if dare I say it) by your love."

"By my love indeed, Flesh of my Dreams. Although I will help you with your Poems and although you will, I hope, invoke and praise me in them, those Poems will not be acts of worship devoted to a *Muse*. Your Poems (our Poems, my Love) will illustrate and illuminate the workings of another, greater, power, a power who cannot be seen, who hardly exists without the songs and dances and pictures and stories of you and your fellows, My Poet."

"Light of my Soul, what or who is this greater power? For greater than you I cannot conceive."

"Nor need you, for you have already conceived. You will write Poems which mortals will not willingly let die?"

"I will try, Lamp of Light."

"Your Poems will please every nation?"

"They will if you so ordain, Majesty Divine."

"You will not write for one age but for all time?"

"For all time, Great Goddess."

"What is the secret of pleasing all ages and all nations?"

"Your presence, Beloved Muse. Grateful submission to your laws."

"Which are?"

"To embody and reflect and create and illuminate the fullness of the mortal soul at its greatest extent and highest reaches."

"So what is the quality that enables a work to please many and please long?"

"I know not, Lamp of Light."

"Nothing can please many and please long but just representations of the joy and the dance and the song of the general, universal and eternal human spirit interacting with the circumambient universe ..."

"... or Nature."

"And that, and that, My Only Beloved, is my gift to you."

"So you are ..."

"I am, I am."

"Herself?"

"Herself. The Source and End and Test of Art! Behold!"

The Goddess let her hieroglyphic robe drop to the floor. All NATURE stood revealed. She took her trembling Poet in her long, slender arms and kissed him on the lips with a touch more soft and sweet than anything on earth.

"Dear heart, how like you this?"

"O lovely Goddess, Heavenly Beauty, Sweet Lady, Celestial Mover, less than ever do I understand."

" Let me explain, My Love. I have done what I could with the world. I have emptied all my store and exhausted the possibilities of my self.

For a long, long while I was content with nothingness, and with the contemplation of matter unformed and void.

I studied the potential of limitless energy in the vast profundity obscure. Then, for a time, I was dazzled by the speed of light, ethereal, first of things, pure quintessence. I wondered at the infinite finiteness and uncertainty of mass. And then, for a while, I was pleased with suns and orbs, the mighty spheres and moons. I pricked with light the infinite darkness and sowed the sky with stars. A thousand thousand, worlds revolved on heaven's great axle. The music of the spheres delighted me. I plotted the circuits and trajectories of a million worlds, and watched the inexorable implementation of predetermined law. The problems of probability fascinated me.

But I ran against the limits of myself. Your earth, self-balanced on her centre, hung desert and bare, unsightly, unadorned. So I filled the deep with warm prolific humour and, for a while, enjoyed the fascination of the self-replicating, the infinite permutations of the double helix. I thronged the seas with spawn, and set to work millions of spinning worms. With a full and unwithdrawing hand I covered the earth with odours, fruits and blossoms, bringing forth the tender grass and herbs of every leaf and stately trees. Earth in her rich attire smiled complete, completed, lovely.

But I grew bored with the stationary, the wind-driven, and the tide-borne. I filled each creek and bay with swarming fry. Innumerable living creatures glided under the green wave. On land, a million, million eggs burst with kindly rupture. I rejoiced in creatures of serpent kind winding their snaky folds in wondrous length, and in the great lizards and the small – and (like you, my Beloved) in the crocodile. The winged air was dark with plumes: the multitudinous sea grey-green with squid and great whales.

But again, there were limits fixed. I had done what I could with the world. I had

emptied all my treasure houses. There seemed no more that could be invented or supplied. The selfsame scene of things appeared constantly, perpetually, inexorably. Life was still only life. There was nothing new to give. I ran again, every year, the round I ran before.

Until, one day, I made an astonishing discovery among the monkeys. A new universe appeared. I was no longer alone in contemplation. A new creature now walked the earth, upright, self-knowing, and fit to govern all the rest. My pleasure was unbounded. A new scene of creation had come into being. My new creations are now all in the Mind of your race – the race of mortal men and women – my last, my best, my darling work. And the mortal Mind can find full, lasting, expression only through you, my love, through you. I have discovered how the Mind of Man may becomes a thousand times more beautiful than the earth on which he dwells."

You my Poet, my Blessed Hope, my New Creation, my Only Joy, have learned some few of my Arts with (almost) all the aptitude for which I longed. You shall now learn those secret and hidden mysteries without which no mortal man can be a Poet. Night draws on apace. Now the lily folds up all her sweetness and slips into the bosom of the pool. So fold thyself, my dearest, slip into my bosom, and be lost in me."

The Goddess enwrapped her Poet as the woodbine enrings the barky fingers of the elm or the honey suckle entwines the oak, and led him to her bower, blushing like the morn.

No more is known of their conversations during that long night. But the constellations must have shed their happiest influence. Our Hero must have learned his lessons well, for since that night all the world has been filled with Poetry.

Book Three

The Arts of Listening

Part One:
To Catch the Westron Wind

63. Poems, Minds and Souls

The morn was bright and fair in the Garden of the Muse. Our Hero woke early, his spirits airy light. Joy was in his steps and in his heart. He skipped and ran and felt his limbs, as if for the first time. His Muse, as was her custom, spread before him the riches of herself, all Nature, and of her garden. Her Poet fed hungrily on sweet fruit from the trees, and clear water from the fountain of Art. Breakfast done, they lay together on a bank of hyacinths, smiling into one another's eyes but saying nothing all the while. It was hard to tell if the Muse was more enamoured of her Poet, or the Poet of his Muse. At last she spoke.

"Well, My First and Dearest Poet, are you pleased, are you satisfied with what you have learned?"

"Beyond the wildest, highest dreams of mortal hope. However ..."

"However?"

"So wonderful, so complex, so comprehensive, so mysterious, so spacious, so intricate, so subtle, so wild, so fine, so bold are our Arts, that I cannot see how mortals, wandering on the earth below, may ever grasp their fruits, their results – our makings. I have had the benefit of your instructions, your inspiration and your love. How will ordinary mortals understand; how will they be able to comprehend – particularly when you and I are not there to tell them what to look for – when we are not there to perform my Poems with the force and delicacy they demand?"

"Explain your fears, Dear Heart."

"How will they know what I meant? How will they know that I was who I was, and thought what I thought? How will they make any sense of my work when they speak, perhaps, a different or (worse!) a changed language, when they are young perhaps and I am old, when their assumptions, beliefs, predilections are utterly different from mine? How will I be heard by future generations loving different things, holding different things in esteem or contempt, consciously or unconsciously, under the pressure of different concerns, moulded by different times and different places?"

"With the greatest difficulty."

"But it is possible?"

"*Just*. They will have to learn."

"Who will teach them?"

"Your Poems will teach them."

"Even when my Poems are only so many marks on a stone or a page? I do not see how this may be done."

"Listening to Poetry is, My Beloved, like the composition Poetry itself, an Art – a great and mysterious process, a discipline of inspiration. When listening to, or reading a Poem, mortals cannot merely sit back in the vague hope that they might be moved or in some other way stimulated. A Poem is more like a musical score than a performance. Worse, it is like a musical score without key signatures, expression marks, bar-lines, time signatures or instructions on instrumentation. The poetic equivalent of all these will, as you say, have to be deduced from a few black marks on a page – most of them words, but some of them other kinds of sign.

In order that these black marks may form themselves in their Minds into something they can recognise as a Poem, mortals will have to think and practise hard. They will have to re-arrange experiences they might have had in their own lives into an order or pattern prompted by those black marks. They will have to make good the inevitable limitations of their personal experience, to recover what they can of the experiences of other humans, living and dead. Mortals will have to dig deep into that vast body of unacknowledged learning which they all carry somewhere in their Minds as speakers of a language that is the product of successive civilisations. And there will inevitably be gaps in this learning, which also will have to be made good."

For all these reasons – and more – listening to Poems will never be an easy matter. Poems are, as I have shown you, Dearly Beloved, the fruits of Nature's most intricate creation, the Mind of a Poet. Almost every other human activity is performed with only a very small part of the Mind. But a Poem can only be composed by a Mind in full possession of itself, and with easy access to its own mysterious recesses. A Poet's Mind, like yours, My Darling, is much larger than his brain. It extends to his muscles, stomach and finger-tips. It includes what he knows, what he feels, and what he guesses from those shadows of perception which seem to fleet between his conscious thoughts.

A Poem, accordingly, can only be heard by a Mind striving to become appropriately large, receptive and reflective, similarly alive to the full range of its own thoughts and feelings, as they exist separately and in conjunction one with another. Poets will believe that a Great Poem is the noblest work of which the Human Soul is capable. Compared with such an effort of comprehensive concentration, learning and feeling, all other human endeavours are limitingly specialised, partial and selective. The Poet demands from his readers more than a faint echo of his own passionate learning and finely-discriminated feeling.

It is therefore not surprising that mortal Minds are hardly ever up to the task. Mortals hardly ever have unblocked access to all the thoughts and feelings which they have experienced, or might potentially experience, in the way that a Great Poem *demands*. Worse, the Mind forges its own manacles, and leads itself into labyrinths and blind alleys. The Mind is lazy and does not always welcome being stirred into violent motion by the power of a Poem. Laziness

when challenged easily turns into resentment. And, since all Poems contain some sentiments which most Minds find it uncomfortable to entertain, resentment can be confounded with fear, and harden further into downright hatred.

The human Mind will always defy human understanding. Its workings have seemed, do seem, and will seem as unfathomably mysterious as a bottomless well. Part of the mystery of the human Mind is that it never appears to work as a single entity. It has always seemed to contain many faculties in a state of perpetual civil war. The mental harmony required for reading a Poem is thus likely to come rarely, if at all. If it came, it would only be in a moment of truce or rapprochement between the warring factions of the Mind. And at such moments, 'Mind' no longer seems to be quite the right word. The Mind seems only to be a gateway – a part of some greater whole.

Know that the interior workings of the Mind – of every single mortal Mind – contain three inter-dependent but autonomous Faculties, known as Memory, Imagination and Judgement. These Faculties are sisters and demi-goddesses. They sit behind the eye and the ear and the other senses, attempting to interpret, categorise, apprehend and comprehend everything that occurs in the world outside. Although they feel themselves to be divine, they (like many poetical demi-gods and demi-goddesses) know, or half-know that they are really servants of a greater, more mysterious power.

Have patience, Child of my Dreams, I shall describe the personalities of these three Sisters, these Faculties, and then we will sit together and watch them in action as a Mind meets some short Poems for the first time."

64. *Memory*

"I am afraid, Dearly Beloved, that Memory, the eldest sister, tends to be a bore. She is also hopelessly unreliable. She hardly ever seems to provide what is needed, but constantly floods the discussion with irrelevant matter. The information which gives her most pleasure is that which she is proud to possess – as a collector is proud of his collection – rather than that which her sisters wish for. She likes to fit whatever is before her into the category or slot which she had already prepared, and so, in effect, likes everything to resemble everything else. She is therefore often blind to what is actually before the Mind, whether it be a Poem or an event in human life.

On the other hand, she is absolutely essential, both to the understanding of Poems and of ordinary human events. Although Judgement and Imagination may be able to guess the meaning of a single new word from those around it, or speculate about the shape of an unfamiliar object or event, they are completely lost in the vast majority of cases without Memory's assistance. But Memory is never sufficient. If she is to be of any help to her fellows at all, she has always to refresh herself. Judgement has always to be sending Memory to various sources of replenishment – to men and women of wisdom or, in times to come, to dictionaries, concordances, bibliographies, histories, biographies, encyclopedias, grammars, and etymologies, in order to make good her own deficiencies and blanknesses.

Memory also possesses an invaluable fund of *general notions*. She has a considerable store of particular examples and a general collection of large categories. She knows what kind of thing a chair or a bed or a Poem is, and what might be expected to be found associated with a chair, a bed or a Poem.

But more important than Memory's supply of information is her store of *experience*. Mortals could hardly understand what a Poem is if they had not already heard some Poems (or at least heard Poems talked of). They would be even more hopelessly at sea if they had never themselves used language passionately or delicately or subtly, or tried desperately and urgently to invest their words with force and meaning. Mortals would be hopelessly, irredeemably lost, were nothing in their lives to correspond in any way with what is in the Poem before them.

Memory is by no means an impassive or merely intellectual character. She may sound at times like a pedant or some dull orator, but she is just as likely at other moments to be carried away on a flood of emotion. When she recalls the past, whether it be the experience of literature or of life, the facts of the matter are invariably accompanied by emotional colouring. Among her rich stores, there are many items she would wish away; items which at any moment may possess her completely and force their way out, wracking her with pain. For this reason Memory's sphere of activity is not – or at least does not seem to be – confined to the brain. She seems to recall taste with her tongue, touch with her fingers, agony in the pit of her stomach.

In compensation, Memory seems to have some mysterious access to the recesses of whatever it is that lies behind, uses, or includes the Mind. Imagination and Judgement provide her constantly with matter – very little of which she retains or makes her own. But that which she does take for her possession grows and mingles within her, affecting the actions and operations of her sisters without their knowledge.

Memory is at her most useful when she is serving others.

Most importantly she continually provides Imagination with images, personalities and thoughts to re-arrange and re-combine. She also provides Judgement with recollections of her own former decisions and procedures, reminding her of how she has come to arrive at satisfactory conclusions in the past, and of the lines of enquiry by which Judgement arrived at those conclusions.

Most useful of all is her profound capacity to recognise and to retain *patterns* of all kinds. This is the secret source of all her powers."

65. Imagination

"Imagination is as dangerous as she is essential to the Mind. It is she who forms the disparate and incoherent messages from the senses into images, pictures, words, ideas, objects. It is she who re-assembles and re-arranges these images, pictures, words, objects, ideas to form malleable materials for the inventions of the Mind.

Imagination is the source of all human sympathy, in Art and in life. (Memory feels only for herself.) All mortal joy or sorrow for the happiness or calamities of others is produced by the operations of Imagination. She realises the event (however fictitious) or approximates it (however remote) by placing the Mind for a time in the condition of the mortal whose pleasures and sufferings are contemplated. While the deception lasts her sisters, believe they feel whatever motions would be excited by the same good or evil as if it were happening to themselves.

Imagination is no less physical than Memory. She can picture the singeing heats of hell in her finger-tips, hear a spirit-wind in her hair.

However well his Memory performs, no mortal could even begin to hear a Poem without Imagination. Until Imagination is engaged, the Poem is only a series of sounds on the ear or marks on the page, and lies outside the listener's Mind.

Without the exercise of Imagination, mortals cannot be said to be hearing at all. The practical effect of words is to suggest images, thoughts, sensations, speculations, to Imagination. Memory may tell her sisters what the word meant last time. But since words never mean *exactly* the same on any two occasions, it is up to Imagination to guess or invent or intuit the new connotation.

But, Dear Poet, I must warn you again, Imagination must never be trusted.

Those mortals who do not believe that Imagination is a dangerous, vagrant Faculty have none themselves.

For Imagination, though essential, is wild. She is a wanton, unsteady and licentious creature, prone to every extravagance, and, unless watched very carefully, she will lead her sisters into mazes or pure fantasy. She is almost entirely unable to distinguish between her own operations and those of the outside world. That which she *takes* to be the case, IS the case.

She is no less emotional than Memory, and makes great contributions to the Mind's pleasures and pains.

But her very pleasures are dangerous. She is often reluctant to relinquish the delight of inventions that are purely her own in favour of inventions that have been directed and controlled by the words on the page. She enjoys the exercise of her own power, particularly her astonishing ability to combine the most heterogeneous images and ideas into a whole. But that whole may be only *apparently* coherent. Imagination is, alas, always likely to prefer her own combinations to yours, My Sweet soul, to ours. She is fixed in a mistaken belief that she is cleverer than her sisters, and has a quicker and surer path to Truth.

Nevertheless, there are at least four ways in which Imagination helps the Mind to apprehend Poems. She can invent a complete set of circumstances to account for how a Poem came into being. She can give ample, various (and contradictory) accounts of the story told by the Poem. She can supply a seemingly inexhaustible supply of speculation about *what kind* of object it is that stands before the Mind. And at her best, she can help her sisters to see, and feel, or believe that they feel and see, whatever it was that you, My Beloved Poet, planned or hoped they might feel and see – and know."

66. *Judgement*

"Last, Beloved, comes Judgement, fair of form (though often crabbed of feature). Poor Judgement is the weakest and most anxious of mortal Faculties. She is the youngest of the sisters, but believes herself to be most wise. For, although she is entirely dependent on Memory and Imagination, she cannot trust them. She finds it extremely difficult to express any simple preference for one over the other. Even when her sisters concur, Judgement is on her guard. As she sees it, the material which Memory provides may be, and probably is, the most useless and distracting irrelevance. Imagination, Judgement thinks, will say anything whatsoever that occurs to her. Judgement considers it her own job to bring order and sense to the meanderings of her fellows. She likes to balance one thought against another, and to create order and a semblance of form out of the chaos with which she is presented. She likes to subvert, destroy and question, in order to build.

But, in truth, she has no more easy access to the secrets of the inner Mind or to the reality of things than do her sisters. She often cares more about achieving surface tidiness than about being faithful to the precarious and awkward paradoxes of human truth. She can be altogether too staid and too decorous, too concerned about what others may think of her, and so worried about not appearing a fool that she adopts a caution which is itself a form of stupidity.

And Judgement is a manic depressive. At one moment she is full of elation at the order and form, the shapeliness, which she has created. The very next instant, she is perversely despondent and unsure of herself, wondering whether the order, form and shapeliness were not, after all, mere delusions. She is considered by her sisters (and indeed sometimes by herself) to be grudging and mean-spirited, pedantic and hair-splitting. She, too (like her sisters) is not a Faculty of the mortal brain alone. Her constant anxieties and her occasional certainties are felt as pain and joy are felt – along the blood. The operations of mortal Judgement are far – *very* far – from free.

Nevertheless any discussion at which Judgement is *not* present will be in the end worthless, for, without the shaping and ordering provided by Judgement, the promptings of Imagination and Memory could never be communicated to the outside world – coherently, or at all. Nor could the listener ever perceive the shape of a Poem with any sustained clarity."

"It seems to me, Goddess," said Our Hero, who had listened to his Muse with increasing despondency, "that my Poems and those of my sons will not fare well amongst such company. With this Judgement as their guide they are sure to end in the mire."

"That is true; that is the inevitable state of things. But do not be downhearted, O My Beloved. The lines which Judgement draws, though faint, may be drawn right. Your Poems *will* live (as I have promised they will live) in the hearts of mortals. You will find an audience (fit though few) in every age."

"Divine Instructress, I find it easier to believe in the few than in the fit."

"Come to the Fountain! Come to my Pool! Let us look deep into the Theatre of Future Time! I will show you the Faculties of Mind struggling with a Poem. I will show you first the most extreme and difficult case – a Mind from our Northern Isle, in the midst of a Dark Time (an age many millennia hence), faced with the work of a Forgotten Poet from several centuries earlier, a work about which little *can* be known, some twenty words scrawled on a single sheet of rag paper in a tenor part book – in an old song book."

Our Hero stared into the pool. He saw (or thought he saw) a mortal figure squinting at a piece of yellowed paper. And then he saw (or half-saw) through the body and into the Mind. He seemed to see the three Faculties, and seemed to hear them speak – all at once, always at odds.

"Lamp of Light," he began sadly after listening for some minutes, "I think it would be easier to catch the wind in a net than for these sisters to comprehend what they have before them."

"We shall see, Dearly Beloved, we shall see."

67. First (Halting) Steps

Imagination, Memory and Judgement are sitting in the darkness of a Mind. The space around them appears to be infinite. From time to time, one or other Faculty will rise from her seat, as if intending to take a stroll. But she will not get far. Although they do not know it, the Faculties of the Mind are confined to a very small circumference, and bound, irrevocably, each to each. Behind them, somewhere in the gloom, is a great gate, resolutely shut. Before them is a scrap of paper at which they peer for some time in silence, Judgement and Memory with attention, Imagination intermittently – if at all.

JUDGEMENT - [ponderously] *Come, come, Sisters, I assume that the marks on this paper are human marks. I assume that in one sense or another they have or may be given* **meaning**. *I would like to know that meaning.* [to herself] *(Meaninglessness worries me.)*

MEMORY - [glad to help] *I recognise these marks as a combination of letters and musical notation, dating probably from very early in the sixteenth century.* [proudly] *I have seen such things before.*

JUDGEMENT - [suspiciously] *Can these letters, if letters they are, be made to form words?*

MEMORY - [happily, confidently] *I recognise the marks on the page as corresponding to these words:*

> WESTRON WYNDE WHEN WYLLE – *or* –
> WYLT THOW BLOW THE SMALLE RAYNE
> DOWNE CAN RAYNE CRYST THAT – *no* –
> YF MY LOVE WERE IN MY ARMYS AND I
> YN MY BED A GAYNE.

JUDGEMENT - [not believing her] *Can these words, if words they are, be seen to form a shape?* [to herself] *(Shape is necessary to meaning).*

MEMORY - [with assurance and aplomb] *The phrases marked in the music seem to correspond (more or less) with a rhythmical pattern which I have often seen before:*

> WEST-ron WYNDE when WILT thou BLOW the
> SMALLE rayne DOWNE can ...

IMAGINATION - [her attention suddenly riveted] *Oh yes, yes;* **blow the small rain down**. *I see it all! It is a snatch of a lovely old sea-shanty –* [singing] **blow the small rain down boys, blow the small rain down** ...

MEMORY - [ignoring Imagination] *... and there appear to be rhyme words. The words* **rayne** *and* **a gayne** *seem to rhyme. Patterns such as the one I seem to recognise here are usually arranged as groups of four lines:*

> *Westron winde when wylt thow blow*
> *   The smalle rayne downe can Rayne*
> *Cryst yf my love were in my Armys*
> *And I yn my bed A gayne*

JUDGEMENT - [pedantically] **'armies'**? *Doesn't that interrupt your regular pattern?*

IMAGINATION - *Perhaps the sailors pronounced* **'armies'** *as we do* **'arms'** *when this sea-shanty was first sung, out on the stormy ...*

MEMORY - [as if settling the matter] *I have seen such things before.*

JUDGEMENT - *It is given a single note in the music (if it is music).*

MEMORY - *Such a regular shape of words – four lines and two units of sense...*

JUDGEMENT - [sharply] *Sense? I see no sense.*

MEMORY - [ignoring Judgement]... *would then resemble that of ballads I have seen. I will now recite a ballad called* **The Unquiet Grave**:

> *The wind doth blow today, my love,*
> *   And a few small drops of rain:*

I never had but one true love
In cold grave she was ...

IMAGINATION - [interrupting and taking fire] *Yes, I see it all. Our words must be part of an ancient song called* **'The Sailor's Return'**. *[passionately] Storm-tossed and desperate the brave mariner pulls at his rope, defiantly singing* **'blow wind blow'**, *but inside, his heart is breaking. He longs for his true love, unaware*

MEMORY - [condescendingly] *There is no difficulty, Sister. Once I have recognised the genre – in this case Late Medieval Ballad Fragment – I have only to identify the appropriate Medieval Theme. [triumphantly] And, indeed, I recognise this ballad fragment as a clear example of some late-medieval* **topoi**. *The first two lines, addressed to the West Wind,*

Westron wynde when wylt thow blow
The smalle rayne downe can Rayne

that she is already buried in the cold earth. [pathetically] One night his true love's ghost appears to him while he is on his long night watch. She warns him of the dreadful fate which ...
JUDGEMENT - [morosely confused, hesitant] *Not so fast! I still do not know whether these words we have before us are an accidental grouping ... a mere fragment of a manuscript ... or if (as you both seem to be assuming) these words do form a poem ... whether it is a whole poem or part of a ballad ... and if these words are a ballad ... I don't know whether or not they resemble* **The Unquiet Grave** *... and if they do resemble* **The Unquiet Grave** *... I don't know ... I don't know what help that resemblance might be to me in my search for form and meaning ... or if ... I don't know ...*

are similar to many medieval prayers for rain, for the growing of crops – for fertility – and lines three to four, addressed to Christ,

Cryst yf my love were in my Armys
And I yn my bed A gayne

are **clearly** *a parallel prayer for the return of the lover.*
JUDGEMENT - [miserably confused] *No, I can't see that ... or that there is any connection AT ALL between the first two lines and the two that follow.*

MEMORY - [undaunted] *As in many works of this period, the parallelism of form overcomes the contrast of content, so that ...*

IMAGINATION - [rhapsodically] *That doesn't matter. It is very beautiful. The longed-for lover is involved in the natural cycle of the seasons. And then Christ appears as a wonderful spirit of fertility, a harbinger of spring and the season of glorious abundance ...*

MEMORY - [catching, and feeding Imagination's enthusiasm]*... when zephyrs gently blow over England and the warm currents, laden with moisture from the Gulf Stream, resuscitate dormant nature and ...*

IMAGINATION - [with a wriggle of ecstasy] *Yes, yes, and the word **'small'** evokes for me the exact feel and sound of sifting rainfall, softly and joyfully setting the spirit of man aglow in the blessed revival and ...*

JUDGEMENT - [with a touch of temper] *Sisters, you have lost me. I can't see any connection whatsoever between* [pointing to the scrap of paper] *these marks and the wild stories you are both telling me. As far as I can see, neither of you has any real idea what **form** these words might take ... or what **meaning** they might have.* [with resolution] *We must abandon this discussion because, to judge*

from your extravagances, we seem to be faced with a set of words which are incapable of resolution. [with the confidence of despair] *The originator of these words (if these words are words, and do have an originator) has done nothing, perhaps deliberately done nothing, to make either of his statements intelligible. There is no meaning to be had.* [leaving her seat and attempting to abandon the Mind.]

Our Hero, in the garden above, saw and heard the three sisters with increasing anxiety. His Muse soothed him, stroking his fevered brow.

"O Muse, as I feared, all is lost. My Poems will *never* find new life in the minds of mortals on the earth below! Never, never, never, never!"

"Have patience," said the Muse, laughing. "Judgement cannot leave. Memory has found some patterns. All may be well."

"I do not see how such a thing is possible," replied the Poet, his head between his hands. Judgement is deranged. Imagination is an idiot. Memory is a dunce.

68. Wind and Rain

Memory rises up, appalled, despite herself, at the prospect of her Sister's leaving. Imagination takes violent hold of both Judgement's hands, preventing her from going.

IMAGINATION - [imploringly but irritated] *Come back; I want to talk to you. You can't describe the parts of this poem as* **statements**. *They are more like groans of passionate longing, as the poet cries from the depth of his heart.*

JUDGEMENT - [secretly glad not to have been allowed to leave] *Very well, Sisters, let us try again.* [petulantly, and looking, for the first time, at the page itself] *But if you want me to stay here with you you* **must** *look carefully at the words (if you are sure they are words) in front of us. Let us consider the first two lines (if that is what they are):*

> *Westron wynde when wylt thow blow*
> *The smalle rayne downe can Rayne*

These lines, it seems to me, are open to a number of possible interpretations ... or contain a large number of uncertainties. In the first place we need to know what **kind** *of wind is being ... called ... or invoked. Is the Westron Wind to be thought of as attractive or beneficial in itself? Secondly ...*

IMAGINATION - [defiantly and looking to Memory for support] **Obviously** *it is beneficial, since it clearly marks the end of cold dry winter and the glorious coming of the plashy wetness of spring, and ...*

JUDGEMENT - [resolutely] *Secondly, we must ask precisely in what way the wind is connected with, or related to, the rain ... if at all. Is it a wind which produces ...*

IMAGINATION - *... or accompanies?*

MEMORY - *... or prevents?*

IMAGINATION - *... or augurs?*

JUDGEMENT - *... or drives away the small rain? And then,*

thirdly, we have to consider the rain itself.

MEMORY - *Clearly it is the kind of rain which we found in* **The Unquiet Grave** *– a few small drops of rain?*

JUDGEMENT - *Why might it not ... equally plausibly ... be a fine light shower?*

IMAGINATION - [suddenly enjoying the range of possibilities] *... or a clothes-penetrating misery-inspiring drizzle, or a deliciously agonising mingling of rain and piteous tears, or ...*

JUDGEMENT - [rigorously] *Fourthly, does the speaker of the poem want the rain to come or to go?*

IMAGINATION - [reverting to her earlier notion with sudden absolute conviction] *To come, to come, to come!*

JUDGEMENT - [desperately] *I have no idea at the moment how these questions might be answered, and am ... at a loss.*

IMAGINATION - [with genuine pity] *Dear Sister, can't you see that the rain is much more than mere water? It suggests the tears of a lover, the mists of the mind, the emotional release of intimacy, all that is longed for or desired, everything that ...*

MEMORY - [turning to Judgement and ignoring Imagination] *The answer to your questions about the wind depends on where the speaker is standing. If the speaker ...*

JUDGEMENT - [again pedantically] *Shall we say 'putative speaker'. All we have before us are some marks on a page.*

MEMORY - [undaunted] *If the putative speaker of these words is an English sailor wanting to go home ...*

IMAGINATION - [suddenly re-convinced by her own notion] *As he is, he is!*

MEMORY - [still undaunted] *... then a longing for the West Wind would place him in the Atlantic or the Irish Sea. This wind from the west would than distinguish this poem from other medieval lyrics – such as,* **Blow, northerne wynd, send thou me my sueting,** *or from a song like ...* [Memory pauses and then sings] **Blow the wind southerly, southerly, southerly, blow the wind south, send my bonny to me.** [Memory is unable to stop singing despite the frowns of her sisters. She can be heard humming the tune quietly from time to time while the others are speaking].

IMAGINATION - [rising from her chair in consternation] *I can't bear to treat the poem like this. It isn't the **kind** of rain that matters; it's what the poet **feels** about the rain. The speaker is longing, desperately longing, for the wind to bring the rain of emotional refreshment, and ...*

JUDGEMENT - [to Memory] *Is this right ... or even possible? Can these words bear such a sense?*

MEMORY - [pausing] *Probably not. There is considerable grammatical uncertainty in the second line:*

> *The smalle rayne downe can Rayne*

[She turns to Imagination] *You, Dear Sister, are reading the lines as if they meant 'please blow west wind so that it can rain'.*

JUDGEMENT - [confused again] *I rather gathered that that was how **you** took them as well.*

MEMORY - [with a touch of embarrassment] *Perhaps.* [gleefully] *But there is another possibility. The word **can** was often in the Middle Ages (and later, as an archaism) substituted for the word **gan** as an auxiliary of the ingressive present ...*

IMAGINATION - [almost angry] *What are you talking about?*

MEMORY - [continuing unabashed] *In an early MS of **Cursor Mundi**, to cite a pertinent example, the forms **can** and **gan** are constantly interchanged. There is a very interesting later example in **Faerie Queene** I i 50 ...*

IMAGINATION - [scowling at her sister] *This gets worse and worse! What difference does that make?*

JUDGEMENT - [genuinely startled and changing direction] *It **entirely alters** the meaning of the poem — if it is a poem, and if it does have anything which could be called a **meaning**. The words **the smalle rayne downe can rayne** might suggest either that it is raining NOW, as the poet speaks, or, possibly, that it DID rain at some point in the past.*

MEMORY - [unruffled] *I am inclined towards the first of these possibilities, because the poem would than become recognisably an example of the outlaw/exile/wild-wood theme, so common in the Medieval Love Lyric.*

IMAGINATION - [With passion, rising from her seat] *Yes, yes, I see it all. The speaker has been slandered to the king by his lady love's cruel brothers, and he has been driven to the wild bogs of Ireland where it rains all the time (echoing his misery), and where he longs desperately for his warm bed and the soft embrace of ...*

MEMORY - [Catching her enthusiasm, and also rising] *And he would be eating acorns. It was usual on such occasions to eat acorns. There is a famous poem on this theme about a man who 'must go walk the woods so wild' where he says the running streams shall be his drink and acorns shall be his food.*

JUDGEMENT - [trying to change the subject and to check the flow of ideas] *Do I gather from what you are both saying that I should assume that the poem is spoken as if in **great grief**?*

IMAGINATION - [with absolute certainty] *Yes, of course, and with **passion**.*

MEMORY - [also with absolute certainty] *Not at all. It is interesting that the poet addresses the wind as **thow** (rather than you) — which isn't perhaps very respectful: **Westron Wind when wilt thou blow**. He also uses the word **wilt** which at that date implied some element of choice.*

IMAGINATION - [sitting down, but speaking with scorn] *So it is as if he said "O dear old West Wind when will you choose to blow"?*

MEMORY - [also sitting] *Well, more or less. On the evidence before me I consider it a possibility that the first two lines might resemble a jaunty song.*

IMAGINATION - [with conviction] *Never! The suffering is palpable.*

MEMORY - *On the other hand, of course, the poet may use **thow** because he is deifying the wind, and ...*

JUDGEMENT - [desperately] *Are you two talking about the same words? I still can't see any connection between what you are saying and the words I thought we were examining. I am on the point of ... despair.* [again making to leave.]

"Heavenly Muse," said Our Hero, saring at the pool with wild eyes, "why do these wicked sisters not listen —

simply listen to the words? Why do they distract each other so?"

"The Mortal Mind, My Poet, is incapable of repose. But have patience. Imagination is engaged. The Mind is in motion."

69. Confusions Conflated

All three Faculties have now left their seats. Imagination once again restrains Judgement – violently.

IMAGINATION - *Come back, Sweet Sister, come back.* [enticingly] *Even you must agree that the last two lines are as clear as crystal:*

> *Christ if my love were in my armys*
> *And I in my bed agayne*

JUDGEMENT - [wearily] *I'm afraid I can't agree with you.* [sits down] *It is hard to know to what extent (if at all) we are meant (if intention can be attributed to words) to see (or in some way to register) … if we are meant to see the invocation of Christ (if that is what it is) as **jarring** with the amorous longings (if that is what they are) of the speaker (or putative speaker). And then again, is the speaker or the beloved away from home? I can't see how to answer these questions and am …*

MEMORY - [sitting down] *The invocation of Christ of course clearly suggests a prayer …*

IMAGINATION - [waving her arms] *I see it. I see it. A young and beautiful woman is kneeling in a church, passionately praying …*

JUDGEMENT - [desperately] *What are you talking about? What woman? What church?*

MEMORY - [ignoring Judgement, responding to Imagination] *There is a poem by Gerald Manley Hopkins called* **Heaven Haven, A Nun Takes the Veil** *which is **just** like that.* [She recites lovingly. The poem is a favourite possession.]

> *And I have asked to be*
> *Where no storms come,*
> *Where the green swell is in the havens dumb,*
> *And out of the swing of the sea.*

JUDGEMENT - [almost offended] *I see no resemblance whatsoever. That's **nothing** like our poem.*

IMAGINATION - [reassuringly] *Oh but it is! The young nun weeps her rain-like tears and longs for the wind of grace and, for the sweet embrace of the Catholic Church and of Jesus, or perhaps of Death.*

JUDGEMENT - [almost angry] *I have never heard a more foolish suggestion.* [turning too Memory] *What do you think? It makes no sense to me.*

MEMORY - [offhandedly] *Nor to me. Not many Medieval Love Lyrics can be attributed to women.* [confidently] *I do however favour a religious explanation of these words. There is another poem by Gerald Manly Hopkins, where, in his own voice, the poet calls to Jesus:* **Mine, Oh thou Lord of life, send my roots rain**, *which …*

IMAGINATION - [petulantly] *I don't see why it mightn't be a woman speaking – even if the poem was written by a man.*

MEMORY - [attempting a reconciliation] *I must, I suppose, concede that most Medieval Love Lyrics are anonymous; that women take men in their arms, just as often as men take women … and that there is a poem by Wyatt, written only a little later than our manuscript, in which, talking of a woman, the poet says that she took him in her arms long and small, or something like that. It is a very interesting poem. Would you like to hear it?*

> *They flee from me that sometime …*

JUDGEMENT - *No! I do not wish to hear this poem, nor any other distraction. I am hopelessly lost. I don't know what you think this poem (if it is a poem) is like, or what it might be about (if poems are **about** anything), or what it means, or might have meant, or even if I'm asking the right questions.* [to Memory] *I've lost count of all your suggested parallels and* [to Imagination] *all your **fantasies**.*

MEMORY - [without a moment's hesitation] *Seven possible interpretations have been suggested. First, it was implied (very sensibly, perhaps) that these words might be a stanza of a lost ballad. We were not, however, able to deduce what that ballad might have been about. Secondly, it was suggested that the poem was an expression of a fertility myth about the natural cycle of the seasons. Thirdly (and also sensibly) someone put forward the view that the poem was an example of the outlaw/exile/wild-wood theme. Then there was the notion that the poem might be a Christian work, spoken perhaps by a nun, yearning for the return of God's Grace. Fifthly ...*

JUDGEMENT - [imperiously] *Stop! Enough! How can we choose from between these possibilities?*

IMAGINATION - [laughing] *Why do we have to choose? I like poems to have as many meanings as possible — the more the merrier. Choose as you please.*

JUDGEMENT - [suddenly furious] *I will not stand for this. Many of these suggestions are downright contradictory. They cannot co-exist. They cancel one another out. The poem cannot be both about a weeping nun and a storm-tossed sailor ...*

IMAGINATION - [under her breath] *Oh yes it can ...*

JUDGEMENT - [in real distress] *I like to make sense of things and I like things to make sense. From a poem I expect more sense than is usually to be found in the world, rather than less.*

Very few things do make sense in this difficult life we lead — and now you two seem to be deliberately cultivating confusion. If you persist with this attitude, I really will leave — and never return. [Judgement appears to be on the point of tears.]

"Why are these sisters so determined to 'interpret' these words? Why can they not let them be?" wailed Our Hero.

"Out of confusion may come certainty," answered the Muse.

"Not until they speak with one voice," said the Poet, without hope.

"Do not fear. The Mortal Mind cannot contain such a degree of internal contradiction for long. Something or someone must give way."

70. Backing Down

Memory and Imagination are distressed by this outburst, and, on this occasion both Sisters make moves to restrain Judgement.

IMAGINATION - *No, please, Sister, do not leave us.* [preoccupied and serious] *I can make up stories for myself any time I like, but I suppose that, if it is possible, I would most enjoy the story the poet wanted to tell. Though it might not always seem like it, I'm actually happiest when I am filled with someone else's story.* [imploringly] *If it will help, I'm quite prepared to give up some of my ideas. I'm not sure, for instance, if I really can hear a nun speaking in this poem.*

MEMORY - [rather grimly] *Since we are confessing, perhaps I had better concede that there is no specific mention of the green wood or an exile or a fertility myth* **as such** *in the words before us.* [with a feeble attempt at self-mockery] *I too am not irredeemably stuck in my ways. If there is some new story in these words, I would like to learn it.*

JUDGEMENT - [suddenly calm] *Where do these handsome recantations leave us? What are we left with?* [almost happily] *Are we not worse off than before?*

IMAGINATION - [pondering] *No, I don't think so. What first attracted me to this poem still intrigues me. Nothing we have said alters the fact that the poet invokes Christ as part of a sexual longing:*

> CHRIST *that my love were in my arms*
> *And I in my bed again.*

That still seems extraordinarily interesting.

MEMORY - *It must be the most powerful and significant word in the language.* [suddenly overcome] *I know one other case where it is used in a similar context – but it is not perhaps suitable for the present occasion.*

JUDGEMENT - [hurriedly] *Let us try to attend to the matter before us.*

MEMORY - [desperately embarrassed, but unable to control herself] *I am afraid I must tell you this –* [urgently] *I can't help it:*

> Darling Flo
> I love you so,
> Especially in your nightie;
> When the moonlight flits
> Across your tits –
> Jesus Christ Almighty!

IMAGINATION - [genuinely interested and trying to cover her sister's embarrassment] *Yes, yes; that's IT! That's it exactly! In these words, too, the weight and power of feeling (such as it is) is conveyed by the daring, apparently inappropriate, even slightly blasphemous, invocation of the deity ...* [laughing] *... but I take it that in our poem the exclamation has none of the colouring of an expletive?*

JUDGEMENT - [ignoring the interruption, but nevertheless taking the point and laughing despite herself] *Can we then agree that longing (of some kind) is the keynote of our poem – as it is of Memory's little ditty? And that, if we take our poem* **as a whole**, *there must be a connection (of some kind) between the poet's longing for the West Wind and his longing for his love and his bed?*

MEMORY - [recovering quickly] *I am sorry for that interjection – But, yes, we can agree.*

IMAGINATION - *Yes, we can ... but somehow you are ignoring other things which we know about the poem – that the longing is beautiful for example.* [smiling] *In Memory's offering it was NOT.*

MEMORY - [pondering] **Longing** *is a word which covers a great many different experiences.*

JUDGEMENT - *Can we limit the term in any way?*

IMAGINATION - *Yes, there are certain kinds of longing which we can now rule out. We can be pretty sure that it is love-longing rather* than lechery, for example. [Turning to Memory] *Come out of your books again for a moment, forsake authority and make experience our guide.*

MEMORY - *I'd rather not talk about it.* [after a struggle with herself] *I suppose the speaker's wish might be for warmth in all senses of the word, rather than for sexual solace alone.* [in answer to an unspoken question from her sisters] *I'm sure I am acquainted with some such emotion.*

IMAGINATION - [pressing her point] *The word **bed** too would suggest security wouldn't it? The poet after all speaks of 'my bed', not his or her bed, or any old bed.*

JUDGEMENT - [with an air of finality] *So we can all agree, can we, that we have, dictating our sense of these words, an imagined speaker longing for a change in the wind, or for wind of some kind, either to bring or to stop a rain which is either fine or intermittent? As part of that longing he, or indeed she, wishes for the warmth and solace of a lover's arms? And that all these longings are strong ... perhaps very strong.*

IMAGINATION - *You make it sound too oblique and prosy. The last two lines are as passionately direct as it is possible to be.*

[with calm clarity] *The poet has used brevity of form as an expression of delicacy and strength of feeling.*

JUDGEMENT - [her air of certainty a little ruffled] *So we can also agree that these words make something we can call a POEM even though we must remain unsure about the precise connotations of some of the parts? Shall we leave it there?*

IMAGINATION - *Perhaps we should. I have exhausted myself.*

Judgement and Imagination rise from their seats as if to attend to other business or to leave the Mind.

Above, in the Garden of the Muse, Our Hero and his Instructress were, if no longer on the point of despair, rather depressed by the motions of this Mind.

"Will they stop there?" asked Our Hero in some distress. "Judgement called the words a Poem – but she has no notion of what that might be."

"But the sisters are, at least, no longer shouting each other down," said the Muse, attempting consolation. "Their passion for a complete explanation has subsided. And, look, they have not done."

71. A Final Distraction

Judgement and Imagination are about to depart to welcome rest, but Memory, flurried with agitation, blocks their path.

MEMORY - [In desperation] *I'm afraid I can't do that. I can't leave now. I must recite some lines from a famous poem I learned long ago. I* **must***.* [desperately to Judgement] *It is very similar to* **The Westron Wind** *and* [turning to Imagination] *it will please you, Sister.* [Memory recites with much musicality of voice and much passion but little understanding.]

O that 'twere possible
After long grief and pain
To find the arms of my true love
Round me once again!

When I was wont to meet her
In the silent woody places
By the home that gave me birth,
We stood tranced in long embraces
Mixt with kisses sweeter sweeter
Than anything on earth.

A shadow flits before me,
Not thou but like to thee:
Ah Christ, that it were possible
For one short hour to see
The souls we loved, that they might tell us
What and where they be.

[Memory remains silent and still for some time.]
IMAGINATION - [enthralled, resuming her seat] *Yes, yes. The poet who wrote that must have read* **The Westron Wind***.*
JUDGEMENT - [puzzled, a little angry, still making to depart] *Why do you say that? It seems to me to be so overloaded with emotion that meaning becomes secondary. All I can see are a few slight resemblances — mentions of lovers' arms, appeals to Christ and so on, while the differences are ...*

IMAGINATION - [slowly and deliberately, considering her words] *It is much more than that, Sister. These are both poems of powerful and mysterious love-longing — so powerful and so mysterious that it does not seem too much for the poet to invoke religion and the forces of nature.*

JUDGEMENT - [angry, but secretly interested; resuming her seat] *Mysteries! I don't know what you are talking about. Sister, please use words to which some definite meaning may be attached.*

MEMORY - *But you agreed just now that* **Westron Wind** *is a poem expressing longing.*

JUDGEMENT - *Some general and indefinable longing perhaps, but ...*

IMAGINATION - *And this poem which Memory has recited for us gives us* **exactly** *the same feeling.*

JUDGEMENT - [mimicking Imagination with heavy sarcasm] *Exactly the same feeling ... even though the sense (or what may pass for sense) is almost opposite?*

IMAGINATION - [astonished] *Opposite?*

JUDGEMENT - *Yes. This poet wants his dead lover to tell him what and where she is ... he wants to ask a metaphysical question ... But even if this new poem does resemble the* **Westron Wind** *in some vague way (and I'm not at all convinced that it does) the second poet must have been given to rhapsodies (rather like yours, Sisters). He has invented a set of circumstances — silent woody places and such like — which can hardly be said to* **derive** *from the first poem — though they are equally imprecise and obscure.*

MEMORY - [surprised] *Obscure?* [musing, preoccupied] *It is true that though I have long been familiar with these words I do not, now you put it to me, recognise the story.*

IMAGINATION - *Oh, come on, you two! This poem is written as if by a man in terrible pain. He loved more than other men and was loved more than other men. Now his true love is dead, he suffers more than other men. This poem, at any rate, is as clear as daylight.*

JUDGEMENT - *So what is all that about a shadow:*

> *A shadow flits before me?*

MEMORY - *I am afraid I do not recognise the idea.*

IMAGINATION - *Is it the image or the ghost of his lost love?*

JUDGEMENT - *It seems to me to be the very opposite of that:*

> *Not thou but like to thee?*

IMAGINATION - *That's a horrible thought, now I consider it. Some kind of haunting.* [beginning to tremble]

MEMORY - [almost to herself] *Perhaps a succubus ... or is it an incubus, or ...*

JUDGEMENT - *And what do you make of this:*

> *We stood tranced in long embraces*
> *Mixt with kisses sweeter sweeter*
> *Than anything on earth ... ?*

IMAGINATION - *His love was unreal, dream-like, other-worldly ... terrifying.*

JUDGEMENT - [troubled] *I do not – cannot – understand how something which happened on earth could be sweeter than anything on earth.*

MEMORY - [again almost to herself] *(I do. Only too well.)* [beginning to sob silently]

JUDGEMENT - [sighing] *So I cannot see how this new poem, obscure as it is, different as it is, can help us with* **Westron Wind**. *Sisters, we are drifting away from the subject which lies before us.*

IMAGINATION - *You do see (do you?) that the new poem (like the old) is a kind of love poem – a poem which describes love-longing in a way which we can recognise ...*

MEMORY - [to herself, sobbing] *(We can, oh yes we can.)*

IMAGINATION - *... in a way that we can recognise, but which is at the same time new –* [speaking with great emphasis] *that*

both poems offer us a new combination of feeling, more pure and permanent and more lovely than anything we may have experienced ourselves, and ...

JUDGEMENT - *A kind of love poem, yes. But phrases like* **'a kind of'** *are no more use to me than your talk of power and mystery and purity of feeling.* [with mounting desperation] *There is nothing here for me to get hold of – nothing that makes clear and definite sense. Everything is vague and ill-defined ... sloppy and* [turning on Memory whose sobs have become audible] *... it all displays an unhealthy emotionality, a lack of emotional hygiene, and ...*

IMAGINATION - [to Judgement with apparent compassion] *Sometimes, my dear, you verge on the insensitive, and are even just a little crass.*

JUDGEMENT - [nettled] *I will consider fragments of nonsense and undisciplined emotion no longer. In fact, I shall leave.* [withdrawing] *You two may wallow together.*

IMAGINATION - [musingly to Memory] *I don't know what she is so upset about. Both these poems fill me with love and beauty and a kind of pleasing sorrow and a sense of the joy and the mystery of human life and human lives and ...*

MEMORY - [sobbing gently, taking Imagination's hand] *Yes, yes they are both ... they are both strangely memorable ... or haunting.*

Imagination and Memory sit in the dark holding hands. Memory's shoulders shake spasmodically but Imagination, though sympathetic, is smiling.

Our Hero saw (or thought he saw) the words of 'Westron Wind' fly softly off the yellow page (which had fallen from Judgement's hands to the floor), float for a while above the sister's heads and then drift towards the door behind in the darkness – which opened for an instant welcoming them in.

"I don't understand, Lovely Muse," said the Poet. "I cannot believe that there was any real contact between words of that Poem by a Forgotten Poet and the Faculties of this future Mind. But, without the approval of Judgement this Poem seemed to find the passes and touch the Heart?"

"Indeed, that is what happened – or so it seems.

The words of this Poem are too isolated, too detached from any context, for Judgement ever to feel she knows them. Let us now watch this Mind engage with another, and more famous (and therefore, perhaps, more knowable) Poem."

Part Two:
In Search of a Rainbow

72. A Rainbow in the Sky

Judgement, Memory and Imagination sit again, as so often, in the dark. Judgement sits as one who is determined to do great things. Memory sits as one who has done great things already. Imagination, however, is bored, unengaged and restless in her seat.

JUDGEMENT - *We are to consider another group of words generally believed to have been written by a man known as Wordsworth.* [lightly] *I suggest that I read them through first, and that we then discuss them in an orderly manner.*

MEMORY - *On the contrary, the best way to conduct this affair is for me to give a brief account of what is known about this poem.*

JUDGEMENT - [incredulously] **Before** *we have read it?*

MEMORY - *Certainly.* [brooking no interruption] *The poem was first published in 1807 when it formed one of the poems* **Referring to the Period of Childhood** - [unhappily] *or was it* **Moods of my own Mind***?* [regaining composure] *Anyway, it was certainly written on March the twenty-sixth of the year eighteen hundred and two while Wordsworth's sister was getting into bed ...*

JUDGEMENT - *What?*

MEMORY - [unabashed] *... and was revised on May the fourteenth during a night when Wordsworth was very nervous. The poem was known among the Wordsworth household as* **The Rainbow***.* [pompously] *It has often been considered by Wordsworth scholars as a distillation of some of the poet's leading preoccupations ...*

JUDGEMENT - *Thank you very much.* [bored] *Interesting, very interesting, but perhaps we might now consider the poem itself (if it is a poem).* [She begins to read slowly and determinedly]

> *My heart leaps up when I behold*
> *A rainbow in the sky...*

IMAGINATION - [aggressively] *Do we have to listen to this? I hate sloppy poems about people who love Nature so ecstatically.* **Rainbows!** *Could anything be more trite? And the rhythm is so banal* [mockingly]:

> *My HEART jumps UP when I des-CRY*
> *A TEA tray IN the SKY ...*

MEMORY - [genuinely worried] *Your quotation is not exactly ...*

JUDGEMENT - [who has been waiting impatiently as her sisters talk and now speaks with mock politeness] *Might I be permitted to continue?*

> *My heart leaps up when I behold*
> *A rainbow ...*

MEMORY - [considering Imagination's comments, ignoring Judgement] *I don't recognize this as a poem about Nature. The word* **behold** *suggests a different category.*

JUDGEMENT - [distracted despite her intentions] *Why? What is the difference between* **when I behold** *and* **when I see***?*

MEMORY - [after a pause and trying to disguise the fact that she is reading from a book] **Behold** *is a word familiar to us from the Bible where it means* **to look on a thing with our eyes** *and also* **to think over a thing in our minds** *and also, on some occasions ...*

JUDGEMENT - *Thank you again, but may I be allowed to finish reading the words?*

MEMORY - [unstoppably] *... and the rainbow, of course, was the* token of God's promise to Noah and all his descendants in Genesis:

...and the bow shall be in the cloud: and I will look upon it, that I may remember the everlasting covenant between God and every living creature.

So this poem is clearly not about Nature at all but about the poet's joy at being reminded of God's promise. [triumphantly] There is no need for further discussion.

IMAGINATION - I agree. It's like some awful hymn:

Our hearts rejoice when we behold
God's goodness up on high ...

JUDGEMENT - Please may I read the words. [desperately] You are confusing me.

My heart leaps up when I behold
A rainbow in the sky...

IMAGINATION - [with no attempt to hide her contempt] How silly: a rainbow **in the sky**. Where else might a rainbow be seen? The poem would have been better if the rainbow **was** in an odd place. Then the poet's heart might well leap up. **My heart leaps up when I behold a rainbow in the bath**. At least, then ...

MEMORY - [interrupting but with an entirely different point] Alternate lines of eight and six syllables — Ballad Metre. What we have here is another ballad. The phrase **in the sky** is there merely to fill the line. A certain looseness of structure is generally considered permissible in ballad form. Moreover ...

JUDGEMENT - [almost screaming] Will you two never be still? [to Imagination] Sister, I cannot hear the words. Your extravagant hostility drowns them out. [to Memory] I cannot find the sense. Your knowledge distracts me.

"O Heavenly Muse," cried Our Hero, in despair, "how unforgiving, how unsympathetic is this Mind!"

"Have patience, My Poet. Imagination is engaged."

"Imagination is engaged in direct opposition to my poor son's words. She is a brutal, remorseless, unfeeling creature."

"The Mind is in motion. Imagination must weary of her hostility. All may yet be well."

73. When My Life Began

Imagination and Memory, shame-faced, fall silent. Judgement resumes her seat.

JUDGEMENT - [gritting her teeth] *I am going to read this poem if it is the last thing I do.*

> *My heart leaps up when I behold*
> *A rainbow in the sky.*
> *So was it when my life began...*

IMAGINATION - [breaking in] *No, it's not really a ballad or a hymn. Its too cloyingly personal for that.* [exulting] *I can see it all now. When Wordsworth was a little William, his mother, who smelt like new-mown hay and wore a cotton dress with a floral pattern, led him gently towards the window and said –* **Oh look Willie, look! It's a RAINBOW! Look at the pretty rainbow, Willie ...**

MEMORY - *His Aunt ...*

JUDGEMENT - *What?*

MEMORY - [plaintively] *It might have been his Aunt. I was ... a friend of mine was shown the beauty of the rainbow by his Aunt. It was a bright fresh morning in April. And there was a smell, not of new-mown hay, but of stale tea and toothpaste and ...*

JUDGEMENT - [testily] *Please, please, pull yourself together! We are reading ... or trying to read ... a poem (or some words that might be a poem).* [gloomily] *I shall have to start again:*

> *My heart leaps up ....*

IMAGINATION - [to Memory, sharply] *Did your heart* **leap** *when your aunt - your friend's aunt – pointed out the rainbow in the sky? Did your heart actually jump for joy?*

MEMORY - [querulously] *I'm not quite sure ... not sure about the joy...*

JUDGEMENT - [briskly] *Sisters, that is neither here nor there.* [controlling herself] *Perhaps you would allow me to go on reading without interruption:*

> *My heart leaps up when I behold*
> *A rainbow in the sky.*
> *So was it when my life began;*
> *So is it ...*

MEMORY - [interrupting shamelessly] *I see I was wrong about the metrical form; and that seems a very strange way to talk about infancy:* **when my life began**. *I don't think I have met this set of words before. Could you explain them to me?*

IMAGINATION - *Its only a funny way to talk about childhood if you forget how appallingly sentimental this poet is. He's so enamoured of natural beauty that he dates the life of his soul from the instant that his mother or his Aunt (or whoever it was) first showed him this Oh so wonderful rainbow. I can see it all. It's sickening! For little Willie, the leap of his heart when he saw the rainbow was more important to his real life – his spiritual life – than the beating and pulsing of his corporal organs, and ...*

JUDGEMENT - [completely at sea] *Thank you again. May I continue?*

IMAGINATION - *If you must,* [glancing at the book disparagingly] *though I can't see that we can get anything out of it.*

JUDGEMENT - [reading carefully with suppressed fury]

> *So was it when my life began;*
> *So is it now I am a man...*

MEMORY - [again interrupting] *At least we can agree that in this poem the speaker is male.*

IMAGINATION - [bitterly] *Yes, but the silly poet is trying to mean much more than* **adult male** *when he says* **now I a man.** [springing up with something like loathing] *The poet is sitting there telling us in his solemn grown-up voice that the thing that makes him a man is that he still feels as a child feels. Next he'll be telling us that his school days were the happiest days of his life.* [with a shudder] *Or perhaps he just wants us to notice how sensitive he is. His heart leaps about* **now he is a man** *just as it used to leap about when he was a coy little thing gawping at flowers. This poem makes me feel sick — it's so crude and phoney, and ...*

JUDGEMENT - [overcome] *I will not be defeated. I will not be defeated, even though we have been unable to reach a single effective conclusion. You two are running ahead of me and of each other, and indulging your own inclinations rather than genuinely cooperating (as I would wish).* [to Imagination] *Please, dear Sister, please don't bully me so!*

Our Hero, in the garden, was not enjoying himself. He stared at the pool and at the Faculties with increasing despondency.

"These sisters are so busy, so full of themselves and their own energy, that I fear for the fate of this poor little Poem."

"Have patience, My Poet," said the Muse, offering an embracing arm in consolation.

"So you keep saying, Celestial Light. But the more I see the more it seems impossible for a mortal Mind to accommodate itself to a Poem."

"Impossible? No, My Dearest, no."

"You are pleased that the Mind is in motion. But it seems to me that stillness and quiet are required if these poetic words are ever to be heard."

"Quite so. Quite so. Imagination may be astonished into silence. Let us wait and see."

74. *Sudden Astonishment*

JUDGEMENT - *Sisters, may we make a bargain? Let me read to the sixth line of this poem, and then you can be as rude as you like for as long as you like:*

> My heart leaps up when I behold
>   A rainbow in the sky.
> So was it when my life began;
> So is it now I am a man;
> So be it when I shall grow old,
> Or let me die!

IMAGINATION - *Good Heavens!*

MEMORY - *That's peculiar!* [troubled] *I have never come across anything* **quite** *like that before.*

JUDGEMENT - *What's peculiar?*

MEMORY - *Well, for one thing, the metrical scheme has gone to pot ... I don't think I've ever met a pattern of words like these:* **so was it... so is it... so be it. So be it** *usually means reluctant acceptance or decision ...*

JUDGEMENT - [tentatively] *But here it expresses resolve (of some kind) ... doesn't it?*

IMAGINATION - *I can see that an old man might, towards the end of his days, accept the inevitable with the phrase* **so be it**, *but this lunatic ...*

MEMORY - [confused] *I don't recognise the poet's theology. Unless he means that he would like to die a spiritual death if he were no longer assured of God's mercy, or ...*

IMAGINATION - [unstoppable in her disgust] *... but this lunatic loves the rainbow so much that he thinks that as long as his heart is able to keep leaping up he will be happy even in decrepitude.*

JUDGEMENT - [almost angry] *Why do you keep calling the poet a lunatic?*

IMAGINATION - *Because no sane man would ever hope to die just because he started to find rainbows boring. And I can't see a liar or a pseudo-intellectual writing such baby words.* [in answer to Judgement's unspoken astonishment] *I can't see a grown-up person saying a whole sentence – a sentence about which he has thought, and in which he believes – entirely in words of one syllable ...*

MEMORY - *Except, of course, for the word* **'behold'** *which ...*

IMAGINATION - **Let me die** *in particular. Only a petulant child or a madman would say that, and ...*

MEMORY - *Lovers say it. In the* **Canterbury Tales** *lovers are always saying that unless they have their lady's love, they will die.* [glancing at Judgement who appears incredulous] *You may sneer, but this is more than a literary convention believe me ... believe me.* [becoming incoherent] *... There is a pain ... true love is as strong as death ... and ... and ...*

JUDGEMENT - [torn between anger and a desire to console] *Now, now, it's only a poem and, so far as I can tell from what you have been saying, it concerns joy rather than sorrow. All this talk of lunatics, lovers and theologians is distracting me from any sense there might be in these words. But I will not cease from inquiry, nor shall ...* [breaking off as she notices Memory looking distinctly bored and Imagination stifling a yawn.]

"Great Muse," cried Our Hero in despair, "astonishment has been followed by stagnation rather than rational admiration! All hope is gone!"

75. Child and Man

JUDGEMENT - *Perhaps, now you have both had your say, I might read the next line.* [imploringly] *Just one line?*

The Child is father of the Man ...

IMAGINATION - [with the air of one who has had her case proved] *I told you he was mad, quite mad.*

MEMORY - *The child is **what**? What is the poet talking about now? I don't recognize this statement. I can't see how this fits in with the rest of the hymn.*

JUDGEMENT - [astonished] *Are you saying that you still think these are the words of a hymn?*

MEMORY - *Not really.* [pausing] *But it's more like a hymn than anything else I can think of.*

JUDGEMENT - *But you can't see how such a statement as this one, that the child is father of the man, is related to a Christian position?*

MEMORY - *No; I am trying to find some theological explanation.*

JUDGEMENT - *Perhaps you have to make a jump between the two statements as in the 'Westron Wind' poem – I mean, between the earlier wish that the poet might continue to joy in the rainbow and the new statement.*

IMAGINATION - [as if experiencing illumination] *Perhaps he's not mad after all. Perhaps it's a very beautiful story – or two very beautiful stories. The first story would be about a father and a child – not a mother or even an aunt. But it is the story we heard before. The father draws the child's attention to a rainbow in the sky. In the second story the ghost of that child guides the attention of his adult self to the wonder of the rainbow.*

MEMORY - *In both cases, then, you would take the word **father** not in a biological sense, but to mean 'protector', 'guide', 'counsellor'? All these meanings are possible, I am glad to say, and ...*

IMAGINATION - *Yes, I suppose I would.*

JUDGEMENT - *You've changed your tune, haven't you?*

IMAGINATION - *Yes. I was astonished by the last line, and a sudden new idea came to me which made everything quite different.*

MEMORY - *That line:*

The Child is father of the Man...

*is rather like something I found in **Paradise Regained**. Milton there writes something like:*

... the childhood shews the man
As morning shews the day ...

JUDGEMENT - *It's not quite like that, though, is it? Milton's idea is a more conventional one – that in a child we can see the promise of an adult ...*

MEMORY - *Perhaps.* [only momentarily daunted] *Well here is a line from Dryden that is even more like the Wordsworth:*

Men are but children of a larger growth

IMAGINATION - [with profound scorn] *That's **nothing** like Wordsworth's story! It's the kind of cheap joke which bored wives make about their husbands!*

MEMORY - [not giving in or up] *Can I have one last attempt to illuminate Wordsworth by quoting another author? Alexander Pope in the **Essay on Man** wrote:*

The boy and Man an Individual makes.

Individual *here, of course, means something which cannot be divided. The thought seems to me to be identical with ...*

JUDGEMENT - *Yes, I can see that that idea is very similar to Wordsworth's. I can see the sense of that.*

IMAGINATION - *No it's not! Pope's is a boring old platitude. Wordsworth's is a beautiful story. Everything depends on the words* **father** *and* **child** *– on the child being the father of the man. I would like to fill myself with these words forever and forever.*

JUDGEMENT - *I am becoming confused again ... and just when I was beginning to hope we were getting some-where. I fear, Dear Sister, that there is not sufficient clarity discernible here even to half-fill my capacious desires for* **meaning** *and* **sense**.

"I, too, Lamp of Light," said Our Hero to his Muse, "I too am becoming confused."

"Why, Flesh of My Dreams? Are things not improving?"

"Not really. Imagination has changed her tune but Judgement is still sending them all in a vain search for sense, sense, sense. The words of the poem do not seem to be able to find their way beyond the busy shallows. There is no quiet place, no still centre in this Mind."

"Are there no glimmerings?"

"Perhaps I see some light *somewhere* in the encircling gloom."

76. Natural Piety

The three sisters sit staring gloomily at each other and at the book for some time. Judgement suspects Imagination of knowing more than she will tell. Imagination suspects Memory of being deliberately distracting. Memory, her strongest feelings scorned, begins to consider other things. Judgement looks from one face to the other with increasing disquiet.

JUDGEMENT - [with an effort regaining composure] *Perhaps it would help to clarify our notions on this question if we finished reading the poem:*

> *The Child is father of the Man;*
> *And I could wish my days to be*
> *Bound each to each by natural piety.*

MEMORY - [irrelevantly] *I can't see how the last two lines rhyme.*

JUDGEMENT - [with her customary mock-gentility] *Perhaps, now you have kindly allowed me to read the whole poem, we might begin to look at it more sensibly. For one thing, the line:* **The Child is father of the Man**, *which I thought a surprising new statement, isn't quite that. It's really a large general proposition sandwiched between a resolve and a prayer, isn't it?*

MEMORY - [stuffily] *Are you calling:* **'And I could wish my days to be bound each to each by natural piety,'** *a prayer?* [contemptuously] *It isn't much like any prayer I have ever heard.*

IMAGINATION - [pondering] *No? I think it is fair to call it a prayer. When the poet says that* **the Child is father of the Man** *he is stating a truth which becomes, in the last two lines, a beautiful prayer that he should never forget the power of his own childhood self to guide, counsel, educate and protect him – to keep him fully human.*

JUDGEMENT - [wishing, but unable, to follow] *But to say that, one needs to understand what the poet means by the final phrase of the poem,* **natural piety.**

MEMORY - [with genuine sorrow] *I'm afraid it is not a phrase I recognise instantly.*

JUDGEMENT - *Perhaps we can make some sense of the poem by making some connections between the words* **natural** *and* **piety** *– or by allowing the poem to make connections for us.*
[She reads as if pressing each word to yield its store of sense, to declare its relationship with all the others]

> *The Child is father of the Man;*
> *And I could wish my days to be*
> *Bound each to each by natural piety.*

MEMORY - [with reviving spirits] *Well, the most obvious meaning of* **piety** *is a devout observance of the beliefs of the Christian Church.* [pompously] *I have been arguing all along that this poem is a Christian poem ...*

IMAGINATION - [irritated] *Well, I've never been at all happy with that notion. For me the word* **natural** *almost contradicts the word* **piety**. *I think the poet is making a religion out of Nature.*

JUDGEMENT - [turning to Memory] *Is* **piety** *only linked with Christianity?*

MEMORY - [unhappy again] *Well, no. The word actually comes from the Latin and implied reverence for one's father, say, quite as much for the gods.*

JUDGEMENT - [hopefully] *Perhaps it could be used for reverence in general – rather than something which is enforced by any doctrine or set of rules?*

MEMORY - *Yes. The word* **natural** *would then imply that it is part of man's inherent nature to be pious.*

IMAGINATION - *I think it implies that the piety is* **instinctive**.

MEMORY - *Pope uses the phrase* **natural piety** *about old king Priam in the* **Iliad***; the old king had a generally reverent attitude to the power of the gods ...*

IMAGINATION - [interrupting] *I think the poet is indicating that man's piety should be most properly directed at natural things.*

JUDGEMENT - [happy for a moment] *These ideas are not necessarily contradictory. By suggesting all these possibilities of* **natural piety** *but not settling for any one of them, the poet has set up resonances out of which he has created what might be called a new concept of piety.* [suddenly despondent] *But I still can't get any clear sense of what the new natural piety might be …*

IMAGINATION - [suddenly very sure of herself] *But don't you see? – the new idea is at one and the same time both very general and very specific. It is very simple to see and to know and to feel, but impossible to formulate.* [with renewed passion] *To attempt such a thing would be to insult the purity of the poem and …*

MEMORY - [angry] *Well, that's not very helpful, is it? You say it's new and not like anything I have ever met before, but you won't tell me what it is!*

IMAGINATION - [petulantly] *It is not that I* **won't** *say. I simply* **cannot***. The words of this poem may not be represented in any form other than themselves.*

JUDGEMENT - [to Memory] *I must agree with you, Sister. Unless we can persuade our dear Imagination to let us in to her little secrets, we might as well give up.*

IMAGINATION - *I think we should. I have said all I can say.*

[Judgement and Memory stare at Imagination imploringly, angrily.]

Our Hero peered into the pool anxiously. It seemed to him that some sort of progress was about to be made. But whether or not it would be progress in the right direction, he knew not. His Muse, he noticed, was smiling, but without, he thought, much confidence or real hope.

77. Bound Each to Each

Imagination at last breaks down before the pressure of her sisters' eyes.

IMAGINATION - [only half-inclined to be consolatory] *I think that one of the things that may be holding me back is that we keep talking about ideas and concepts and statements, but this is a POEM.*

JUDGEMENT - [still irritated] *Yes, of course. We know that. What do you mean?*

IMAGINATION - *I mean I can't see the poet saying to himself,* **I think I will illustrate a concept or two this morning. To do so I will employ the well-known symbol of the rainbow** *and so on.*

JUDGEMENT - [baffled. For her there is no other way of thinking] *How* **do** *you see the poet?*

IMAGINATION - *Well, looking at the poem on the page, I can see that it is written in a very tight form, but listening to it when you read it aloud is quite different. Then it sounds as if a man were talking to himself, in a moment of absolute seriousness. I think he used so many little everyday words because he was trying to avoid that kind of pseudo-thinking that turns on* **concepts** *and* **ideas** *and* **symbolism**. *I think he has managed to do that so precisely, that any other form of words would have destroyed the point or meaning of the poem.* [turning aside] *This poem doesn't need us. If we talk too loudly or too pretentiously about the poem, we would be intruding.*

JUDGEMENT - [with barely restrained fury] *But can't you overcome your fine feeling just for a moment to help those less sensitive than yourself to understand what is meant by* **natural piety**?

IMAGINATION - *I don't think that this phrase can be taken out of the poem. It is a phrase that sends us back to the beginning again. The whole poem is one thought.*

JUDGEMENT - *I don't understand.*

MEMORY - *Nor I.*

IMAGINATION - *This poet does not think like you in an orderly sequence. First A, then B or C, and so on. The poem is one prayer, one wish, one hope, one acknowledgement of the continuity of thought and feeling which connects the fragments of the poet's life together and links them to other lives and to the natural world. Or something like that ...*

JUDGEMENT - *Perhaps some such explanation is plausible.* [pause] *But there is one further problem. What are we supposed to associate with the word* **bound** *in the lines:*

> *And I could wish my days to be*
> *BOUND each to each by natural piety?*

MEMORY - [with confidence] *They might be* **tied together** *or* **imprisoned**, *or they might owe each other obligations.*

JUDGEMENT - [unhappier than ever] *I have no idea which meaning to choose.*

IMAGINATION - *I don't think you need to go beyond the poem to answer that question. The answer is obvious ...*

JUDGEMENT - [irritated] *To you, perhaps, who prefer intuition to sense...*

IMAGINATION - [undaunted] *The bonds by which the poet wishes his days to be bound each to each are the same bonds that bind father to a child and an individual man to his past and future selves.*

JUDGEMENT - [looking anxiously at Memory] *Does that make sense? Does that use of the word* **bound** *square with other uses of the word we might have come a cross?*

MEMORY - *Well, of course, the most common and powerful* **bonds** *are those between members of the same kin group. But here* **bound** *is being applied to days. I have never come across this before.*

IMAGINATION - [with fire] *But don't you see? The poet's days ARE people. They are his past and future selves. This is a poem about his whole life — what he was, what he is, and what he will be.*

JUDGEMENT - [abashed] *Aren't you going too far? It is only a short poem.*

IMAGINATION - *Yes, but it concentrates entirely on essentials. For instance, look at the middle section. I hear two poems there. One goes like this:* [almost chanting]

My life began
I am a man
I shall grow old

MEMORY - *Anyone could have written that.*
IMAGINATION - *Exactly. Those lines contain what you might call the facts. But there is another poem:* [again with passion]

So was it
So is it
So be it

which expresses the poet's joyful acceptance of the inevitability of those facts.
MEMORY - *But you said earlier — and we more or less agreed — that* **so be it** *is not a phrase of acceptance, but a phrase of hope, a wish, a prayer.*
IMAGINATION - *Yes, yes, it is. It is* **when the two short poems are brought together** *with the rest, and in particular with that passionate outcry:* **or let me die** ...

My heart leaps up when I behold
*   A rainbow in the sky.*
So was it when my life began;
So is it now I am a man;
So be it when I shall grow old,
*   Or let me die!*

The Child is father of the Man;
And I could wish my days to be
Bound each to each by natural piety.

JUDGEMENT - [astonished] *Are you saying that this is not just a poem about the whole of life, it is a poem which transforms the whole of life?*
IMAGINATION - *Yes, I suppose I am.*
JUDGEMENT - *I could never bring myself to say such a thing. It is an enormous claim for a few small words.*
IMAGINATION - [with a degree of self-satisfaction] *It is, isn't it.*
JUDGEMENT - *Far too large for me, I'm afraid. But you like the poem now?*
IMAGINATION - *I like it enormously. I think it represents a kind of perfection of art.*
JUDGEMENT - [in eternal doubt] *Well I'm not sure about that, but it does seem to be expressing something very sensible.*
IMAGINATION - [patronisingly and happily] *O come, come! Can't you see that it is trembling with life, beauty and Imagination?*
MEMORY - [rather sadly] *All I can say is that it is probably memorable.*

Our Hero was not sure whether or not to be pleased with the outcome of the sisters' conversation. He could not make out if the door in the dark had opened. He stared at the pool, for a time and then turned to search the lovely face of his beloved Instructress.

"Heavenly Muse, did these Faculties possess that poem, or did they not?"

"It is hard to say. The truth that is the object of art is found in the whole Mind, not in its separate faculties, and its effect is one of repose, expansion and substantial possession."

"But these Faculties, as we saw long ago, are incapable of repose."

"Perhaps the Poem will come to them – really come to them – when they are not attending to it directly, in the night, perhaps."

"Am I to be content with this – this partial, momentary, half-contact, with my audience? Can I hope for no more than dreams?"

"I am afraid, My Chosen Soul, that many and many a time your Poems will form themselves no more securely than this."

"Is there always so much noise in the mortal Mind?"

"Noise – or the silence of vacancy."

"But you promised me love and fame. You said my

Poems – my spirit even – would live again so long as humans are human, and life is life."

"And so they shall. Let us try another case – another Poem."

"And another Mind."

"There is no need. Another day – another moment in this same future Mind – will suffice. One Mortal Mind differs as much from itself from hour to hour as it differs from another Mind. We will try to discover this set of Faculties on a good day, with the work of a Poet unusually concerned to make his words the image of his mind: to speak so that mortals might know him."

Part Three:
Ten Stories and a Visitation

78. God the Moneylender

Imagination, Judgement and Memory are once again gathered before a poem. The interior of the mind is, as usual, dark, but lightens considerably with the progress of the discussion.

Judgement is reading from a large folio.

JUDGEMENT - [looking round with a slightly forced smile] *Sisters, I take it as agreed that we have resolved to try as hard as we can on this occasion ... to maintain a decent sociability ... and to speak to one another as friends ... and not as competitors. Here, for our consideration, is a set of words assumed to be a poem, which ...*

MEMORY - [as if ending the discussion] *... which is the forty-fifth in a collection of short poems by Ben Jonson which he called* **Epigrammes.**

JUDGEMENT - *... a set of words assumed to be a poem which I will now (if I may) read.*

[Judgement reads stumblingly, without enthusiasm or understanding]:

ON MY FIRST SONNE. / *Farewell, thou child of my right hand, and ioy; / My sinne was too much hope of thee, lou'd boy. / Seuen yeers tho'wert lent to me, and I thee pay,/ Exacted by thy fate, on the iust day. / O, could I loose all father, now. For why / Will man lament the state he should enuie? / To haue so soone scap'd worlds, and fleshes rage,/ And if no other miserie, yet age? / Rest in soft peace, and, ask'd, say here doth lye / BEN. JONSON his best piece of poetrie. / For whose sake, hence-forth, all his vowes be such,/ As what he loues may neuer like too much.*

IMAGINATION - [yawning] *Not much has occurred to me on one reading. It seems pretty dull — much duller than the last two poems. There is no music for my ear or images for my inner eye.*

JUDGEMENT - [with an attempt at enthusiasm] *In that case we might be able to understand it very quickly.* [rapidly] *It is clear, isn't it, from the title and the general drift, that the poet is talking about the death of his son?*

MEMORY - [catching Imagination's yawn] *Yes, I suppose so. But everything else is a chaos of half-recognised, and therefore half-understood, phrases, together with some half-heard snatches of rhythm.*

I suppose I could recognise some ...

JUDGEMENT - [momentarily inclined to give up] *Shall we leave it at that?* [to herself] *(I am always initially repulsed by what I do not immediately comprehend.)* [reviving] *If we do go on ... if we do go on and give the poem a second read-through* [despondent again, to the point of incoherence] *... it will only be because some small part ... perhaps no more than a word or a phrase ... because some small part has surprised you ... one or both of you ... has surprised you into pleasure ... however mild.* [imploringly] *I can do nothing without you.*

[There is no reply]

[encouragingly] *I am sometimes persuaded of the attractions of words that seem to reflect what we already know (or think we know) ...*

[There is no reply]

... at other times I am intrigued by sentiments which seem to offer a challenge to our preconceptions.

[Still no reply]

I am open to suggestions... any suggestion. [desperately, brightly] *Where shall we start?*

IMAGINATION - [offhandedly] *It doesn't much matter where we start.*

JUDGEMENT - [worried] *Why doesn't it matter?*

IMAGINATION - *If the black marks are a poem, each piece will, I'm sure, be connected to every other - beautifully. But I haven't heard anything which would want to make me try.*

JUDGEMENT - [desperately] *Nothing? Nothing interested you? Nothing whatsoever?*

IMAGINATION - [with a shrug] *Sorry.*

MEMORY - [after a pause] *Well, since you ask, I was mildly surprised during our first reading by the word* **exacted** *at the beginning of what I suppose is the fourth line:*

Seuen yeers tho'wert lent to me, and I thee pay,
EXACTED by thy fate, on the iust day.

It surprised me because (going, as I suppose it does, with **pay***) the word* **exacted** *seems to be a term from the world of moneylending — which I have not come across in association with laments for the dead.*

JUDGEMENT - *Please, please go on.*

MEMORY - [doubtfully] *Well, I have a vague notion that I have met the word* **exacted** *in Shakespeare's* **The Merchant of Venice**.

IMAGINATION - [mildly interested] *Tell me the story.*

MEMORY - [gladly] *A rich Christian merchant, Antonio, sardonically begs the Jewish moneylender Shylock (a man he holds in complete contempt) to make him a loan. Antonio knows that, if he goes bankrupt, Shylock, who hates him, will demand his pound of flesh, will* **exact** *the penalty — a penalty which will mean, for Antonio, certain death.*

IMAGINATION - [engaged at last] *If the word exacted is the kind of word it seems to be, the poet would be telling a story in which fate, or God, played the role of a cruel moneylender, inexorably calling his money in at the appointed time.* [speaking slowly, boldly and with great deliberation] **My son was a loan and not a gift. My son was lent to me. I knew not for how long. Now, after a short time - only seven years - the loan is recalled, and I must pay. I must, I must.**

MEMORY - [unimpressed, unmoved] *It is true that in some parts of the Old Testament, God* **does** *from time to time appear to men as a being to whom dues must be paid without question or remonstrance.*

IMAGINATION - [excited] *Give me an example.*

MEMORY - *When Job, weary of his life, complains, in the bitterness of his soul, of the unjust miseries of his existence, his friend rebukes him vehemently:*

Know, therefore, that God exacteth of thee less than thy iniquity deserveth.

JUDGEMENT - [tentatively] *Might this suggest that the story of the cruel moneylender is not ... is not the only story being told? I am considering the word just.*

Exacted by thy fate, on the JUST day.

MEMORY - *Quite.* [happy to help, but happier still with the sound of her own voice helping] *The word* **just** *has two meanings (at least). It could mean* **precise***, and refer to a particular date stipulated in a moneylender's bond. Or a second meaning would imply that the* **exacting** *took place by the operation of than ungainsayable right which is called* **Justice***.*

JUDGEMENT - *If this second meaning were uppermost, would the story be one of a man receiving a loan on just terms, which was justly recalled, and justly repaid?*

IMAGINATION - *Yes, it is a terrible, an unbearable story. God the real father or owner of the child had sent him to live, for a while, with the poet.* [speaking with emotion and care] **God in his infinite goodness allowed me that most precious of gifts, the gift of a child. The only terms on which such a treasure may be granted are that the gift may be rescinded in any manner, and at any time that God wishes. Life is a loan which cannot be granted in perpetuity. My son was recalled. I have paid. Thanks be to God.** [suddenly but profoundly moved]

Dear Sisters, there is no more to be done with these words of suffering, this sad poem. There is no more to say. My heart is broken. We should all weep – weep and say nothing. [noticing that, while Memory seems willing to acquiesce, Judgement is restless] *Please, please, let us sit still for a while – feeling in silent testimony.*

As Imagination was speaking, Our Hero, in the Muse's garden above, saw (or thought he saw) the ghost of a shadow enter (or seem to enter) the margin of this twentieth-century Mind. The Faculties were no longer alone. The Mind was inhabited (or so it seemed) by a strange and foreign being.

79. A Father's Farewells

Imagination sits silently for a while, inwardly weeping. Her sisters, however, are largely unconcerned, although Judgement, as usual, is worrying away.

JUDGEMENT - *But neither of these stories would lessen your first surprise at the word* **exacted** *would it?. Am I to gather that in the case of either story, the pain of bereavement is being talked about in an extraordinarily harsh ... an almost brutal ... manner?*

[Imagination refuses, or is unable, to answer]

MEMORY - [pompously] *Yes, these are not the kind of sentiments I am used to in the newspaper obituary columns – or anywhere else for that matter. I am baffled.*

IMAGINATION - [musingly, reluctantly] *There is something strange here.*

MEMORY - *Something unrecognizable, yes.*

JUDGEMENT - *Help me Sisters.*

IMAGINATION - *I am beginning to suspect the underlying presence of a way of thinking and a civilisation different from the one in which we live.* [turning to her sisters] *What do you think?*

JUDGEMENT - [rapidly turning to Memory] *I'm afraid I cannot comment. Can you help us?*

MEMORY - *The Greeks and Romans often wrote of life as a debt that had, sooner or later, to be repaid without rancour.*

IMAGINATION - [without enthusiasm, still full of tears] *Tell me more.*

MEMORY - *Often, on their gravestones, the bereaved are depicted paying a fond but dignified farewell to their departing loved ones. Usually the place of parting is not shown. It is almost as if the loved one has to go, by mutual and uncontentious agreement, on a long journey.*

IMAGINATION - [engaged, despite herself] *Yes, the opening of our poem is clearly such an address to a departing loved one. The poet, a noble, stoical Roman stands by the river ... the river ...?*

MEMORY - [infuriatingly] *... Lethe, Sister, the river Lethe. Yes the language of the first line would otherwise be puzzlingly remote and formal:*

Farewell, thou child of my right hand, and ioy;

IMAGINATION - [working hard] *It also seems strange that, for the duration of that line, the son seems almost to be present and alive.*

JUDGEMENT - [never satisfied] *But even if we dwell on the Roman story, and see the poet taking a fond and formal farewell of his son ...*

IMAGINATION - *Clasping him to his bosom, perhaps, or arm to arm.*

JUDGEMENT - *... there still seems something very odd about the phrase* **child of my right hand** *which ...*

MEMORY - [proudly] *I have a story, from the Old Testament, about Jacob, which might help.*

IMAGINATION - *May we hear it?.*

MEMORY - *Jacob's wife bore him a son, but died of the birth.* [moved] *She cried out in her agonies that the boy should be called* **BENONI** *which means* **Child-of-my Sorrows** *but Jacob averted the evil omen by calling the boy* **BENJAMIN** *which means* **Fortunate** *or literally* **Child-of-my-Right-Hand** *– child of my strength, child of my potency, child whom I shall honour...*

IMAGINATION - [with passion] *... child who is as close to me as my own right hand.*

JUDGEMENT - *And* **Benjamin** *was the Christian name which both father and son, poet and subject, shared ... was it?*

MEMORY - [with mounting enthusiasm] *Yes, and the poet, in drawing out the literal meaning of the name, reminds us both that Christ, the son of God who died, sat at the right hand of his father, and that ...*

IMAGINATION - [holding Memory's hand in warm sympathy] *... and that the poet's son was a child of joy to him – a joy in himself and a child of joy – the child of a joyful marriage perhaps:*

Farewell, thou child of my right hand, and JOY

JUDGEMENT - [pained] *I don't understand.*

IMAGINATION - [smiling] *The poet is telling three stories at once.*

JUDGEMENT - [still lost] *Three stories?*

IMAGINATION - [with her usual absorption when possessed by a story] *In one story, he bids a gracious last farewell to a valued adult friend:* **may your journey be safe and easy, may you fare well.**

JUDGEMENT - *I can see that that makes ... some kind of sense.*

IMAGINATION - *And in another story, he takes a despairing farewell to his joy – the son of his joy and the cause of his joy:* **farewell all light of life, and farewell youth.**

JUDGEMENT - *I am not sure I follow that.*

IMAGINATION - [ignoring her sister, concentrating on her stories] *And, in the third story, the poet takes a sacred, a religious farewell to the offspring of his loins:* **farewell, you whom I have made, prop and stay of my unquiet mind, progeny of my sacred Soul.**

JUDGEMENT - *I am afraid, Dear Sister, that, while I am prepared to believe that you are right, I do not see how you arrive at all these stories from these few words.*

As Imagination was telling her stories Our Hero saw (or thought he saw) the shimmering figure on the margin of the Mind begin to assume something like a human form and move towards the three sisters.

80. The Sins of Fathers

Imagination, with more to concern her than simple grief and more to animate her than mere sympathy, is happy. Memory, conscious of her usefulness, is content. But Judgement is still worried.

JUDGEMENT - *It is not entirely clear to me why you want to use the word* **religious** *so early in the poem ... or quite what the word* **religious** *might mean in this context. It is sometimes helpful to me ... and, I take it, to Imagination to know stories ... true stories ...*

IMAGINATION - *... or (better still) apocryphal stories, or (best of all) interesting speculations ...*

JUDGEMENT - *... about a poet's life.* [turning to Memory] *Is anything known about this poet's religious life?*

MEMORY - [mournfully] *Usually there is all too little to be known.* [brightening] *In this case, there is a story which Jonson told himself.*

IMAGINATION - *Can we hear it?*

MEMORY - *With pleasure. In 1603, his thirty-first year, Jonson left home to stay with a friend in the country. One night, in a vision, he saw his only son, whom he had left behind in town, appear to him with the mark of a bloody cross on his forehead, as if he had been cut by a sword. Jonson was amazed and prayed to God. His friend persuaded him it was only a fantasy, at which he should not be dejected. But then there came letters from his wife, telling of the death of the boy. In the dream, the son appeared fully grown – which Jonson thought might be the way he would appear at the Resurrection.*

IMAGINATION - [surprised] *I find that moving, useful and interesting.* [abstractedly] *One of the most useful and interesting things about this and all such stories is that it shows us that the world of the past is both very like and very unlike the world we live in – and I enjoy that. I can move freely and breathe deeply in such a world.*

MEMORY - [full of herself] *Yes. The story shows that Jonson, just like a modern parent (or indeed any human being), lived a life in which he was continually, pressingly, preoccupied by thoughts about his absent loved ones.*

JUDGEMENT - *But it also shows us ... (does it?)* [looking at both her sisters] *... shows us that the divisions in the mind of an intelligent human between the everyday and the spiritual worlds were ... were ... different in his day.*

IMAGINATION - [crisply] *Jonson, clearly, lived in a world in which dreams could easily be thought of as direct messages from God about the earthly and heavenly future. The real and spiritual worlds were, for him, co-extensive and continuous.* [almost to herself] *It must have been both comforting and terrifying – uplifting and depressing.*

JUDGEMENT - [genuinely at a loss] *Do such thoughts help us when we come to consider why it might be that Jonson was so quick to use the word* **sin** *when reflecting on the death of his son?*

IMAGINATION - [momentarily repelled] *That is awful, terrible, unbearable. It seems as if Jonson regards the death of his son as somehow a* **punishment** *meted out on the father by a just God.*

MEMORY - [consolingly] *A sin, for a Christian, is an act committed against the will of God, and therefore against the eternal rightness of things. A sinner, conscious of his sin, grieves, and offers repentance, seeking forgiveness.*

IMAGINATION - [anxiously] *I don't understand. What* **sin** *has the poet committed?*

MEMORY - [laboriously] *In trying to help you to understand what might have been in Jonson's mind to prompt him to use the word* **sin** *in relation to his feelings about the death of his son, I might mention that I have heard that many bereaved men and women, young boys and little girls, consider themselves in some way directly responsible for the death of their loved ones, almost as if they had caused the fatal accident or disease themselves.*

IMAGINATION - [quickly] *It must be natural to feel that the pain of such bereavement is inflicted as a punishment. This natural feeling must be strongest when there do seem to be some grounds, however slight, for the bereaved person to blame himself for his loved one's death.*

MEMORY - [preoccupied] *In Shakespeare's* **Macbeth**, *Macduff, a good and noble Scots lord, goes to England to join the forces who are determined to end Macbeth's usurpation of the Scottish throne. While he is away, his wife and children are brutally, savagely,* massacred. The news is brought to Macduff in England. His first articulate thought is that God has punished him not merely for being absent, but because of his intrinsically sinful nature. He is told to bear his grief **like a man**, and replies: [she recites with real force of feeling]

> I shall do so;
> But I must also feel it as a man;
> I cannot but remember such things were,
> That were most precious to me. - Did Heaven look on,
> And would not take their part? Sinful Macduff!
> They were all struck for thee. Naught that I am,
> Not for their demerits, but for mine,
> Fell slaughter on their souls; Heaven rest them now.

IMAGINATION - *Oh the poor man! But if this helps me to see why, for a Christian, the loss of a son might be felt as the just retribution for sins, I am still surprised that the poet* attributes the nature of his sin to **hope**:

> *My sin was too much HOPE of thee, loved boy*

MEMORY - [at a loss] *Yes, it is surprising.* **Hope** *is, after all, in many ways part of a Christian's virtue, and has at all times been thought to be one of the principal things which make human life bearable. Hell was often thought of as the only place in God's universe where Hope never comes.*

JUDGEMENT - *So how, or why, could, or should,* **hope be a sin**? *This poem doesn't make sense. I am afraid that there is no meaning to be had from these words. I cannot understand how can something so essentially human be a* **sin**?

With the insistent repetition of that question, it seemed to our despairing Hero that the shimmering figure receded a little way back away from the three Faculties and into the dark.

81. Loving and Liking

All three Faculties sit for a while in silence pondering, musing, or dreaming.

JUDGEMENT - [with a wry laugh] *I am confused as usual.* [solemnly] *It is difficult, from what you two are saying, to see how the first two lines of the poem, separated only by a semi-colon, should be connected ...*

IMAGINATION - [equally at a loss] *... or could be made to seem part of the same world.*

JUDGEMENT - *Shall I read them again?* [she reads deliberately and very slowly, as if the words would explain themselves if spoken carefully enough]:

Farewell, thou child of my right hand, and joy;
My sin was too much hope of thee, loved boy ...

MEMORY - *It is difficult.* [trying hard] *The first line is elevated, and allusive both to the classical and Old Testament eras. The second (a string of ten monosyllables) seems plain and conversational, but is charged with New Testament resonances.* [apologetically] *I'm afraid that doesn't help much.*

JUDGEMENT - [getting a grip on herself] *While feeling around for a possible coherence in these apparent contradictions, we might turn to the end of the poem.* [hopefully] *If Jonson thought of himself as repenting of a **sin**, there may be some indication of the nature of that sin in his final vow.*

...henceforth all his vows be such,
As what he loves may never like too much.

IMAGINATION - *But this vow is itself perhaps the greatest surprise so far. If we were to make a distinction between loving and liking in a similar context, we would probably reverse Jonson's distinction.* [glancing at Memory] *If, for example, we had just escaped some disastrous love affair, we might think to ourselves along these lines; "Henceforth, we will try to arrange matters so that those we like we do not love too much. Then we won't get hurt again".* [innocently] *Does something like that correspond with your experience Sister?*

MEMORY - [changing the subject rapidly] *I'm afraid I have a piece of information which may increase our puzzlement even further. For it seems that, while composing the ending of his poem, Jonson recalled an epigram by one of his favourite Latin writers, Martial, which ends:*

quidquid ames, cupias non placuisse nimis

which means something like: **Whatever you love, take care that it doesn't please you too much.**

JUDGEMENT - *That is strikingly similar to Jonson's line.*

MEMORY - [glad that her distraction has worked] *Yes, but it is strange that Jonson recalled this particular Martial epigram in the present context, since the boy grieved over was a slave and not a son, and the love spoken of may be sexual love.*

IMAGINATION - [interested] *Tell me the story.*

MEMORY - *I am afraid I do not know it very well, but I think it goes like this: Martial loved the boy (who was born on his own farm) for his beauty, wit and grace. The boy died in his twelfth year. In the poem I mentioned just now, Martial laments this death and advises a friend not to let the gods know that he feels more than liking for **his** boy, for fear they should become jealous and therefore, as is the way with gods, doom the boy to destruction.*

JUDGEMENT - *This would seem to be in every way different from any distinction between **loving** and **liking** that Jonson might have had in mind in this poem.*

IMAGINATION - [with another teasing glance in Memory's

direction] *Perhaps we should move away from literature and consider life for a while. Perhaps* [to Memory] *you, dear Sister, could tell us something ...*

MEMORY - [rapidly avoiding the issue] *If, however, we recall the Latin we find that the word which Martial used for **liking** was **placere**, a word which refers exclusively to the pleasures given to a lover by his beloved.* [coming up with what she hopes is another distraction] *Indeed the word **like** in this poem might well mean the same as Martial's **please**. **It likes me well – it pleases me** – Jonson might have said.*

IMAGINATION - [as if experiencing sudden illumination, and shocked into solemnity] *That changes everything.*

JUDGEMENT - *I don't understand*

IMAGINATION - *If we take that hint back to the second line of Jonson's poem:*

My sin was too much hope of thee, loved boy

and assume that liking – being pleased – **too much** was connected closely in Jonson's mind with **hoping too much**, we might begin to see the outlines of another story.*

JUDGEMENT - *Another story?*

IMAGINATION - *It is the story of a father who delighted in the birth of a son exclusively because of the pleasure which the child's life might give him. **I was proud that this son bore my name. I looked forward with eager expectation to the days when my son should be accorded those honours which had been denied to me.** His pleasure, that is, was the self-regarding pleasure of one who seeks to live out his own hopes and dreams in the life of another, whatever that other person might hope or want for himself.*

JUDGEMENT - [happily, as things seem, to her, to be going well] *But we still need yet another story ... don't we? ... the story of what might have been in the past, and what Jonson vows will be in the future ...*

IMAGINATION - [again looking at Memory] *... a story of true love, perhaps?*

MEMORY - [hurriedly assuming the mantle of learning] *The word **love** in the English language almost always carries with it a submerged memory of its use in relation to a God who so loved the world that he gave his only begotten son. Unlike **amor** in Latin and **eros** in Greek, the English word **love** can seldom be used simply to express desire, sexual or otherwise.*

IMAGINATION - *What?*

MEMORY - [undaunted] *It was, after all, the word **love**, a word which had been used by many generations of English men and women to describe their strongest feelings for each other, which William Tyndale used to translate the Greek word agape when rendering St. Paul's great hymn to the spiritual quality which he saw as informing the life of all true Christians.*

IMAGINATION - *What?*

MEMORY - [reciting, clearly, deliberately]

Love suffereth long and is courteous. Love envieth not. Love doth not frowardly, swelleth not, dealeth not dishonestly, seeketh not her own, is not provoked to anger, thinketh not evil, rejoiceth not in iniquity, but rejoiceth in the truth, suffereth all things, believeth all things, hopeth all things, endureth in all things.

IMAGINATION - *I think that is very beautiful.*

JUDGEMENT - *Yes, yes ... perhaps, but do we now have the outlines of the story we needed?*

IMAGINATION - [gleefully] *Yes, we seem to.* [sombrely] *The father in the story in the poem says: **I feel great sorrow, and because I feel, I realise for the first time, now it is all too late, that I had not loved the boy as I should have done – with a love exclusively focused on its object, a love which shuts out all purely selfish hopes and desires; such a***

TEN STORIES AND A VISITATION: LOVING AND LIKING

love that seeks only the good of the beloved, will endure anything for that good, even to the point of accepting that the death of the beloved might be, in some sense, for his own good, and therefore not a proper cause for my sorrow.

While Imagination told her story, Our Hero to his great joy saw the figure in the shadows become substantial and move again out of the dark and into the forefront of the Mind.

82. Better off Dead?

The Faculties are now thoroughly engaged but temporarily silent. Their last thought has set them back in their seats.

JUDGEMENT - [slightly shocked] *That notion – that a child might be* **better off dead** *– is presumably one that it is difficult for any of us to accept. All of us would probably regard it as a ... cruel sentiment. I find it contrary to reason. Memory will find that it ... contradicts habitual association, and it is in every way, I suppose, repulsive to Imagination. The poet has not made it easy for himself ... or for us* [she reads slowly, pondering]:

> *O, could I loose all father, now. For why*
> *Will man lament the state he should envy?*
> *To have so soon scaped worlds, and fleshes rage,*
> *And if no other misery, yet age?*

MEMORY - [puzzled] *No, indeed, the poet has not made it easy. It would be natural for a Christian to have mentioned an after-life or heaven. It is a Christian commonplace that there is no need to mourn for souls in bliss.*

IMAGINATION - [with some urgency] *But for this poet, don't you see, merely to be at peace, simply to avoid the world's agonies and the torments and limitations of occupying a human frame, is a state to be envied.* [trying to involve her sisters] *After all, the miseries of life are pressing on him at this moment with unusual force – his only son has died.*

MEMORY - [unmoved] *Yes. For this poet, clearly, "the world, the flesh and the devil" is more than just a proverbial tag.* [happily] *In another poem he makes a virtuous gentlewoman say that she must bear the inevitable sorrows of life:*

> *...I do know that I was born*
> *To age, misfortune, sickness, grief...*

JUDGEMENT - *But in that poem the misfortunes can be borne. The poem before us now forces us to ask ... (does it?) ... what state of mind must a man be in to believe that death is preferable to life?*

MEMORY - [unfeelingly] *The particular experience – the death of an only son - which lies behind Jonson's poem is not one which all humans have to face, though it was commoner in Jonson's day than it is in ours. I do not know it myself.*

IMAGINATION - *But we can probably recreate it by extrapolating from the losses we have suffered ourselves, and from those we have read about.* [turning to Memory with some irritation] *Since you have no lived experience to bring to bear, it would help me if you would recall some moments in the great books of the world where a father's grief over the death of his son is seen as the greatest grief which a man can know.*

MEMORY - [coldly] *Homer summed up his sense of the sorrow and torment of the Trojan war in the grieving of King Priam for his dead son, Hector. It was a Classical commonplace that it was infinitely preferable to die oneself than to have to watch one's child smouldering on a funeral pyre.*

IMAGINATION - [untouched] *Thank you. Anything more specific?*

MEMORY - *When, in the Old Testament, King David hears the news that his son Absalom (who had rebelled against him, and become his most bitter enemy) has been killed, caught by the hair in the brambles of a tree while riding his horse, he breaks his heart in anguish* [Memory recites pausingly – as if suddenly but profoundly stirred to the core of her being]:

And the King was much moved, and went up to the chamber over the gate and wept; and as he went, thus he said, O my son, Absalom, my son, my son Absalom! Would God I had died for thee, O Absalom, my son, my son!

JUDGEMENT - [cooly] *It is beginning to come over me that, despite its formal and self-contained control, this is a poem written out of an agony of grief.*

IMAGINATION - [moved, almost angry] *Of course it is! Isn't this what I have been saying from the start? Jonson knows that he should envy the dead and be glad his son is at peace, but he also knows that neither he nor any man can avoid feeling the loss of a loved one as some kind of dismemberment. He knows that man **will** always lament – despite all that his conscious mind and religious convictions might tell him to the contrary.*

JUDGEMENT - *And so? Help me Sisters!*

IMAGINATION - [with absolute seriousness] *So the story of the father who quietly, even gladly, bade farewell to his son on his journey to peace is matched with this story – **the story of the father who wished he could unburden himself of all that part of him which was associated with his being a father, with everything that fathers have felt and done since the beginning of human time, with the ease that one might shed a cloak or a burden from one's back.***

JUDGEMENT - [dry-eyed as ever] *Yes. And yet, in the very grammatical form and cadence in which the wish is expressed, the poet recognises the impossibility of its accomplishment;*

O, COULD I loose all father now ...

IMAGINATION - [sobbing] *Oh, poor man, poor man! Poor humanity! Poor me! Now, surely Sisters, surely we have said enough?*

As Imagination wept, Our Hero thought he saw the figure in the shadows seem to come to stand over her. Perhaps a soft hand of comfort was laid on her shoulder.

"You see," said the Muse triumphantly, "mortal Minds (despite everything) ARE capable of comprehending Poetry?"

"Capable of ordinary human sympathy, certainly," replied Our Hero, "and of comprehending poetry ... perhaps."

83. His Best Piece of Poetry

Imagination, Judgement and Memory have reached an almost complete accord. They have moved close together; three heads over one book.

JUDGEMENT - [glad to understand] *The poet's* **fatherhood** *then — all the hopes and pleasures which he derived from his son's connections with himself — is the price he has to pay, it is what it costs him, to arrive at the equanimity which he has achieved by the end of the poem?*

IMAGINATION - [full of the poem] *Yes, and that equanimity is displayed in the invention of another lovely story.* [with deliberation] **In this story, a wayfarer is imagined pausing by the tomb in which the son is laid, and being addressed by the spirit of the dead boy ...**

MEMORY - [irrelevantly] *Strangely enough, since Jonson was a Christian, that happens at the end of one of Martial's poems on his dead boy. Roman graves were often placed by the roadside and ...*

IMAGINATION - [ignoring the interruption and entirely serious] *What the dead boy tells him is the last, and, to me, the most extraordinary of all the stories which the poem contains.* [she reads lightly, delicately, inhabiting the words]

> *Rest in soft peace, and, asked, say here doth lie*
> BEN. JONSON *his best piece of poetry.*

'My father,' *says the boy, who is happily at peace,* **'my father is a POET ...'**

MEMORY - [this time trying to help] *A poet, as the Greeks knew in giving him the name* **poietes**, *is a Maker and the things he makes are Poems —* **poiemata**.

IMAGINATION - [inspired by Memory] **'My father**,' *says the* boy, **'loves his poems very much. He is intensely proud of his Art and his calling, and regards ...'**

MEMORY - [inspired by Imagination] *Yes. Jonson used to quote*

Cicero's description of how poetry (like a combination of good wife, mother, father, husband, daughter, friend)

> *... nourisheth and instructeth our youth, delights our age, adorns our prosperity, comforts our adversity, entertains us at home, keeps us company abroad, travels with us, divides the times of our earnest and sports, shares in our country recesses and recreations ... leads on and guides us by the hand to action with a ravishing delight and incredible sweetness.*

IMAGINATION - [rapt] **'Yet**,' *says the boy,* **'my father thinks that none of his Makings equal the art of Poetry, the act of Making, which he achieved in begetting me.'** *That is a beautiful thought. May I enjoy it in quiet?*

JUDGEMENT - [with a slight note of self-satisfaction] *By now the interlocking stories which we have been collecting may be beginning to arrange themselves in something like a shape, a shape in which all the apparent contradictions have an underlying unity.*

IMAGINATION - [musingly] *And if that is beginning to happen, it would be confirmation that this poem was a truly loved child of Jonson's heart and brain. If it has an existence here amongst us, then it is something which has the capacity to live independently of its progenitor.*

MEMORY - [irrelevantly again] *At the end of Chaucer's* **Troilus**, *the poet addresses his own poem in a similar vein. I have always thought this lovely:*

> *Go little book, go little myn tragedye...*

JUDGEMENT - [ignoring Memory, deeply intrigued by the poem and by herself] *If the poem is forming a unified shape, that very unity will subsume within itself the various pieces of information with which Memory had to provide the rest of us before the shape could form. The work we had to do in trying to make sense of our first fumblings with the black marks on the page is like a ladder which we kick away once the desired summit has been reached.*

IMAGINATION - [almost to herself] *What has happened in our assimilation of Jonson's poem is only partly that Ben Jonson has communicated his emotions to us so that we grieve with him as we might grieve with a grieving friend, for what we have amongst us is not raw grief but a harmonious creation, made out of sorrow, but itself resting softly at peace.*

JUDGEMENT - [profoundly satisfied] *Its harmony derives from the fundamental art of poetry, the art of achieving consonance between felt thoughts and sounds. As we read the poem over, we become increasingly conscious that the various stories are held within just bounds by the reticence of Jonson's utterance and by the discipline of his lines.*

MEMORY - [experiencing her own kind of pleasure] *More than this, they are joined one to the other in a subtle relation by being included within a single metrical pattern. I am now forced to recognise, for example, that* **thou art** *is pronounced as one syllable,* **th'art**. *And the same must be true for* **Seven**. *It is to be pronounced* s'en – **Se'n years thou'rt lent to me, and I thee pay** – *and I see why my attention was attracted to the word* **exacted** *amongst all those monosyllables, and to the more stressed word* **will** *at the beginning of the line –* **For why / Will man lament the state he should envy.** *And I can now begin to see why this poem can be classed as an* **epigram** – *a work where brevity and point are of the essence and ...*

JUDGEMENT - [listening to her sister with only half an ear] *Increasingly, perhaps, we have begun to feel that this pattern is complete, that it could not be one line or one word longer or shorter than it is, that nothing could be added or taken away, and that it*

contains within itself the determining reasons why every tiny part should be exactly as it is and not otherwise.

IMAGINATION - *Is it true that, although this poem sometimes sounds like a transcript of direct speech, and although the vocabulary contains very few of those words which are used by poets alone, the effect of the whole is not at all like anything ever spoken by one man to another outside the realms of art?*

MEMORY - *Indeed. The characteristics of spoken language in real life (particularly under the pressure of extreme emotion) are incoherence, hesitancy, incomprehension, incompleteness and formless ugliness — the antithesis, in fact, of the poem which may by now have shaped itself among us.*

IMAGINATION - [surprised by herself and half-regretful] *And yet, and yet, this poem has not broken as entirely from the poet and become as completely realised in song as some parts of the others we read or heard earlier.*

JUDGEMENT - [irritated by the merest hint of a further complication] *That is your reservation alone. For me, this poem attains, as a whole, an easy dignity and gentle grace which no human could ever hope to achieve in life. The most complicated and subtle blend of thoughts and feelings are expressed with lightness and clarity. Each word is weighed, yet none is ponderous.*

IMAGINATION - [glad to agree] *Yes. A voice speaks, and it speaks with a natural voice, but it is not the voice of an individual or a personality.*

MEMORY - [having a moment of inspiration] *Jonson is able to tell us of his suffering and resolution, because he had weighed his own suffering and resolution with that of other men in other ages. It is thus not merely his individual suffering and resolution about which he is writing, but a suffering and resolution which exists and has existed, at least as a possibility, for all men and women. The poem is not Ben Jonson speaking. It is the child of his human, and therefore inherited, soul.*

IMAGINATION - *Yes, but I'm not sure that Jonson's resolution is easily available to us in the way you suggest — even as a potential. I think what I most enjoy in this poem is everything that I could not possibly feel myself without the poem. It is not so much that Jonson is accommodating himself to me, to what I am already, but that I am transformed or translated so that I* **become** *his poem — something very different from my normal self. Jonson's poem is not something I could say myself... not in a thousand thousand years.* [with conviction] *Something new is made. Something is brought into being. Jonson's poem is an act, a vow, a promise made to a divine power; an act of devotion, by which part of life is consecrated to a particular purpose.*

Farewell, thou child of my right hand, and joy;
My sin was too much hope of thee, loved boy,
Se'n years thou'rt lent to me, and I thee pay,
Exacted by thy fate, on the just day.

O, could I loose all father, now. For why
Will man lament the state he should envy?
To have so soon 'scaped world's, and flesh's rage,
And if no other misery, yet age?
Rest in soft peace, and, asked, say here doth lie
BEN. JONSON his best piece of poetry.
For whose sake, henceforth, all his vows be such,
As what he loves may never like too much.

Our Hero, looking in the pool, saw the sisters reading the poem. But the voice that spoke the lines was none of theirs.

"Illuminator of all Darkness, I am satisfied," he said, exulting as the great Gate of the Soul opened wide.

"Beware of over-confidence", warned his Muse. "That particular poem and that particular Mind were unusually suited, perhaps."

Part Four: Idle Tears

84. *Involuntary Recollections*

"But wait", said Our Hero, peering intently into the pool. "Look, look there! Are there yet further stirrings in that dark future Mind?"

"Indeed, there are, My Beloved", said the Muse, smiling sweetly, "the mind of mortals is never at rest. One impulse breeds another, peopling the vacuity."

Although, as usual, the sisters are half-inclined to part from one another, something, as always, detains them. On this occasion their attention is focused on a strange expression on the face of Memory – a grimace somewhere between pleasure and pain.

MEMORY - [murmuring, as if to herself] *Ah! dark and strange the days that have passed by. No that's not it. Oh wild and ...*

IMAGINATION - [stifling a yawn] *What? What was that, Sister?*

MEMORY - [in half-explanation] *I was under the impression, perhaps mistakenly, that you were not fully satisfied by the last poem we looked at.* [slightly nettled] *I am trying to help by attempting to provide something you might, just possibly, like.*

IMAGINATION - [reluctantly] *Yes, it's true. The last poem did seem to put limits, put restrictions on me.* [as if to herself] *I am not sure whether I liked or resented those limits.*

JUDGEMENT - [interrupting peremptorily] *Well I was ENTIRELY satisfied. I could not ask for more. I am ...*

IMAGINATION - [teasingly] *"Satisfied"! Were you no more than satisfied, Sister? "Satisfied" doesn't sound like much to me.*

JUDGEMENT - [surprised] *Is there more? Can a poem do more than* **satisfy***?*

MEMORY - *That is what I am wondering.* [reflectively] *That last group of words filled me, I suppose.* [pausing] *They filled me but I am not haunted by them.*

JUDGEMENT - [incredulous, irritated, amazed] *"Haunted"! Why on earth should you want to be HAUNTED by a group of words?*

MEMORY - [sighing deeply, but insisting on her dignity] *I find that is sometimes my condition.*

JUDGEMENT - [aghast at the possibilities] *Clearly it would be better for all of us if we passed on to consider other matters than poetry – other worlds, more solid concerns, real meat for the mind ...*

IMAGINATION - [only half mocking] *No, please! I would quite like to hear what haunts my Sister.*

MEMORY - [almost to herself] *I'm not sure where I first found these words ... my grandmother, perhaps, gave them to me ... and I'm even less sure that I have them right ... but I'll try to drag them up from somewhere.* [reciting in a strange poetry-voice] *Dum dum-di dum ... Tears dum-di tears, I know not what they mean. Tears, tears ... tears ...*

JUDGEMENT - [at a loss] *"Dum-di"?*

MEMORY - [happily] *I've got it.* **Tears, idle tears** *...*

JUDGEMENT - [bitterly, to herself] *I preferred "dum-di". (Non-sense is better than bad sense – or semi-sense.)*

MEMORY - [intensely and sonorously] **Tears, idle tears, I know not what they mean. Tears** *...*

JUDGEMENT - [indignant but laughing cruelly] *It is hardly surprising that you "know not" what these (ha! ha!) 'idle' tears might 'mean'.* [brutally] *In your case tears don't 'mean' a great deal. Tears. senseless tears!*

MEMORY - [trying to ignore her sister] *Tears from the pit ... no depth, of some di-dum ... no, of some divine anguish ... no some* **divine despair rise in the heart and gather in** *.. no, to the eyes .. in ... on ... no ...* [momentarily grief-stricken] *Oh dear, I've lost it.*

JUDGEMENT - [outraged] *Just as well! A moment ago you said you didn't know what the dreadful tears meant – but now you seem to know exactly where they come from!*

MEMORY - [without apology] *These words are not* **mine***. I am not responsible for them.*

JUDGEMENT - [with heavy irony] *I am glad to hear that! They words have no meaning at all.*

IMAGINATION - [quickly] *Not so. These are words of an aged man crying over some vague regret he knows nothing of and we care nothing about!*

JUDGEMENT - [again heavily] *It must be embarrassing to have even heard of these words.*

IMAGINATION - [suddenly, from nowhere] *How can despair be divine?*

MEMORY - [glad of a distraction, clicking into her professional role] *It is true, of course, that despair is usually considered to be a sin. In Spenser's* **Fairy Queen**, *for example, there are several occasions ...*

JUDGEMENT - [crossly] *We've heard all this before. I certainly don't want to hear it all again.* [seriously] *I suggest we abandon this nonsense.*

IMAGINATION - [pursuing her own interests] *What's he ... what is the person who was unfortunately responsible for these words doing?*

MEMORY - [suddenly the words have come to her] *...* **gazing on the happy autumn fields and thinking of the days that are no more.**

JUDGEMENT - [with not-entirely-well-meant laughter] *Good God! This is appalling. "Happy autumn fields"!*

IMAGINATION - [joining the joke] *Yes – why not petulant pastures, sorrowful spring meadows, woeful winter forests, heart-rending heath-lands ...* [to Memory with elaborate mock-civility] *It is very kind of you, Sister, to try to provide me with something pleasing, but I am – how shall I put it – SURPRISED that you think that I might be pleased with the wailings of a sad old man – the self-indulgent outpourings of premature senile dementia. These words are, I'm afraid, simply silly.*

JUDGEMENT - [taking Memory's hand] *Such a grave mistake,, such a grievous error, is extremely worrying. Are you sure you are feeling well?*

Imagination and Judgement contemplate the strange aberrations of Memory, in silence and contempt. She is torn in two. Intense embarrassment is at war with some pressure within, forcing the words to her reluctant lips.

"Alas", said Our Hero, "my works can have no life in such a Mind, among such cruel sisters. They have learned *nothing*. What is it in nature that breeds such hard hearts?"

"Blame not Nature", said the Muse laughing. "A poet should always trust Memory."

"I don't see why. I can never trust mine."

85. The Mortification of Memory

Memory struggles with her self and her sense of her sisters' indifference. But she cannot remain still for long.

MEMORY - [anguished, pacing up and down] *Is it like that?* [in desperation] *Is it all like that?* [reciting rapidly as if checking the words for faults] **Fresh as the first beam glittering on a sail that brings our friends up from the underworld. Ah! fresh ...**

JUDGEMENT - [her face between her hands in mock-agony] *O God there's more — more nonsense!* [briskly] *Our friends don't come up from the underworld.*

IMAGINATION - [laughing] *... but from Exeter or Swansea ...*

JUDGEMENT - [curious, despite herself] *What is this underworld anyway?*

MEMORY - [pained, reciting the words as if for the first time] **Fresh as the first beam glittering on a sail that brings our friends up from the underworld.** [a long pause] *I'm afraid I don't know what this underworld might be.*

JUDGEMENT - [amazed] *You've had these words for heaven knows how long — and you don't know!* [with a sharp look] *You've no idea?*

MEMORY - [with a shrug] *Sorry.*

IMAGINATION - [brightly] *There is a ship and a shining sea and a beam on a sail. As the old man watches from the shore he sees a sail coming over the horizon. It is the sail of the ship that brings his friends on a visit to ...*

MEMORY - [pedantically] *"OUR" friends.*

JUDGEMENT - [scornfully] *The old man is attempting generality.* [pausing] *But I still don't understand this 'underworld'.*

MEMORY - [didactically] *The underworld is, I suppose, a pre-Christian notion. Aeneas and Odysseus both ...*

JUDGEMENT - [genuinely questioning, looking into the faces of her sisters] *Do we care?*

MEMORY - [determinedly unabashed] *... but I am not sure that I ever heard of friends coming from there. The idea of the underworld occurs again in the poem.* [reciting, as usual, in her poetry-voice] **Fresh as the first beam glittering on a sail that brings our friends up from the underworld. Sad as the last that reddens over one, sad as ...**

JUDGEMENT - [puzzled despite her irritation] *Sad as the last WHAT? Reddening over one WHAT?*

IMAGINATION - [quickly] *The last beam reddening over one last sail?*

MEMORY - [ignoring her sisters] **... sad as the last that reddens over one that sinks below the verge with all we love. So sad, so strange ... no ... so fresh the days that are no more.**

JUDGEMENT - [as if pleased to be proved right] *This is pure drivel! "The verge" I ask you! "All we love"! What meaning is there in that? "Sad and fresh days"! I won't, **can't**, allow these words to speak for us.*

IMAGINATION - [kindly, turning to Memory] *It does seem terribly vague, you know, and weak. So sad, so sad, so very-very-very sad the days that are long gone.*

JUDGEMENT - [also turning to Memory with concern, as to one who is ill] *How CAN you be interested in such a set of words — coming from such a weak mind?*

MEMORY - [apologetically] *I suppose these words seem ... somehow rather ... unusual to me. There is something ... somehow ... different from other words I have met.* [reciting mechanically as if to emphasise that the words are none of hers] **Sad and strange as when ... no ... as in dark summer dawns the earliest pipe of birds to dying ears when unto dying eyes the casement slowly grows a glittering ... no, a glimmering square. So sad, so strange the days ...**

JUDGEMENT - [half-attending] *I thought he was crying in the happy autumn fields.*

IMAGINATION - [quickly, dismissively] *He is. This talk of dying and dawns is merely illustration of how terribly sad he feels about it all.*

JUDGEMENT - [sharply] *What "all"?*

IMAGINATION - [smiling] *That's the problem. It's so vague, so sad ...*

JUDGEMENT - [laughing dismissively] *... and so, so strange!*

IMAGINATION - [pausing] *It IS strange, isn't it – the singing of birds in the dawn heard by a man for whom this day will be the last?* [to Memory who is now too abashed to reply] *Don't you find it strange?*

JUDGEMENT - [still laughing] *And the old man uses such quaint words – "the pipe of early birds"!*

IMAGINATION - [noticing Memory's distress] *Perhaps some of the words are a little precious, but I like the glimmering casement, the window slowly appearing in the gloom.*

JUDGEMENT - [irritated by Imagination's sudden engagement] *IF that's what it IS doing. Who can tell?*

IMAGINATION - [happily] *I am genuinely glad of that fragment. It allows me to see for an instant through the eyes of a dying woman.*

MEMORY - [apologetically] *I'm afraid there is more.*

JUDGEMENT - [quickly] *Oh NO!*

IMAGINATION - [soothingly] *Go ahead. There might be something in it.*

JUDGEMENT - [bitterly] *NOT very likely – or not for me.* [to no one in particular] *No sense, no sense, you see.*

MEMORY - [encouraged, quietly persistent] ***Dear as remembered kisses after ...***

JUDGEMENT - [laughing, to herself] *Dear, dear kisses. We will have 'sweetness' soon.*

MEMORY - ***Dear as remembered kisses after death ...***

IMAGINATION - [also laughing] *After WHOSE death? Is the bereaved woman remembering the dear, dear kisses ... or is it the ghost?* [to Memory, pulling herself together] *I'm sorry.*

MEMORY - [refusing to give up] ***Dear as remembered kisses after death, and sweet as those ...***

JUDGEMENT - [triumphantly] *As I predicted. Sweet, sweet kisses to add to the dear, dear ones!*

MEMORY - [with resignation] ***... sweet as those by hopeless fancy feigned on lips that are for others ...***

JUDGEMENT - [dwelling on the alliteration with contempt] *"By hopeless Fancy Feigned"! This language is patently unreal.*

IMAGINATION - [laughing despite her better intentions] *Yes, this is all too much a poem. This is art that jumps up and down proclaiming itself. The sentimental old man is attempting the grand style!*

MEMORY - [dwelling on the words in defiance] ***Deep ... deep as ... as love ... deep as first love ...***

JUDGEMENT - [attempting a new method of distraction] *Correct me if I am wrong, but is it not generally accepted that first love is a mere infatuation, best forgotten.* [looking hard at Memory] *Do you know something of this, Sister?*

MEMORY - [not taking the bait] *I'm afraid I can't comment. These words have nothing to do with me.* [with conviction, however, and, as she recites, some emotion] ***... deep as first love and wild with all regret ...***

JUDGEMENT - [genuinely questioning, despite herself] *"Wild"? How "wild"?*

IMAGINATION - [laughing] *Really wild!*

MEMORY - [with increasing emotion, trembling] ***... deep as first love and WILD with all regret, O death in life the days that are no more.***

JUDGEMENT - [with ponderous politeness] *Ah ha! "Death in life"? And what, Dear Sister, might **that** be?*

MEMORY - [unable to answer, the tears of which she has been speaking suddenly breaking forth] ***O DEATH IN LIFE the days that are no more.***

IMAGINATION - [surprised] *What IS the matter, Sister?*

MEMORY - [sobbing uncontrollably] ***O DEATH IN LIFE the days that are no more.***

JUDGEMENT - [after a pause during which she looks at her sister aghast] *Pull yourself together can't you?*

MEMORY - [not responding] ***O DEATH IN LIFE the days that are no more.***

JUDGEMENT - [looking around as if for help] *This is terrible!*

MEMORY - [desolately, as if doomed to repeat these words for ever] ***O DEATH IN LIFE the days that are no more.***

237

Imagination and Judgement stare silently at their weeping sister with horror and desperation. At length, Judgement, under the impression that there is a danger of hysterics, slaps Memory's face. It is Judgement herself, however, who is most in danger of losing self-control.

"Oh dear, oh dear", said Our Hero, rubbing his eyes. "I am not sure I want to be responsible for causing such turbulence in future minds."

"Memory at least is moved", said his Muse, comfortingly.

"But, alas, she knows not how or why."

86. Judgement Objects

JUDGEMENT - [shaking her sister furiously] *It won't do, you know. It just won't do.*

MEMORY - [plaintively] *What won't?*

JUDGEMENT - [decisively] *These appalling words and your deplorable behaviour.* [in answer to her sister's silent incomprehension and her own feeling that intellectual grip is urgently called for] *I have two objections — closely connected and extremely powerful objections. The first is to the sentiment expressed in or by these words. The second is to the **means** of expression. The sentiment is clearly unhealthy. The right course for any decent human mind is to let the past be past and old bygones be. This longing for what is gone must lead inexorably to a loss of any effective hold on reality.*

MEMORY - [very quietly] *Are you sure?*

JUDGEMENT - [glad of what she takes to be a show of submission] *Of course I'm sure. Such sentiments are thoroughly reprehensible.*

IMAGINATION - [as if to herself, smiling] *Fancies hatched in silken-folded idleness.*

JUDGEMENT - [happily, since things seem to be going her way] *Exactly! Furthermore, the expression is hopelessly imprecise. The voice is sickly and yet indeterminate; the tone pure plangency and ...*

IMAGINATION - [smiling again to herself] *It is a sad, slow voice haunting the mouldered lodges of the past.*

JUDGEMENT - [with apparent confidence masking some desperation] *Precisely! The old man is wallowing in an emotion which is reprehensible in itself and which is here expressed (or half-expressed) in a language — with a diction — that leads us* [looking hard at Memory] *(or some of us) away from experience and from that painful struggle to comprehend experience which constitutes our existence, Instead we are turned towards an imaginary never-never world ...*

IMAGINATION - [again lightly] *A fairy world, the Elfland of sub-literature.*

JUDGEMENT - [emphatically] *Entirely! An old man who allows himself such a loss of control is not to be trusted. We must resist. We must stand up and fight.*

MEMORY - [apparently without irony] *I am sorry I ever began. I will never mention these words again so long as I shall live.*

JUDGEMENT - [triumphantly] *That is well. We will be most glad of such restraint.*

IMAGINATION - [to Judgement, suddenly coming out of herself] *Not so fast, Sister! Don't put words in my mouth. There were some things in this poem — not many I admit — some things for which I am grateful.*

JUDGEMENT - [appalled] *That cannot be! Nothing is given or described in such a way as to allow you even the lightest hold. These words represent mere wallowing in a mood which is savoured precisely because it is a vague, unmeaning thing. The man who is responsible for them should have pulled himself together — just as Memory is (I am glad to see) pulling herself together now. There is nothing there for any of us. These words are the direct product of a diseased and ageing brain.*

IMAGINATION - [going along with Judgement despite herself] *Or, perhaps he was merely trying to please a sentimental audience that needed to be distracted from present realities?*

JUDGEMENT - [severely] *In which case it was a **wicked** collusion. Whatever they were originally, for us these are dangerous words. As we have seen* [with an acid glance at Memory] *they induce a dangerous emotionality, a sickly mood, a weakness of ...*

IMAGINATION - [interrupting briskly] *Do these words suggest a mood? an emotion? Is that all?*

JUDGEMENT - [sharply] *Well of course it is — a mere emotional swell inviting the weak among us to go along with it without question. After all what are we given? Idle tears — from divine despondency ...*

MEMORY - [mechanically] *Divine despair.*

JUDGEMENT - [ignoring the interruption] *... rising tears — the heart — happy fields — beams on sails — ships sinking with all we hold dear ...*

MEMORY - [again automatically] *All we love.*

JUDGEMENT - [with increasing volume] *... glittering casements —*

MEMORY - [who cannot help it] *... glimmering.*

JUDGEMENT - [almost shouting] — *sweet kisses — dear lips — and a good helping of Ah!s and Oh!s. These are so many hooks for a sentimental reader in a sentimental age to hang any loose despondency upon. I say again, these words are the vague, reprehensible expression of vague, reprehensible emotion.* [as if clinching a case] *After all, the old man himself tells us that he doesn't know what his tears MEAN.*

IMAGINATION - [not abashed by her sister's onslaught] *Perhaps he is working that out, thinking it through.*

JUDGEMENT - [shrilly] *Thinking! No, he merely goes on to tell us self-indulgently what the tears feel like to him.*

IMAGINATION - [calmly, thoughtfully] *I'm not sure it is as you say.* [turning to Memory] *Might I hear the words I liked again? Don't worry about Judgement.* [laughing] *I am certain that these words will do you no lasting harm. Speak them, if you please, as it seems they ask to be spoken.*

MEMORY - [immensely grateful for what looks like kindness] *You mean the words about the window. I'll try.*

> *Ah, sad and strange ...*

JUDGEMENT - [to Imagination in a failed attempt to raise an easy laugh] *There you are. Ah sad and strange indeed!*

MEMORY - [encouraged by a smile from Imagination, reciting in ringing tones]

> *Ah, sad and strange as in dark summer dawns*
> *Th'earliest pipe of half-awaken'd birds*
> *To dying ears, when unto dying eyes*
> *The casement slowly grows a glimm'ring square;*
> *So sad, so strange, the days that are no more.*

JUDGEMENT - [bitterly] *Sad and strange, so sad, so strange, The old man can't get beyond that — that unmeaning moan. These words convey nothing to me.*

IMAGINATION - [with real curiosity] *Not even when tied to an example? Doesn't the story of the dying man's last dawn help with the words "sad" and "strange"?*

JUDGEMENT - [with finality] *No, it doesn't help me at all.*

MEMORY - [happy no longer to be the target of both her sisters' mirth] *Not having died (though you sometimes make me feel as if I had) I can't help directly. Nor can I recall much that is similar from stories I have heard.*

JUDGEMENT - [to Imagination, heavily] *This wonderful story is, it appears, very much your exclusive province, Sister.*

IMAGINATION - [defiantly but thoughtfully] *Well I still like it. I find the sadness and strangeness felt by such a dying man at such a moment engaging to consider ... though the effect is hard to describe ... the joining of the sad and the strange ... the sound of the birds ... the strangeness of the sensation ...*

JUDGEMENT - [pouncing] *There you are, "sensation", mere sensation!*

IMAGINATION - [with enthusiasm] *But it is NOT sensation on its own ... or, rather, I find that it is difficult to distinguish sensation from other things that are felt or thought. I find myself considering what the dying man must be thinking ... What thoughts must arise in the breast of one who knows that this day is his last! The symbols of a new beginning are noticed for the last time and are for him signals of the opposite, What is fresh for the rest of the world is infinitely sad for him and ...*

JUDGEMENT - [trying a new tack] *Is "dawns" a noun or a verb?* [forcing herself to laugh] *Does the earliest (ha! ha!) pipe of (ha! ha!) half-awake birds DAWN or are there many dying ears and dying eyes, many piping birds and glittering squares every dark summer morning? No syntax: no sense!*

IMAGINATION - [pausing] *It depends, perhaps on how you say it. As I hear it –* [reciting in her own passionate version of a poetry-voice] **as in dark summer dawns the earliest** ...

MEMORY - [with a sudden burst of inexplicable excitement] *Yes, yes, that's it!* [to Imagination] *I like your story very much, but it was the beautiful, slow movement of these words which, now I consider it, made me want to offer them to you.* [reciting slowly and intently]

> *Th'earliest pipe of half awaken'd birds*
> *To dying ears, when unto dying eyes*
> *The casement slowly grows a glimm'ring square* ...

IMAGINATION - [catching her sister's feeling, rapturously] *Yes, yes, the perfect harmony between words and feeling, the sweet slow sounds of sadness and of slow dawning light amidst the encircling dark* ...

JUDGEMENT - [furiously] *The sound of darkness! Sweet slow sounds! This is madness! Let me see something solid beneath the sounds of emotional vacuity. Open the window of sense to clear the stinking air!*

"Alas", said Our Hero, again rubbing his eyes, "I am worried for the inhabitants of this dour mind."

"This is a human mind and is not at risk", replied his Muse.

"Human! All too human!"

87. *Imagination Tells a Story*

Now it is Imagination's turn to pace up and down in frustration. After some time she turns towards her sister and crouches at her feet.

IMAGINATION - [calmly but reprovingly] *I know nothing of your precious 'sense'. I'm happy enough with pictures and sounds — particularly if they are connected in a story — and especially if the stories are connected one with another.*

JUDGEMENT - [desperately] *I can't follow the 'stories' which you say are in these words ... and I see no connections of any kind. What connections can be found between one piece of non-sense and another?*

IMAGINATION - [as if it should be plain to all] *We get, in these words, a series of stories where the beginnings and endings of things happen simultaneously.*

JUDGEMENT - [out of her depth] *The beginnings and endings of THINGS? Can't you be more precise ... or more helpful to me?*

MEMORY - [also as if it were a matter of course] *The beginnings and endings of life and love and friendship.*

JUDGEMENT - [desperately] *Friendship? How can words about boats and beams tell us anything about friendship? — if those are the words you are considering.*

MEMORY - [all her old confidence returning] *Just those -*

> *Fresh as the first beam glitt'ring on a sail*
> *That brings our friends up from the underworld,*
> *Sad as the last which reddens over one*
> *That sinks with all we love below the verge;*
> *So sad, so fresh, the days that are no more.*

[to Imagination] *You said before that this was a story about some friends coming to visit.*

IMAGINATION - [thoughtfully] *I was wrong — or half-wrong. The idea perhaps is something like that — but it is the **beams** that are fresh, and then sad.*

JUDGEMENT - [staring blankly] *Does that make a difference?*

IMAGINATION - [slowly] *I suppose so ... though it is hard to explain. The sense, the thought, is in the pictures ... The friends are merely an example.*

MEMORY - [passionately] *... and the lovely slow words ...*

IMAGINATION - [with a nod] *... and the pictures, both of them, are sweet to me. I see, perhaps, a boat arriving at the start of life and departing at the end. But my attention is concentrated on a glittering and a reddening **beam**.*

JUDGEMENT - [too surprised to be bitter] *I really don't follow at all.*

IMAGINATION - [without hesitation] *It is not so much that the gaining or loss of friends is fresh and sad but that the pictures themselves* [becoming incoherent] *— the knowledge in the pictures ... captured in the pictures ... held in the pictures ... two instants held against eternity ...*

MEMORY - [excitedly] *... and the lovely words ...*

> *Sad as the last which reddens over one*
> *That sinks with all we love below the verge ...*

JUDGEMENT - [to Memory] *Can you help me? What is our sister speaking about?*

MEMORY - [refusing to speak to Judgement] *I can give support for both the sense of freshness, of expectation, and the sense of sadness, of finality. A sense of such things is part — inevitably part — of human life.*

JUDGEMENT - [furious again] *A 'sense' of this and a 'sense' of that. This is not the sense I need. I want THOUGHT. I want something specific, something solid. Where, where can I find it?*

IMAGINATION - [calmly] *In the pictures, and in the notion that friends come to us from another world to which they return. In the underworld they exist and do not exist, so that ...*

JUDGEMENT - [all her exasperation welling up again] *That*

is a nonsensical notion and palpable untruth. That's not the return I want. I want the poet or the poem to return upon himself or itself with some sign of intelligent life, some criticism of his, or its own self-indulgence, some thought that [becoming incoherent] ... well ... the past is past ... it may be sad but life goes on in the here and now. To me this man is listing things, merely. These words are no more than a list of sad things – or of would-be sad things ....

IMAGINATION - [sweetly] They are not only sad things. They are at the same time fresh things, or dear things, or strange things, or deep things. The days that are no more come back – they exist with that freshness and that sadness, both. These words tell of the coexistence of the present, the past and the future – the inextricable mingling of those things in human perception, and apprehension. They give me a wonderful sense of the abiding in the transient. Isn't that a kind of thought? Isn't that a kind of sense?

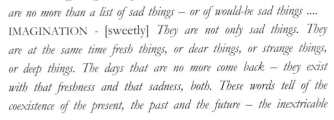

JUDGEMENT - [bursting into tears] Not to me, not to me!

Judgement's tears of irritation, confusion and mortification fall for a while in near silence. Memory is puzzled by her sister's behaviour; Imagination mildly annoyed.

In the garden of the Muse Our Hero winced.

"Have patience, Child", whispered his fair Instructress, "all may yet be well".

88. *Wild With all Regret*

Now it is Memory's turn to attempt to comfort her anxious sister. She sits close to Judgement, hanging her head and speaking softly, while Imagination, stands aloof.

MEMORY - [with a surge of genuine affection] *Calm down, sister dear. I am sorry I ever brought these words up.*

IMAGINATION - [without sympathy] *I can't see what the matter is – or what the fuss is about.*

JUDGEMENT - [sobbing] *It is just that I can't bear to see you two going into ecstasies about senseless notions such as 'abiding in the transient'. To me, you see, these words are cloyingly obscure.* [trying to smile] *Just think of all that wild love and all those kisses! Any vestige of sense is entirely dissipated when we come to those. You MUST see that.*

MEMORY - [confident since the boot is now on the other foot] *Not really.* [reciting this time with controlled passion]

> *Dear as remember'd kisses after death,*
> *And sweet as those by hopeless fancy feign'd*
> *On lips that are for others; deep as love,*
> *Deep as first love, and wild with all regret*
> *O Death in Life the days that are no more.*

JUDGEMENT - [laughing through her tears] *O death in life to have to hear these words!*

IMAGINATION - [to Judgement, severely] *There is, you will* **have** *to admit, a difference between the dearness of the kisses that were won and lost and the sweetness of those that were purely imaginary – the sweetness of kisses never granted.*

MEMORY - [coyly] *Such differences exist in human perception.* [in answer to an unspoken scepticism of Judgement] *They do, they do.* [recovering] *... or so I have been told. And the words chosen – poetical words, it seems, which you didn't like – the*

hopeless feignings of fancy – enforce that difference and ...

JUDGEMENT - [genuinely at a loss, looking into the faces of both her sisters] *So what?*

IMAGINATION - [confidently, patiently] *So again we have a story that combines near-opposites within a unity. Both kinds of kisses exist in the present when they are recalled...*

MEMORY - [quickly] *... or recall themselves ...*

.JUDGEMENT - [incredulous] *Are you saying that this is a poem about love – and that all the old man is regretting is lost love of one kind or another?*

IMAGINATION - [thoughtfully] *Perhaps. The movement of the words does seem to become most passionate here* [reciting] *–* **deep as love / Deep as first love** *...*

MEMORY - [enthusiastically] *Yes, the lovely impassioned movement of the words. And "wild" does seem to be an unusual word in this ...*

IMAGINATION - [turning to Memory] *Is it the wild regret of the continued existence of love in unfulfilment? Is regret one of the strongest of human passions?*

MEMORY - [pausing] *So it seems. (Although embarrassment can come close.)* [with growing rapture] *The three slow verses which culminate in this intense bursting out are drenched through and through in the heavy dew of long and living sorrow for love just touched but unattained. Perhaps the wildness of regret is that it cannot be over-mastered?* [frightened by her own notion] *It may return at any moment with full and terrifying force.*

JUDGEMENT - [almost apologetically] *I still think the old man should have overcome his infatuation.*

IMAGINATION - [who has been working on her own] *No, as I consider the matter, lost love cannot be the well-spring of this set of words. Rather, the unfelt kisses and the depth of first love are the most telling, touching examples of what the tears are like —-* [a sudden notion occurring to her] *– which becomes an explanation ... or a near-explanation ... of what the tears at the days that are no more MEAN.*

JUDGEMENT - [incredulous again, but subdued] *Mean! Do tears mean anything? Can tears mean anything?*

"I begin to grow weary of this Judgement", cried Our Hero.

"All poems, real poems, must offer a challenge to *some* part of the Mind. Do you want easy victories?" asked the Muse, smiling.

"I think, on this evidence, I would settle for a decent truce."

89. Poetry, Sense and Feeling

Imagination, fully engaged, paces up and down in excitement.

IMAGINATION - [as much to her self as the others] *The despair would not be divine were it merely that – merely a poem of love regret.*

JUDGEMENT - [advancing a challenge] *So why is the regret divine? And what kind of poem is it?*

IMAGINATION - [quietly] *I'm not sure. I'm not sure that these words do constitute a man (or a woman) speaking to us –– though that was the impression I received at the start. How did it go?*

MEMORY - [obliging]

> *Tears, idle tears, I know not what they mean,*
> *Tears from the depth of some divine despair*
> *Rise in the heart, and gather to the eyes,*
> *In looking on the happy Autumn-fields,*
> *And thinking of the days that are no more.*

JUDGEMENT - [surprised] *"Thinking"? Why does he say that he is thinking of the days? Wouldn't we expect to be told what happened on those days if he were* **thinking** *about them?*

IMAGINATION - [musing on her own] *The contrast between the unexpectedness of the tears on the one hand, and the depth from which they rise (or seem to him to rise) on the other, must prompt thought ... or something like thought. The contrast is so extreme – between the idleness of the tears and the happiness of the fields on the one hand, and the depth of the heart and the depth of the sudden despair on the other – that it must give rise to something more than personal feeling.*

MEMORY - [happily] *I agree, I agree. It must. It does. The feeling is not anchored in particulars* [to Judgement] *– each of which can be, as you say, 'got over' – but to a more general sense of the past intervening in the present.*

IMAGINATION - [confidently] *Yes, he is not grieving over lost love. He – or she – or the poem – is pondering, feeling ... pondering by feeling ... THINKING.*

JUDGEMENT - [after a long pause] *Perhaps I am now beginning to understand something of what you mean by 'thinking'. And I can now dimly make out one principle of construction beneath the apparent obscurity. Is 'depth', as it were, the governing idea?*

IMAGINATION - [pausing] *Perhaps. Where do these tears come from? Can we find that out by examining what they taste like, as it were? The tears are both physical and spiritual. They rise in the heart and gather to the eyes. There is a continuity between the emotional and the material.* [to Memory] *What are the words which are used to describe the days that are no more?*

MEMORY - [unhesitating] *They are:* **fresh, sad, sad, fresh, sad, strange, sad, strange, dear, sweet, deep, deep, wild***. The whole impression culminates in the phrase* **'death in life'**. *These are simple, common words.*

JUDGEMENT - [genuinely questioning] *Don't these words allude to experience rather than give it to us? Are these not vague, unmeaning words? If I used a list like this, would you not laugh?*

IMAGINATION - [smiling] *We probably would. But I like your notion that these words qualify and amplify an idea of 'depth'. On the other hand, these words are not those of an individual man or individual woman speaking to individual men or women.*

JUDGEMENT - [anxiously] *So what are they?*

IMAGINATION - [carefully] *A voice speaking to itself and to all humanity but not to any intermediate audience listening in the 'real' world. This poem is written in the language of men but the words are not used as men use them, but ....*

MEMORY - [suddenly] *It's a lovely song.*

JUDGEMENT - [shocked] *A song?*

MEMORY - [joyfully] *It doesn't rhyme, of course, but there is something like a refrain – di dum di dum the days that are no more.*

IMAGINATION - [nodding] *It starts as one voice speaking but finishes as a set of words that all men and all women might sing.*

MEMORY - [caught up in her own pleasure] *Have you noticed the pattern of the passion?*

JUDGEMENT - [jumping as if stung] *What?*

MEMORY - [pleased, now, with herself] *It's a song in blank verse. Very unusual. I've been trying to tell you … well. tell myself … all along that it was the sound, the shape, or pace of these words which haunted me. When you were laughing at me I should have pointed to the supreme control – the perfection of the movement. It is at once conventional and extraordinary. The exclamation you hated –* **O Death in Life, the days that are no more** *– is carefully worked towards and justly arrived at.*

JUDGEMENT - [looking at each sister alternately] *So what are you telling me? that thought and emotion are here one and the same? – that, by dwelling on, by developing the feeling, the song arrives at a kind of realisation? – that this realisation – that the days that are no more constitute a coexistence of death in life – is both heart-breakingly bitter and also somehow an acceptance? – an* **understanding** *of something?*

IMAGINATION - [with admiration] *I'm not sure we were telling you that – but it sounds true, now that you say it. That kind of story is – or so it seems to me – on the very verge of what can be said in words.*

JUDGEMENT - [smiling] *I still don't understand which days are being lamented … or described … or evoked in these words.*

MEMORY - [not seeing the point of the question] *The days that are no more.*

JUDGEMENT - [unbelieving] **All** *of them?*

MEMORY - [confidently] *All of them ….*

IMAGINATION - [rapturously] *… all present in one moment. The song is almost overcharged with thought. Its depths and implications are boundless – the days that bring and those that take our friends, the days of death and those of love, days of waking and of dying, days of …*

JUDGEMENT - [anxiously] *This is a mystery to me. Is that why the despair is divine? Because it touches on or derives from what you two call the mysteries of life, the most inexorable and perplexing laws of human existence?*

IMAGINATION - [serenely] *That must be why.*

MEMORY - [suddenly, out of the blue] *This poem arrests the vanishing apparitions which haunt the interlunations of life.*

JUDGEMENT - [glancing sharply at her sister] *What?*

MEMORY [apologetically] *Just a few words I picked up somewhere … words that seem … somehow … appropriate …*

JUDGEMENT - [also apologetically] *The interlunations of life are the very things that bother me – (not that I know what they are).* [she glances at both her sisters in turn] *You are seriously telling me that these words represent, or embody, or encapsulate, or somehow suggest a vast comprehension and expanse of thought?*

IMAGINATION - [quietly] *Sufficient to fill me completely. As I dwell on the words I am astonished.*

JUDGEMENT - [laughing] *I can see that .. but are you sure you are right to be astonished.*

IMAGINATION - [with a shrug] *I can't help it. These words seem to me to marry exultation and horror, grief and pleasure, eternity and change. Anything that does that astonishes me – permanently.*

JUDGEMENT - [who can never rest easy] *Yes, but …*

MEMORY - [interrupting politely but confidently] *I am grateful for all your comments and I'm sure all you say is true, but would it not be better to hear the words themselves?* [reciting to no one in particular]

Tears, idle tears, I know not what they mean,
Tears from the depth of some divine despair
Rise in the heart, and gather to the eyes,
In looking on the happy Autumn-fields
And thinking of the days that are no more.

Fresh as the first beam glitt'ring on a sail,
That brings our friends up from the underworld
Sad as the last which reddens over one
That sinks with all we love below the verge;
So sad, so fresh, the days that are no more.

Ah, sad and strange as in dark summer dawns
Th'earliest pipe of half-awaken'd birds
To dying ears when unto dying eyes
The casement slowly grows a glimm'ring square;
So sad, so strange, the days that are no more.

Dear as remember'd kisses after death,
And sweet as those by hopeless fancy feign'd
On lips that are for others. Deep as love,

Deep as first love, and wild with all regret;
O Death in Life, the days that are no more.

JUDGEMENT - [permanently astonished] *I see what you mean by saying that these words are* **overcharged** *with thought.*
MEMORY - [after a long pause] *I like this poem.*
IMAGINATION - [to Memory] *Thank you, Sister, thank you. So do I.*

"Well, I suppose that will have to do," said Our Hero, shrugging his shoulders. "But if this Mind makes such heavy weather over little poems, how will future mortals fare with the *mighty masterpieces* that my sons are to compose in future times for men unborn?"

Part Five:
The Arts of Criticism

90. *The Art of Criticism*

It was late evening in the Garden of the Muse. The sun was slowly sinking in the west. Our Hero was once again more or less happy. He watched the ripples in the pool long after the visions had faded. He knew, without being told, that the time was drawing nearer when he would have to return to the earth below. Although his heart was full of hope, he noticed one doubt flying somewhere amongst his more conscious musings.

"Heavenly Goddess, I am satisfied that the Poems of my progeny (or some shorter poems, at least) will (somehow, more or less) form themselves in the Minds of future generations and that their spirits (or something very like their spirits) will live (or almost live) again. But I was unable to tell if the Faculties (or the Minds they serve) placed any great *value* on the experience or on the Poems."

"Value, My Poet?"

"The Faculties were almost overcome and defeated by the shortest of works. How will they fare with the grand master-works you are urging me to make, unmake and make again? I have not yet seen what effect my Great Poems will have on the sum of things."

"In that Mind, my Chosen Soul, you saw (however dimly) the Art of Criticism in action."

"And what is the Art of Criticism, My Muse?"

"The Art of Criticism, My Beloved, is part of the Art of Listening and part of the Art of Poetry. Poets need this Art to make their poems, and listeners need this Art from the moment when they start to try and decide whether the jumble of words somewhere between the page and their minds *is* a POEM.

Anyone who lives and anyone who reads is a critic. Mortals cannot help it. It is as inevitable as breathing. The critical potentiality is one of the abilities they employ in making sense of the strange and terrible place they gradually find themselves to have been born into. They are critics whenever, in laughing at a joke, they recognise that different things belong to different orders of importance. They are critics whenever, in bursting into tears, they recognise that some things cost them a great deal to lose.

Mortals use their critical faculties in choosing their friends and their enemies, their homes and their holidays, their husbands and their wives. They use the critical faculties in deciding how to spend their money or their time, this evening, or tomorrow, or the rest of their lives.

But, as we have seen, Dearly Beloved, most mortals most of the time, are lamentably *bad* critics.

There are many reasons for this. One of them is that human life is so incoherent, so muddled, so constantly *not* what they expect, that they never seem to have lived long enough, or to have thought deeply enough. All they seem to have to go on is a set of feelings, sometimes strong, sometimes less distinct, often conflicting and intermittent, which make up the only sense they have of themselves. They hardly ever believe other people's experience or listen to other people's helping words. Most of them, perhaps, most of the time believe that the Doom of Man has been specially reversed for them alone; that they live an individual life divided from the rest of their kind.

As it seems to be in life, so it seems to be in Poetry. Mortals have the same misplaced confidence in their Judgements as they do in their watches. None goes just alike, but each believes his own. They may, sometimes, pay lip-service to the opinions of others, but in their secret heart of hearts they know that they are right and they alone.

And that is why Criticism has to be an Art, and why mortals have to learn it, and why they have to learn it from other people.

Some people have cared about Poetry and Criticism more than others. Some have cared about Poetry and Criticism more than anything in the world.

Lie back in the grass, My Beloved, drink deep from my Pierian spring; I will tell you the story of a man who (if all goes well between you and I) will care so much about Poetry and Criticism that he will happily be (or would happily have been) a martyr for their sake."

91. *Natural Modesty*

"Once upon a future time there lived a bright-eyed boy called Alexander. Even as a child, Alexander knew that there was only one thing for him to do in his life – to be a Poet. Rhythm and rhyme and lovely-sounding, strange, mysterious words gave him – as they give most mortal children – infinite pleasure. When he was about twelve he wrote an epic Poem which he called '*Alcander, Prince of Rhodes*. It was full of flamboyant vocabulary and extravagant sound-effects:

> *Shields, helms and swords all jangle as they hang,*
> *And sound formidinous with angry clang.*

But as he read through this epic which he had been so very proud to complete, he saw almost immediately that *something* was wrong. Even though he had stolen little bits from every author he had been able to lay his hands on, he saw that something **essential** was missing.

There must be some law or laws known to the Poets on whose works he had drawn, but which were as yet undiscovered by himself.

In search of these laws, the young man asked himself which Poems most pleased him, and which Poems had most pleased most readers down the ages. Luckily they were the same. His favourite Poem was the first and most famous Poem in the world, the Poem about the wrath of Achilles, about killing and being killed on the battle-fields of Troy, about the cruelty of the gods and what was terrible and the wonderful in the souls of men. It was the ILIAD of HOMER.

Then he asked himself what kind of pleasure this Poem gave him and in what ways that pleasure differed from the other pleasures of life.

He knew the Poem gave him very great pleasure indeed – but then, so did a good meal or a ride in the country. He was not quite in control of himself as he read it – but then, neither was he when attempting to speak to a very pretty girl. Whenever the people in the Poem spoke, he was compelled to listen – but so was he when addressed by old, wise, friends. Whenever the people in the Poem did anything, he watched with rapt attention – as he watched any extraordinary event in life.

The difference, he suddenly realised, was that the other pleasures of life were either elusive and impermanent, or palled, dulled, and faded with repetition, but the more he read this Poem, the more possessed he became, until he felt he was racing through the story in a fiery chariot of delight.

And so he decided that he must read the Poem every day, and meditate upon it every night. He discovered that his pleasure in the Poem compelled him to try and understand *everything* that might be understood about it. And the more he understood, the greater his pleasure was.

Despite his great love of the ILIAD, there were some parts of the Poem which baffled Alexander, and other parts which bored him. He saw that if his pleasure in the Poem was to be complete, he would need help.

He turned first to the wise men of the past. But they were almost no use at all. He found it strange that, of all the commentators upon Homer, there was hardly one whose principal design was to illustrate the beauties of the author or demonstrate the power of his Art. Their remarks were philosophical, historical, geographical, allegorical, or, in short, anything rather than critical and poetical.

And so he returned to Poetry. The most useful help he found was contained in other Poems rather than learned commentaries. Some of these Poems were translations or re-workings of the ILIAD. Alexander paid particular attention to the ways VIRGIL used HOMER's Poem when writing his AENEID. He also learnt from Poems which had drawn on the ILIAD for a moment or two, and from others which seemed to be dealing with  similar subjects or which seemed to be using similar arts.

Before his study of these other Poems, Alexander had thought that he knew almost everything there was to know about the ILIAD. But now, as he began to see what other Poets had made of the great old Poem, he realised that he hadn't even begun. Studying the Art of Poetry was for him (as for you, Dearly Beloved) as hard as climbing mountains. He had started from a low valley, and had thought the first mountain was the last. But now he trembled as he saw an endless succession of peaks rising over each other. It was exhilarating and daunting, uplifting and humiliating, enervating and inspiring – all at once."

92. Re-living the Iliad

"And then one day, some eight or nine years later, when almost every moment of the great Poem had come fully alive for him, Alexander thought that he had discovered the source, the well-spring of his pleasure in the Poem. His pleasure was the delight of experiencing something MORE SUBSTANTIAL, AND THEREFORE MORE PERMANENT, THAN THE REALITY OF LIFE ITSELF.

He had no other way of accounting for his feeling that every scene and description in the Poem existed in his mind almost as if he had actually been there. And every time he read the Poem, he was there again. The same things happened in the same way – and were delightfully comprehensible and painlessly incomprehensible in the same way.

In the ILIAD the energy of humanity was encapsulated: the current of life ran forever – always in motion, always the same.

It seemed to Alexander that he was a perpetual eye-witness of those terrible scenes around the walls of Troy. He was there right at the start when Achilles, the most courageous of the Greek warriors and the warrior most conscious of his own worth, was consumed with passionate wrath at king Agamemnon's seizure of his slave-girl and withdrew from the fight, leaving his fellows to their fate – or their doom.

He saw Hector, the most dutiful and loving of the Trojan Princes, take his last leave of his wife Andromache before returning to the battle-field to defend his city, to kill and to die. He noticed, sharply, how Hector's baby son clung to his mother's breast, fearful of the nodding plume on his father's battle-helmet. He observed the generous benevolence and natural piety of Troy's aged King Priam towards Helen, the cause of all his city's woes – and all his own. He saw Helen's regret for all that had passed and her pitiful surrender to the charms of her abductor and to the power of the Goddess of Love.

From afar and above, he watched the ominous flickering of the battle-field camp-fires reflected on the distant walls and spires of Troy, during a night-long lull in the fighting.

He was there when the Greeks, sore pressed by their foes, sent ambassadors to Achilles, begging him, imploring him, to relent, to return to the fight, and save them from destruction. And he heard Achilles' reply, first quietly and sullenly resolved, then warming to an extravagantly fiery rage as he awakened and roused himself to a full consciousness of the injuries and iniquities done to him – to *him*, the first of men.

With particular pleasure, Alexander heard the Lycian prince Sarpedon rallying his friend Glaucus to display the selfless courage on the battle-field which alone would justify their position as the aristocratic heads of their tribe. He then witnessed Sarpedon's slaughter at the hands of Achilles' friend Patroclus, and the hideous fighting round Sarpedon's corpse, now lying on the plain and defaced with blood and dust. And he saw Patroclus, dressed in the armour of Achilles, killed by Hector, as his turn came.

Alexander was present too as Achilles writhed on the ground, rending his hair in passionate grief first at the news of Patroclus' death; and then when the great warrior ran amok among the Trojans, killing Hector and dragging his naked corpse behind his chariot round the walls of Troy in full view of all those who loved him.

He understood how and why Achilles, finally awed by Reason's Rule, at last ceased from his manic violation of the laws of god and man, and received Priam as a suppliant, returning the body of the old king's son unmutilated, to receive proper burial.

And in all these actions, Alexander had watched the interventions of the immortal gods – fighting among the warriors, squabbling among themselves, submitting to the overruling might of Jove. And he had seen all the aspects of natural and rural life in which, in lovely similes, Homer had shown the strange continuities between the worlds of animal and inanimate nature and the human actors in the drama of Troy.

All these things, thought Alexander, had happened before his very eyes and would happen again so long as he lived – every time he opened the book or remembered the Poem which, by now, he had by (and in his) heart."

93. *Art and Life*

"Yet although Alexander felt he had seen all things with his own eyes, he also knew that he had been *more* than a mere witness. He had not only stood and watched, excluded and confused, as when he had watched happenings in real life. He had participated with intimate understanding in the actions and sensations and feelings of both men and gods.

He had lamented with the grieving, and rejoiced with the triumphant – sometimes in the same instant. For if the great spirit of the Poem – the spirit that fired Alexander and must have fired HOMER – was a spirit of reality, its reality was distinct from that of the world in which Alexander conducted his daily life.

Though, as he read, and as the story unfolded (or, as it seemed to him, happened), Alexander felt dread, hope, sorrow, joy, foreboding, awe, amusement, amazement, pity, contempt, merriment, elation and dejection by turns, these emotions all had a colouring quite different from that which they had in ordinary life.

The dread was without anxiety, the hope without anticipation, the sorrow was devoid of suffering, the joy was pure, the merriment lasting, the amusement unalloyed, the disgust and contempt were without personal rancour, the merriment was discreet, and the dejection pleasing.

If the young man had seen a naked corpse dragged in the dust behind a chariot in real life, he would have been appalled. When the Poem caused the same action to occur in his Imagination, he was pleased to the very core of his being.

How could this be? How could deep pain and profound joy co-exist in the same instant in the same mind?

The answer, thought Alexander, was that Homer had not simply transcribed from, or reproduced, life, but had produced an imagined world in an exquisite piece of Art – a beautiful imagining, a lovely and lively word-painting.

This imagined world was DIFFERENT FROM life as lived by real men and women but not OTHER THAN life as lived by real men and women.

Homer's world contained many things which were not, which could not be, in any obvious sense, life-like. There were gods lusting after mortal boys and girls and seducing one another on mountain tops: heroes battling with rivers and hiding in magic clouds: horses talking miraculously, and cauldrons moving under their own volition.

Nevertheless, as Alexander raised his eyes from the book to look at the world around him, everything that had happened and everything that had been said in the Poem caused him to see his own surroundings and his own life with freshened eyes, dilated spirits and a more ample heart.

How could this be? How could something different from the world nevertheless reflect the world – or on the world?

The world of the Poem was, Alexander came to see, co-natural but not identical with the world he knew.

Homer had not copied the world as it was, but created a new world according to the Laws that had governed the creation of the old.

The Poem turned sorrow into delight because IT HAD BEEN DICTATED BY THE SPIRIT AND NOT BY THE LETTER OF LIFE."

94. The End and Test and Source of Art

"It began to dawn on Alexander that he had penetrated a great secret.

Like you, Dearly Beloved, he discovered that the spirit, the Muse, who had assisted in the composition of the ILIAD – who had animated it with the power to touch and to move, who had shaped and paced its narrative, and given its verse strength and agility and suppleness – was the Goddess of Nature herself, the same goddess whose laws give shape and strength and agility and suppleness to the minds and bodies of men, and life and vigour and form to all created matter.

NATURE AND HOMER WERE, HE FOUND, THE SAME.

The only difference, Alexander now realised, between the pleasures of Poetry and the pains of reality was that when the Goddess Nature became the Muse she became, without losing any of her force and vigour, a contemplative and consolatory goddess.

As you well know, it is very hard, Dearly Beloved, for mortals to see any Laws of Human Nature when life is raw and undigested. The emotions and events of ordinary life overcome and swamp the Mind. They obscure rather than illuminate any general truth of which they may be an example or an expression.

The ILIAD turned sorrow into delight, Alexander realised, because along with the song which made the reader see and feel what was happening, there was a second, contemplative and consolatory, under-song which told the reader that everything could be borne, that nothing was too much for the Mind of Man to face and comprehend.

These discoveries had taught Alexander an important lesson in the Arts of Criticism. He determined to ensure that he was at each and every moment reading in the same *spirit* in which the author had composed. If the author had been possessed by the Goddess of Nature in writing, he would have to be similarly possessed in reading. It was not the mere words or letters that were the critic's concern, but the life-giving spirit. When that spirit of Nature was moving and heating his mind, he would be feeling the true force of the Poem as a whole. That would save him from mean and petty attention to extracted detail.

Alexander also realised that the only spirit in which criticism could properly be performed was a spirit of *generosity*. Unless the critic's Mind had been fired, there would be nothing to talk about. And if the critic's Mind *had* been fired, he would inevitably be inspired by *gratitude*.

He would be grateful because he was getting from Poetry something he could not possibly find anywhere else.

In the world, human nature was something which was either too painful to contemplate, or which vanished even in the instant it was perceived.

As you well know, Flesh of my dreams, mortals can hardly ever hold – fix clearly in their Minds – even their *own* current view of things.

But as Alexander read his beloved ILIAD, he came more and more to believe that the Nature which animated the cells of his brain as he took the Poem into his system had a steadier, fuller, a more permanent reality than Nature ever had in his ordinary apprehensions, intuitions and observations.

And the vividness and completeness of the ILIAD as it now existed in Alexander's Mind seemed to him to suggest that the Poem he possessed *must* be essentially the same Poem that had existed in Homer's Mind all those centuries ago.

It therefore constituted powerful evidence that Minds can meet across the boundaries of time and beyond the pressures of place.

It showed that, though the behaviour both of individual men and of groups of men is constantly and completely changing, *within* the energy which changes those forms of human behaviour and society there exists a constant, fixed, immutable, self-creating and self-defining human spirit, out of which Poets write their Poems and to which they direct them.

The ILIAD was a very old Poem indeed. It had been written when the forms of social, intellectual and emotional life had been, in every conceivable respect, quite unlike those which obtained in Alexander's day. The legal codes were different. The gods were different. Military and agricultural practices were different. Styles of dress were different. Customs and ceremonies were different. Men and women regarded each other differently. Heroes wept and whined to their mothers. The most fundamental words – those closest to Alexander's words – 'love', 'honour', 'duty', 'guilt', 'heaven', 'hell', 'fate' – implied quite different sets of assumptions. As Alexander read the ILIAD, he was constantly being surprised, perplexed and disorientated.

But the surprise was, in the end, one of *permanently astonished recognition.*

He was being forced to see things which, in a sense, he felt he had known all along. Only he had never –

and without the Poem, could never have – known (or even guessed), that he knew them.

The Poem seemed to mobilise and speak to parts of him which he had never dreamt existed.

He began to see that something in Mankind remains always the same, and that nothing is lost by Nature, though everything is altered.

Alexander had sometimes thought of himself as a bit of an oddity, unlike the rest of his species. But the ILIAD, and the writings of other men and women down the ages who, like him, had admired Homer's poem, suggested that there was something of him in all men and all women, and something of all men and all women in him.

Alexander's reflections convinced him – beyond the possibility of doubt – that Homer had defied the usual laws of transitory and partial human existence and had written a great Poem which was for all ages and for all humankind.

It seemed suddenly clear to Alexander that there was only one Law of Criticism and only one Law of Poetry and that these Laws were the same.

A Poem was something that had been inspired by Nature; something which aimed to create Nature in the Mind of the reader, and something that could, at the proper time, be tested by that spirit of Nature."

95. *Experience and Judgement*

I must warn you, Dearly Beloved, that in some Dark Times it will sometimes be said that this young man was making a terrible mistake. It will be said that any belief in an unchanging Human Spirit is a mere *delusion*. It will be said that I, myself, am (imagine it!) a mere *fantasy*. It will sometimes be said

that it is impossible to claim that one Poem is better than another. It will be thought that Poems are produced by historical forces rather than by inspiration. The fact that Alexander glowed and trembled as he read the Iliad, it will be said, tells us nothing whatsoever about the worth of the work itself.

To Alexander, this would have seemed an appalling blasphemy.

For him, enjoying a Poem and judging it to be wonderful were not two separate acts. Nor were they separable.

If his mind was strongly agitated, if his heart was reached and touched, if his dim imaginings and intuitions were developed and shaped and harmonised, if his own personality seemed to be both extinguished and extended, if his mind seemed to be con-joining with the minds of thousands of other men and women, if the whole of life seemed suddenly to be irradiated with beauty, if the words seemed suddenly to be singing their own perfect harmony, and dancing their own perfect dance, then he KNEW, as surely as it was possible for a mortal man to know anything, that he was in the presence of a spirit so powerful that he was forced to call it energy divine.

For him, that was what a great Poem WAS.

It did not seem to Alexander that he was ATTRIBUTING worth to his great Poem – as value is attributed to beads,

rings, shells or to paper money. The powers of the Poem were intrinsic as the powers of wine and opium are INTRINSIC. The divine energy was attributable to (and demonstrable in) a multitude of detail.

To ignore the divinity of the Poem, to talk about it as if it were something that could be discussed without passion or involvement, was a sin against humanity, since, for Alexander, one of the defining characteristics of humanity was the god-given potentiality to blame the false and value the true, wherever and whenever they were to be found.

Just as he saw that Poems were different from life and yet co-natural with life, so he saw that the decisions which he made about Poems were different from but co-natural with the decisions which he made in his ordinary life.

In life he found it hard but essential to distinguish between the people he met. Some were cruel and some were kind. Some were beautiful but cold, and some were plain but wise. He could be happy to spend his whole life with some: others were to be shunned like the plague.

By a subtle metamorphosis, the principles which he employed when making distinctions in life could, he found, be transferred to Poems. Some poems offered only an evening's dalliance, while others, in which the spirit of Nature was strong, remained friends for life. The beauty of some Poems was skin deep. The plainness of others was the plainness of long-pondered and deeply-meditated sense.

In both cases decisions had to be made – for Alexander, Dearly Beloved, was mortal, and mortal life is far too short to spend much time with folly or deceit.

96. *Alexander's First Vision*

These thoughts were confirmed, and enlarged, and made pressing, when Alexander had a wonderful dream – a vision sent, My Beloved, by me.

He was standing alone under a glowering sky in a vast empty plain in the midst of a Dark Time. On the horizon he could see some ruins; on the ground some skulls and bones.

Then the sky opened in a flood of glory, and he saw a Temple in a region beyond time and place, secure from war, envy, conflagration and decay.

Here he saw his revered HOMER sitting with other patriarch Poets, garlanded with laurel that was for ever green, as if on an altar.

Behind the altar stood a goddess – the Goddess of Poetry and Nature, perhaps, – beautiful beyond dreams, powerful beyond terror, wise beyond imagination.

Beside the Goddess stood a handmaid – the spirit of Just Criticism – who dressed her charms and fanned the Poets' fires.

He heard the Poets sing a song in which all humanity might join with them. They were answered by a general chorus of Mankind. To the altar trooped the critics of all ages and all nations. Before the altar they sang their hymns of gratulation.

And then in his vision Alexander saw generations as yet unborn joining in the hymn of praise – generations from yet-to-be-discovered worlds.

These hymns suddenly turned into a stream – a stream of praise.

The more the stream flowed, the larger and stronger, more vigorous and powerful it grew until it flooded the world in a river of light.

He saw the Goddess of Poetry and Nature become the Goddess of Reason. He saw her driving the clouds of Pride away, and Truth breaking out like a resistless dawn.

He saw Wit, Art and Learning join together. He saw Truth and Candour shine everywhere like the sun, clearing and improving all that it shined upon, gilding all objects but altering none.

He saw the darkness of a Dark Age suddenly lightened.

He saw the Spirit of Greece and Rome shake off the dust, and raise her reverend head.

He saw Sculpture and all my Sisters' Arts revive; stones leaped into form and rocks began to live. He heard every fine temple ring with sweet notes, and all the Arts advance across the Northern World.

He saw the light of Poetry and Nature shine everywhere, subliming wit in the South and ripening spirits in cold northern climes.

He saw that the same sun that shone on past ages might enlighten the present and warm humanity to the end of time.

Then, suddenly, Alexander found himself flying – flying like a sea-bird that had just left its nest, on uncertain wings, in short excursions, content to skim the surface of the seas.

But he knew that he would one day, some day, soar aloft and feel the sun on his wings.

Alexander became determined that his generation and his nation must send representatives to this visionary altar; that they must join the universal chorus.

The more he glowed as he read, the more he trembled as he tried to find words adequate to describe his wonder and his vision. It became a matter of the greatest urgency.

It became the business of his life."

97. *Alexander Becomes a Critic*

"And so Alexander went out into the world of men to be a critic. But he had doubts. 'What makes me think,' he asked himself, 'that I can criticise other people's poems when my own aren't yet much more than 'prentice work, and when, being so young, I might so easily have got my judgements entirely and absolutely wrong?'

The answer came to him one day when he was sitting in a coffee house. At the other end of the room, surrounded by admirers, the fashionable critic-about-town was holding forth. Nothing impeded his eloquence. He mentioned book after book, name after name. And every name and every book he assailed. Poets, he implied with every gesture and in every witty turn of phrase, were clearly not as clever as he was. But as Alexander listened, he noticed something peculiar. The man wasn't really talking to anyone in his audience. The whole show was for the benefit of his *own* ears. The resistless tide of the critic's eloquence had nothing to do with the Truth or with Poetry. It was an exercise in self-praise. The man may have been stuffed full of books, but he was a blockhead. His reading was a kind of ignorance.

Alexander turned aside thinking to himself: 'Now I know why I might have something useful to say after all. I may be able to be a critic, because I know that I'm not one. I know that I don't know and never will know all there is to know about my beloved Homer. I know that I am not even worthy to speak his name. That man babbling away over there is moved only by pride and egotism. The essence of criticism is HUMILITY.'

Alexander realised that if he was going to have the virtues of a good critic, he would also need the virtues of a human being.

And as he began to circulate in the world, he found that the men who were most helpful to him as an aspiring critic and Poet had these virtues in abundance. They were men who had never stopped learning, and who knew that they had never stopped and that there was still much to do, and much to know. Even though Alexander was very young, these men listened when he spoke, expecting to learn as much as they taught. Their love of Poems was such that they never preferred themselves, or any other matter, to trying to determine what might be the truth of Poetry. Some of these men had read as many books as the critic in the coffee-house, but they never imposed that learning on Alexander, or even mentioned it, unless it was immediately helpful. They were tactful and tentative, both to Alexander himself and about Poems, but their tact and tentativeness was always more than mere good manners. When they were speaking boldly of some thought they believed to be true, they also spoke modestly. When they described what they saw as the faults of Alexander's work, they remembered their own.

Above all, Alexander noticed, their knowledge and their thoughts extended both to books and humankind. They were happiest when they could honestly and justly say that a Poem had extended the possibilities of mankind as a sentient species. Alexander decided that these men, his teachers, were talking about Poems in the only way that Poems could be talked about – humanely. He decided that he would try to do the same.

If the special thing which Poetry offered was the opportunity to escape the constrictions of his own age and his individual personality – the opportunity to share in a larger, more comprehensive, Human Nature – then it would be stupidity to pay less than full attention to opinions other than his own. Therefore he resolved to make use of every friend and every foe, past and present.

The business of criticism, he determined, was essentially a corporate pursuit. Poetry was the great common ground where differences of age, sex, religion, politics and philosophy became utterly insubstantial and irrelevant – or were translated into the language of general Nature. Poetry, the young critic had seen in his vision, was something which joined Mankind, healing and welding together all warring factions in a vast empire of human society."

98. Poetry and Criticism

"Up to this point, the story of Alexander might be a heightened example of the story of any young man possessed by a passionate and all-absorbing love of Poetry. But this particular young man, you will remember, Dearly Beloved, was also a Poet. At this point in the story, he made a decision not open to ordinary mortals. He concluded that the only way to teach the world how crammed with life his beloved ILIAD was would be to write a Poem himself, a Poem that followed and re-imagined every moment and every beauty.

And this he did (with my assistance!). He wrote a Poem of his own which re-created every part of the ILIAD. The effort almost killed him. He introduced it in beautiful prose, and accompanied it with a running commentary, full of the very kind of humane tact and insight which he had come to see as such an essential ingredients of any literary criticism worthy of the name.

During the course of this work, the young critic had become a mature Poet. He finished his great work of Poetry and Criticism, of Criticism in Poetry, and sent the book out into the world.

In writing this book, he had performed all the Arts of Criticism.

He had traced the pleasures offered by the Poem to their sources, deep in the Human Mind. He had tried, as hard as it was possible for a man to try, to write in the spirit in which the old Poet had written and to help his audience to read in that spirit.

He had taken account of the thoughts of all the generations who had read his beloved poem before him. He had tested the experience of past Minds against the Poem, and against his own experience. By endless comparisons with the work of other Poets, he had distinguished what he felt to be the particular character of HOMER — that which made him a peculiarly powerful and energetic example of the Spirit of General Nature.

He had tried, as hard as a man could try, to understand all that was alien in the real and literary cultures out of which the ILIAD had been written. He had tried to understand the ancient language, the ancient religion, the ancient way of telling stories, the ancient customs, and the human thoughts and impulses which seemed to lie within those customs.

In order to test whether the spirit of eternal Nature, (which he thought he had discovered within the words and story of the ILIAD), was genuinely that, and not a set of ideas which time had rendered obsolete, he had taken each minute part of the Poem into the world in which he lived. He had listened to men and women talking to each other. He had watched the women putting on their make-up and men playing with their snuff boxes. He had observed the passions in all their variations from the sprightliness of infancy to the despondence of decrepitude. He had noticed the heightened colour on the cheek of the young girl playing cards and the pallor of the fallen politician.

Most of all he had looked into his own heart. He had tried to distinguish those thoughts and feelings which were mere accidents peculiar to himself, or which were the result of living in a particular place and at a particular time, from those which he suspected animated (or might animate) all Minds at all times.

He did all he could to help his readers to make similar decisions for themselves. He wanted his Poem to help men and women to distinguish between strong, but merely temporary, feelings, and those more permanent motions of the heart that underlie or describe human nature.

He wished his work to provide a place to which mortals could turn whenever they were beginning to forget what it is that makes mankind human — now, then, and forever.

He had tried to make his Poem worthy of its great original. It was a work, Dearly Beloved, for which he had high hopes."

THE ARTS OF CRITICISM: A BAD DREAM

99. A Bad Dream

"As is the way with mortal hopes, Alexander's were partly fulfilled and partly dashed. His great Poem was one of the most successful his country had ever seen. It made his fame and it made his fortune.

But for him, that was not the point.

The only people, he began to think, who really seemed to understand his Poetry and criticism were people who didn't need to understand it because they already knew what it had to teach. And the rest of the world went on as if nothing had happened. Ignorance, Stupidity, Mendacity, Superficiality, Pride and Envy encompassed him around.

As Alexander passed into middle age, he began to have bad dreams.

In these dreams, there were two goddesses of Nature. The first was the goddess he loved, the goddess of Life-in-Nature, the goddess of the ILIAD. But the second goddess was a goddess of Death-in-Nature. It was this second goddess who was praised by the world, and who owned all the weapons.

In his dreams, Alexander saw this second goddess of Death-in-Nature extending her boundless reign over the whole of human life. Under her power, Dullness and Ignorance and Superficiality and Stupidity became more than mere privations, they became active and powerful forces.

He saw her inspiring a deep hatred of Art and Thought in the minds of men and women. He saw the spread of the rule of self-promotion and distrust and envy and mendacity through every institution dedicated to the human spirit. He saw education cramping rather than illuminating. He saw school children bleeding from the birch, forced to load the Memory to the detriment of the Mind.

As a result, the deathly spirit was as prevalent among the young and popular and apparently clever as it was among the stuffy and more obviously dull. He saw every imaginative faculty starve through want of nourishment, and every work of Imagination lie unread and unvalued.

The efforts of Intelligence and Poetry seemed to have no more lasting power to resist the Dread Goddess than a momentary meteor has to light the sky. He saw those to whom the preservation of the human inheritance had been entrusted covering Art and Life with the death of their own souls and the cobwebs of their own dull brains.

He saw, under the influence of the Dread Goddess of Death-in-Nature, mortals longing to stay locked in their cosy and comfortable individuality and contemporaneity, happily cramped in the cells of their own dull Minds. He saw the desires of the moment confounded with the needs of the whole being. He saw the fashionable and ephemeral mistaken for the universal and the permanent; the preoccupations of the instant confused with the preoccupations of eternity.

He saw that the world that Poets had made was becoming a forgotten world.

He feared that there would soon would be nowhere for human beings to find themselves – to find their true selves. He feared there would be nowhere for the human spirit to live, and move, and find its being. There would be no place left for the grand, sublime, witty, or wise possibilities that human beings had (over hundreds of generations) created for themselves.

He saw the Arts extinguished one by one.

It seemed that the stars in the sky were dying. He feared that his dream was a portent of the coming of universal night. He believed that the humane spirit had been

THE ARTS OF CRITICISM: A BAD DREAM

extinguished at least once in the past. He knew that precious things had silently passed out of mind or had been violently destroyed.

And now it was all happening again.

The particular horror of his current bad dream was that this time nobody would notice.

The last spark of the humane spirit would expire without anyone realising that anything had happened."

100. *Mankind and Humanity*

"You, Dearly Beloved, may think that Alexander was merely suffering from delusions or nightmares – that his hopes as a young man and his fears as an old were equally wild and extravagant. You may think that what this old man feared and said is what old men have always said and will always fear. You may think that the Human Spirit could no more be extinguished than the stars. Or you may think that Poetry and the Human Spirit have nothing to do with one another – essentially or absolutely.

But you see, in Alexander's sense of things, 'mankind' and 'humanity' were not always or necessarily synonyms.

Mankind and Humanity were not necessarily the same thing at all.

Mankind and Humanity were not even necessarily connected.

Alexander's meditations on the ILIAD had convinced him that what the politicians and merchants and journalists called the 'real world', was no more than a temporary, arbitrary and circumscribed set of social, economic, ethical and political opinions and arrangements. As Alexander saw it, those who lived exclusively in this world, and whose minds were entirely conditioned by the assumptions and values of this world, might be entirely ignorant of themselves – might be quite unaware of the full range of realities, of deep and lasting *pleasures* which, for those whose ears and eyes had been opened by Poetry, could be seen to comprise the Mind and the Heart of Man.

It was possible, as Alexander saw it, to know all about Mankind, but to know nothing of Humanity at all.

As I have told you, Flesh of My Soul, Alexander had been simultaneously shocked and moved by the world that was depicted in the ILIAD. He had felt lost and at sea in the presence of thoughts and actions which seemed entirely alien, and at one and the same moment he had seemed to be on old, familiar, well-loved, well-known territory. While living in the Poem he seemed to be living in an utterly strange world which he nevertheless recognised as his true home.

This paradox constituted for Alexander powerful, incontrovertible, unavoidable, inescapable evidence that there exists in every human Mind and Heart an inheritance of capacities, possibilities, potentialities, imaginings and needs which never find full expression in any one life or any one society.

As Alexander saw it, it might be possible to pass through a life without knowing that Humanity existed.

It might be possible for Mankind to continue as a social species while Humanity quietly gasped and died.

In Alexander's view, Mankind had been provided by Nature and biological inheritance only with potentialities and possibilities. In order for Humanity to realise these potentialities and possibilities – in order for Humanity to come into being, to continue, to live and to propagate itself – quite other and more potent means were called for.

Only the world's great Art could hope to provide Humanity with a place where the full range of human capacities, possibilities, potentialities, imaginings and needs could be discovered, recovered, faced, expressed and passed on. Only great Art, as Alexander saw it, could enable Man fully to know, and therefore to be, himself, and to see his humanity for what it really is – in its *full wonder and horror and terror and truth*.

And that is perhaps why ALEXANDER POPE (for this is the story of that great Poet from our damp Northern Isle) was so worried that his translation of Homer and his ESSAY ON CRITICISM had done so little to uphold the spirit of Poetry in a hostile world, and why he devoted the DUNCIAD, the satirical poem of his last years, to his bad dreams and to his worst fears about the powers which exist to diminish, frustrate, suppress and deny great Art – the powers which were, he thought, destroying the one thing which could give Man true permanent, comprehensive knowledge of himself and his own Mind; which could provide the profound, liberating pleasure which comes from such knowledge, and from such knowledge *alone*.

I must warn you, Dearly Beloved, that Alexander may be (or have been) right to worry.

The power of the goddess of Death-in-Nature, the goddess whom he will call Dullness, is and will be as evident and widespread in every age as it was (or will be) in Alexander's.

Dullness is a goddess who (as is the way with goddesses) works silently, constantly within each and every mortal Mind and Heart. All mortals, whether they will or no, are her devotees.

But while Alexander may have been right to worry, perhaps he should not have despaired.

The ILIAD (along with all the Greater Poems of all my Greater Poets) will possess the same power, the same capacity to excite and shock, to delight and terrify, to transport and mollify, to move readers to laughter and tears in every age, that it had (or will have) when that young man glowed as he read and trembled as he wrote. Their power will be, as I have promised, co-extensive (and co-terminous) with Humanity.

But, in all honesty and in simple truth, I must warn you again, Life of my Dreams, that even the Greater Poems of

my Greater Poets will have this power only as a possibility, a potentiality, a promise, a hope.

That is why it is so terribly important for those who have the opportunity, the inclination or (like you, Dearly Beloved, the inspiration) to write or to read Poems, to exercise the Arts of Poetry and the Arts of Criticism as well as they possibly can. That is why you and your sons – those with lesser strength and those with the force of thirty souls – must try, and try again, to discover the spirit waiting to be unleashed in a page of verse; why you must try, and try again, to resist the Dread Goddess: why you must try, and try, and try again, to join the general chorus of Mankind in testifying to a shared conviction that Poems are the living, breathing progeny of our coming together, Spirit of my Soul – in testifying to a shared conviction that Poems live, and that what they live is the Life of the Spirit of General Nature.

It is terribly important, my Beloved Poet, because the Story of POETRY is part of the Story of ART, which is part of the Story of HUMANITY, which is part of the Story of MANKIND.

Without the STORY OF POETRY there might not be a STORY OF ART.

And without the STORY OF ART the STORY OF HUMANITY might be very short indeed."

269

A List of Poems

Chapter 33

And ten low words oft creep in one dull line
Alexander Pope: An Essay on Criticism.

Chapter 35

This is the excellent foppery of the world ...
William Shakespeare: King Lear I.

Chapter 36

Twinkle, Twinkle little star ...
Jane Taylor: The Star.

War, he sung, is toil and trouble ...
John Dryden: Alexander's Feast.

Chapter 37

The double, double beat of the thund'ring drum
John Dryden: Ode on St. Cecila's Day.

Blow, bugle, blow, set the wild echoes flying ...
Alfred Tennyson: The Princess IV.

Sing ye, sweet angels, alleluia sing ...
Edmund Spenser: Epithalamion.

Slow, slow, fresh fount, keep time with my salt tears ...
Benjamin Jonson: Song from Cynthia's Revels.

Chapter 38

Give me some music: music, moody food ...
William Shakespeare: Antony and Cleopatra II.

There is sweet music her that softer falls ...
Alfred Tennyson: The Lotus Eaters.

Chapter 39

Soft is the strain when Zephyr gently blows ...
Alexander Pope: An Essay on Criticism.

Chapter 44

The time when early housewives leave the bed ...
John Dryden: Virgil's Aeneis VIII.

Night's candles are burnt out and jocund day ...
William Shakespeare: Romeo and Juliet III.

Chapter 45

The busy larke, messenger of day ...
Geoffrey Chaucer: The Knight's Tale.

The morning lark, the messenger of day ...
John Dryden: Palamon and Arcite.

Chapter 46

... yon gray lines/ That fret the clouds ...
William Shakespeare: Julius Caesar II.

... The rosy messenger of day/ Strikes the blue mountains ...
Alexander Pope: The Iliad of Homer IX.

... Magnificent/ The morning was ...
William Wordsworth: The Prelude IV.

Chapter 47

Up rose the sun, and up rose Emily
Geoffrey Chaucer: The Knight's Tale.

Sol through white curtains shot a timorous ray ...
Alexander Pope: The Rape of the Lock I.

Not with more glories, in th'etherial plain ...
Alexander Pope: The Rape of the Lock II.

Chapter 48

... the sun/ Which cometh forth as a bridegroom ...
Psalm IX.

At last the golden oriental gate ...
Edmund Spenser: The Fairy Queen I.

When the first matin-song hath wakened loud ...
Alfred Tennyson: Ode to Memory.

Now the bright morning star, day's harbinger ...
John Milton: Song. On May Morning.

See the morning opes her golden gate ...
William Shakespeare: 3 King Henry the Sixth II.

Chapter 49

Hark, hark the lark at heaven's gate sings ...
William Shakespeare: Cymbeline II.

... Morn,/ Waked by the circling hours ...
John Milton: Paradise Lost VI.

Now rosy Morn ascends the court of Jove ...
Alexander Pope: The Iliad of Homer II.

... Meanwhile/ To resalute the world ...
John Milton: Paradise Lost IX.

The saffron Morn, with early blushes spread ...
Alexander Pope: The Iliad of Homer XI.

Chapter 50

Morn in the white wake of the morning star ...
Alfred Tennyson: The Princess III.

Now Morn her rosy steps in th'eastern clime ...
John Milton: Paradise Lost V.

But look the morn in russet mantle clad ...
William Shakespeare: Hamlet I.

By this the northern waggoner had set ...
Edmund Spenser: The Fairy Queen I.

Chapter 52

And now secure the painted vessel glides ...
Alexander Pope: The Rape of the Lock II.

Chapter 53

... know that in the soul/ Are many ...
John Milton: Paradise Lost V.

Chapter 54

... Nature knows/ No steadfast station ...
John Dryden: Of the Pythagorean Philosophy.

Chapter 55

... I have felt/ A presence that disturbs me ...
William Wordsworth: Tintern Abbey

Chapter 57

Howl, howl, howl; O you are men of stones ...
William Shakespeare: King Lear V.

Chapter 58

O fairest of creation, last and best ...
John Milton: Paradise Lost IX.

Chapter 59

> *Then spak he thus, 'O lady mine, Criseyde ...'*
> **Geoffrey Chaucer: Troilus and Criseyde V.**

Chapter 67

> *Wetron winde when wylt thou blow ...*
> **Anonymous.**

> *The wind doth blow today, my love ...*
> **Anonymous: The Unquiet Grave.**

Chapter 69

> *And I have asked to be/ Where no storms come ...*
> **Gerard Hopkins: Heaven-Haven.**

Chapter 71

> *O that 'twere possible / After long grief ...*
> **Alfred Tennyson: Maud.**

Chapter 72

> *My heart leaps up when I behold ...*
> **William Wordsworth: The Rainbow.**

Chapter 78

> *Farewell, thou child of my right hand, and joy ...*
> **Benjamin Jonson: On My First Son.**

Chapter 80

> *... I shall do so;/ But I must also feel ...*
> **William Shakespeare: Macbeth IV.**

Chapter 82

> *... I do know that I was born/ To age ...*
> **Benjamin Jonson: To the World.**

Chapter 84

> *Tears, idle tears, I know not what they mean ...*
> **Alfred Tennyson: The Princess IV.**